D0281793

GCSE AQA

Biology

Complete Revision and Practice

Contents

How Science Works

Biology 1a — Human Biology

Biology 1b — Environment and Evolution

Biology 2a — Cells, Organs and Populations

Contents

Biology 2b — Enzymes and Genetics

Biology 3a — Life Processes

Biology 3b — Humans and Their Environment

Practice Exams

Published by CGP

From original material by Richard Parsons.

Editors:
Charlotte Burrows, Mary Falkner, Rosie McCurrie.

Contributors:
James Foster, Paddy Gannon, Adrian Schmit.

ISBN: 978 1 84762 660 8

With thanks to Katherine Craig, Janet Cruse-Sawyer, Julie Jackson and Glenn Rogers for the proofreading.
With thanks to Laura Jakubowski for the copyright research.

Graph on page 172: Concentration of Carbon Dioxide from trapped air measurements for the DE08 ice core near the summit of Law Dome, Antarctica. (Data measured by CSIRO Division of Atmospheric Research from ice cores supplied by Australian Antarctic Division). Dr. T.H. Jacka, Glaciology Program, Antarctic Cooperative Research Centre and Australian Antarctic Division.

Every effort has been made to locate copyright holders and obtain permission to reproduce sources. For those sources where it has been difficult to trace the originator of the work, we would be grateful for information. If any copyright holder would like us to make an amendment to the acknowledgements, please notify us and we will gladly update the book at the next reprint. Thank you.

Groovy website: www.cgpbooks.co.uk

Printed by Elanders Ltd, Newcastle upon Tyne.
Jolly bits of clipart from CorelDRAW®

Photocopying – it's dull, grey and sometimes a bit naughty. Luckily, it's dead cheap, easy and quick to order more copies of this book from CGP – just call us on 0870 750 1242. Phew!

Text, design, layout and original illustrations © Coordination Group Publications Ltd. (CGP) 2011
All rights reserved.

The Scientific Process

You need to know a few things about how the world of science works.
First up is the scientific process — how a scientist's idea turns into a widely accepted theory.

*Scientists Come Up with **Hypotheses** — Then **Test** Them*

Hundreds of years ago, we thought demons caused illness.

1) Scientists try to explain things. Everything.
2) They start by observing something they don't understand — it could be anything, e.g. planets in the sky, a person suffering from an illness, what matter is made of... anything.
3) Then, they come up with a hypothesis — a possible explanation for what they've observed.
4) The next step is to test whether the hypothesis might be right or not — this involves gathering evidence (i.e. data from investigations).
5) The scientist uses the hypothesis to make a prediction — a statement based on the hypothesis that can be tested. They then carry out an investigation.
6) If data from experiments or studies backs up the prediction, you're one step closer to figuring out if the hypothesis is true.

Investigations include lab experiments and studies.

*Other Scientists Will **Test** the Hypothesis Too*

1) Other scientists will use the hypothesis to make their own predictions, and carry out their own experiments or studies.
2) They'll also try to reproduce the original investigations to check the results.
3) And if all the experiments in the world back up the hypothesis, then scientists start to think it's true.
4) However, if a scientist somewhere in the world does an experiment that doesn't fit with the hypothesis (and other scientists can reproduce these results), then the hypothesis is in trouble.
5) When this happens, scientists have to come up with a new hypothesis (maybe a modification of the old hypothesis, or maybe a completely new one).

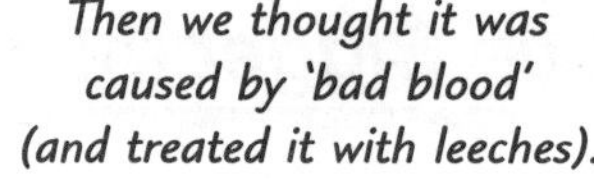

Then we thought it was caused by 'bad blood' (and treated it with leeches).

*If **Evidence** Supports a Hypothesis, It's **Accepted — for Now***

1) If pretty much every scientist in the world believes a hypothesis to be true because experiments back it up, then it usually goes in the textbooks for students to learn.
2) Accepted hypotheses are often referred to as theories.
3) Our currently accepted theories are the ones that have survived this 'trial by evidence' — they've been tested many, many times over the years and survived (while the less good ones have been ditched).
4) However... they never, never become hard and fast, totally indisputable fact. You can never know... it'd only take one odd, totally inexplicable result, and the hypothesising and testing would start all over again.

Now we know most illnesses are due to microorganisms.

You expect me to believe that — then show me the evidence...

If scientists think something is true, they need to produce evidence to convince others — it's all part of testing a hypothesis. One hypothesis might survive these tests, while others won't — it's how things progress. And along the way some hypotheses will be disproved — i.e. shown not to be true.

Your Data's Got To be Good

Evidence is the key to science — but not all evidence is equally good.
The way evidence is gathered can have a big effect on how trustworthy it is...

Lab Experiments *and* ***Studies*** *Are Better Than* ***Rumour***

1) Results from experiments in laboratories are great. A lab is the easiest place to control variables so that they're all kept constant (except for the one you're investigating). This makes it easier to carry out a FAIR TEST.

See page 7 for more about fair tests and variables.

2) For things that you can't investigate in the lab (e.g. climate) you conduct scientific studies. As many of the variables as possible are controlled, to make it a fair test.

3) Old wives' tales, rumours, hearsay, "what someone said", and so on, should be taken with a pinch of salt. Without any evidence they're NOT scientific — they're just opinions.

The ***Bigger*** *the* ***Sample Size*** *the* ***Better***

1) Data based on small samples isn't as good as data based on large samples. A sample should be representative of the whole population (i.e. it should share as many of the various characteristics in the population as possible) — a small sample can't do that as well.

2) The bigger the sample size the better, but scientists have to be realistic when choosing how big. For example, if you were studying how lifestyle affects people's weight it'd be great to study everyone in the UK (a huge sample), but it'd take ages and cost a lot of money. Studying a thousand people is more realistic.

If there's no evidence, there's no science...

You need to think carefully about where evidence has come from. If it's come from an experiment where the variables were controlled, then you can be fairly sure that you can trust the evidence. However, you also need to think about sample size — the bigger the sample, the better the results.

Your Data's Got To be Good

When it comes to evidence, reliability and validity are really important.

Evidence Needs to be **Reliable (Repeatable** and **Reproducible)**

Evidence is only reliable if it can be repeated (during an experiment) and other scientists can reproduce it too (in other experiments). If it's not reliable, you can't believe it.

RELIABLE means that the data can be repeated, and reproduced by others.

EXAMPLE:

In 1998, a scientist claimed that he'd found a link between the MMR vaccine (for measles, mumps and rubella) and autism.

As a result, many parents stopped their children from having the vaccine — which led to a big rise in the number of children catching measles.

However, no other scientist has been able to repeat the results since — they just weren't reliable. Health authorities have now concluded that the vaccine is safe to use.

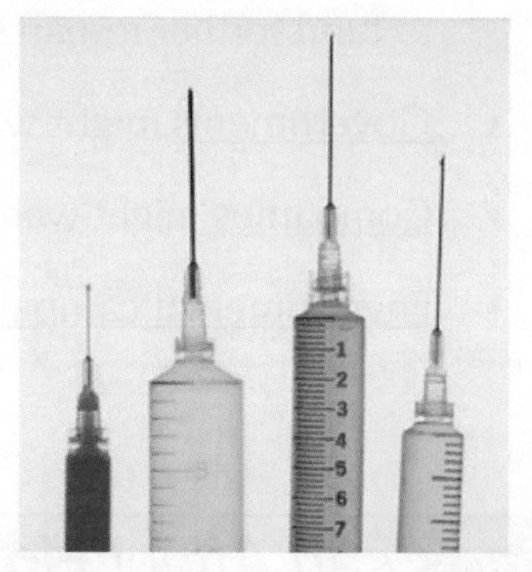

Evidence Also Needs to Be **Valid**

VALID means that the data is reliable AND answers the original question.

EXAMPLE: Do power lines cause cancer?

Some studies have found that children who live near overhead power lines are more likely to develop cancer. What they'd actually found was a correlation (relationship) between the variables "presence of power lines" and "incidence of cancer" — they found that as one changed, so did the other.

But this evidence is not enough to say that the power lines cause cancer, as other explanations might be possible.

For example, power lines are often near busy roads, so the areas tested could contain different levels of pollution from traffic.

So these studies don't show a definite link and so don't answer the original question.

RRR — Reliable means Repeatable and Reproducible...

The scientific community won't accept someone's data if it can't be repeated by anyone else. It may sound like a really fantastic new theory, but if there's no other support for it, it just isn't reliable.

Bias and How to Spot It

When you're given some scientific evidence, you need to think about who's presenting it to you, as well as what it says.

*Scientific **Evidence** can be **Presented** in a **Biased Way***

1) People who want to make a point can sometimes present data in a biased way, e.g. they overemphasise a relationship in the data. (Sometimes without knowing they're doing it.)
2) And there are all sorts of reasons why people might want to do this — for example...

- They want to keep the organisation or company that's funding the research happy. (If the results aren't what they'd like they might not give them any more money to fund further research.)
- Governments might want to persuade voters, other governments, journalists, etc.
- Companies might want to 'big up' their products. Or make impressive safety claims.
- Environmental campaigners might want to persuade people to behave differently.

*Things can Affect **How Seriously Evidence** is **Taken***

1) If an investigation is done by a team of highly-regarded scientists it's sometimes taken more seriously than evidence from less well known scientists.
2) But having experience, authority or a fancy qualification doesn't necessarily mean the evidence is good — the only way to tell is to look at the evidence scientifically (e.g. is it reliable, valid, etc.).
3) Also, some evidence might be ignored if it could create political problems, or emphasised if it helps a particular cause.

EXAMPLE:
Some governments were pretty slow to accept the fact that human activities are causing global warming, despite all the evidence.
This is because accepting it means they've got to do something about it, which costs money and could hurt their economy. This could lose them a lot of votes.

Trust me — I've got a BSc, PhD, PC, TV and a DVD...

We all tend to respect people in authority, but you have to ignore that fact and look at the evidence (just because someone has got a long list of letters after their name doesn't mean the evidence is good). Spotting biased evidence isn't the easiest thing in the world — ask yourself 'Does the scientist (or the person writing about it) stand to gain something (or lose something)?' If they do, it's possible that their evidence could be biased.

Issues Created by Science

Developments in science are happening all the time. New things are being discovered or created that can make our lives easier. But that doesn't mean that they won't create any problems.

Scientific Developments are Great, but they can Raise Issues

Scientific knowledge is increased by doing experiments. And this knowledge leads to scientific developments, e.g. new technologies or new advice. These developments can create issues though.

For example:

Economic Issues

Society can't always afford to do things scientists recommend (e.g. investing heavily in alternative energy sources) without cutting back elsewhere.

Social Issues

Decisions based on scientific evidence affect people — e.g. should junk food be taxed more highly (to encourage people to eat healthily)? Should alcohol be banned (to prevent health problems)? Would the effect on people's lifestyles be acceptable...

Environmental Issues

Genetically modified crops may help us produce more food — but some people think they could cause environmental problems (see page 73).

Ethical Issues

There are a lot of things that scientific developments have made possible, but should we do them? E.g. cloning humans.

Scientific developments aren't all good...

When you hear about a new development in science, think about whether it raises any issues. There will almost certainly be some, whether they're to do with the environment, people, or money. Evaluating issues is the sort of thing that could come up in the exams, so get plenty of practice in now.

Science Has Limits

Science can give us amazing things — cures for diseases, space travel, renewable energy...
But science has its limitations — there are questions that it just can't answer.

Some Questions Are **Unanswered** by Science — So Far

1) We don't understand everything. And we never will. We'll find out more, for sure — as more hypotheses are suggested, and more experiments are done. But there'll always be stuff we don't know.

   EXAMPLES:
   - Today we don't know as much as we'd like about the impacts of global warming. How much will sea level rise? And to what extent will weather patterns change?
   - We also don't know anywhere near as much as we'd like about the Universe. Are there other life forms out there? And what is the Universe made of?

2) These are complicated questions. At the moment scientists don't all agree on the answers because there isn't enough reliable and valid evidence.
3) But eventually, we probably will be able to answer these questions once and for all... All we need is more evidence.
4) But by then there'll be loads of new questions to answer.

Other Questions Are **Unanswerable** by Science

1) Then there's the other type... questions that all the experiments in the world won't help us answer — the "Should we be doing this at all?" type questions. There are always two sides...
2) Take embryo screening (which allows you to choose an embryo with particular characteristics). It's possible to do it — but does that mean we should?
3) Different people have different opinions on it:

Some people say it's good... couples whose existing child needs a bone marrow transplant, but who can't find a donor, will be able to have another child selected for its matching bone marrow. This would save the life of their first child — and if they want another child anyway... where's the harm?

THE GAZETTE
BONE MARROW BABY'S BROTHER SAVED
THE POST
BONE MARROW BABY BORN: WHAT RIGHTS DOES HE HAVE?

Other people say it's bad... they say it could have serious effects on the new child. In the above example, the new child might feel unwanted — thinking they were only brought into the world to help someone else. And would they have the right to refuse to donate their bone marrow (as anyone else would)?

4) The question of whether something is morally or ethically right or wrong can't be answered by more experiments — there is no "right" or "wrong" answer.
5) The best we can do is get a consensus from society — a judgement that most people are more or less happy to live by. Science can provide more information to help people make this judgement, and the judgement might change over time. But in the end it's up to people and their conscience.

Science is a "real world" subject...

Science can't tell you whether you should or shouldn't do something. That kind of thing is up to you and society to decide. But there are lots of questions that science might be able to answer in the future — like whether or not there are other intelligent life forms floating around in the Universe...

Designing Investigations

You need to know all about investigations for your controlled assessment and for your exams. Investigations include experiments and studies. The rest of this section will take you through it all...

Investigations Produce Evidence to Support or Disprove a Hypothesis

1) Scientists observe things and come up with hypotheses to explain them (see page 1).
2) To figure out whether a hypothesis might be correct or not you need to do an investigation to gather some evidence.
3) The first step is to use the hypothesis to come up with a prediction — a statement about what you think will happen that you can test.
4) For example, if your hypothesis is:

Sometimes the words 'hypothesis' and 'prediction' are used interchangeably.

> "Spots are caused by picking your nose too much."

Then your prediction might be:

> "People who pick their nose more often will have more spots."

5) Investigations are used to see if there are patterns or relationships between two variables. For example, to see if there's a pattern or relationship between the variables 'having spots' and 'nose picking'.
6) The investigation has to be a FAIR TEST to make sure the evidence is reliable and valid...

See page 3 for more on reliability and validity.

To Make an Investigation a Fair Test You Have to Control the Variables

1) In a lab experiment you usually change one variable and measure how it affects the other variable.

EXAMPLE: you might change only the temperature of an enzyme-controlled reaction and measure how this affects the rate of reaction.

2) To make it a fair test everything else that could affect the results should stay the same (otherwise you can't tell if the thing you're changing is causing the results or not — the data won't be reliable or valid).

EXAMPLE continued: you need to keep the pH the same, otherwise you won't know if any change in the rate of reaction is caused by the change in temperature, or the change in pH.

3) The variable you CHANGE is called the INDEPENDENT variable.
4) The variable you MEASURE is called the DEPENDENT variable.
5) The variables that you KEEP THE SAME are called CONTROL variables.

EXAMPLE continued:
Independent variable = temperature
Dependent variable = rate of reaction
Control variables = pH, volume of reactants, concentration of reactants etc.

Designing Investigations

There's a lot to think about when you're planning an investigation. Doing a trial run can make it easier to work out the best way to carry out an experiment. Here's how...

Trial Runs help Figure out the Range and Interval of Variable Values

1) It's a good idea to do a trial run first — a quick version of your experiment.

2) Trial runs are used to figure out the range of variable values used in the proper experiment (the upper and lower limit). If you don't get a change in the dependent variable at the upper values in the trial run, you might narrow the range in the proper experiment. But if you still get a big change at the upper values you might increase the range.

> EXAMPLE continued (from previous page):
> You might do a trial run with a range of 10-50 °C.
> If there was no reaction at the upper end (e.g. 40-50 °C), you might narrow the range to 10-40 °C for the proper experiment.

3) And trial runs can be used to figure out the interval (gaps) between the values too. The intervals can't be too small (otherwise the experiment would take ages), or too big (otherwise you might miss something).

> EXAMPLE continued:
> If using 1 °C intervals doesn't give you much change in the rate of reaction each time you might decide to use 5 °C intervals, e.g. 10, 15, 20, 25, 30, 35 °C...

4) Trial runs can also help you figure out how many times the experiment has to be repeated to get reliable results.

   E.g. if you repeat it three times and the results are all similar, then three repeats is enough.

You won't get a trial run at the exam, so get learning...

A trial run can also help you to spot any problems with your method. You don't want to find a load of issues when you're carrying out the real thing. For example, you might find an easier way to do something, or discover a way to do something that makes your results more accurate. And of course, as you've just learnt, trial runs help you work out the best range and interval of variable values.

Designing Investigations

You learnt on page 7 that to make an investigation a fair test, you have to control the variables. But sometimes controlling all of the variables isn't that easy. You might need to use a control group.

It Can Be **Hard** to **Control the Variables** in a **Study**

It's important that a study is a fair test, just like a lab experiment. It's a lot trickier to control the variables in a study than it is in a lab experiment though (see page 7). Sometimes you can't control them all, but you can use a control group to help. This is a group of whatever you're studying (people, plants etc.) that's kept under the same conditions as the group in the experiment, but doesn't have anything done to it.

EXAMPLE:

If you're studying the effect of pesticides on crop growth, pesticide is applied to one field but not to another field (the control field).

Both fields are planted with the same crop, and are in the same area (so they get the same weather conditions).

The control field is there to try and account for variables like the weather, which don't stay the same all the time, but could affect the results.

Investigations Can be **Hazardous**

1) A hazard is something that can potentially cause harm. Hazards include:

- Microorganisms, e.g. some bacteria can make you ill.
- Chemicals, e.g. sulfuric acid can burn your skin and alcohols catch fire easily.
- Fire, e.g. an unattended Bunsen burner is a fire hazard.
- Electricity, e.g. faulty electrical equipment could give you a shock.

2) Scientists need to manage the risk of hazards by doing things to reduce them. For example:

- If you're working with sulfuric acid, always wear gloves and safety goggles. This will reduce the risk of the acid coming into contact with your skin and eyes.
- If you're using a Bunsen burner, stand it on a heat proof mat. This will reduce the risk of starting a fire.

You can find out about potential hazards by looking in textbooks, doing some internet research, or asking your teacher.

The lab is a dangerous place...

There are plenty of things that can cause harm in the lab. When you're designing an investigation you need to think about how you can carry it out as safely as possible — even if it's just wearing a pair of safety goggles. That's not all you need to think about though... In a study, there might be some variables that are just impossible to control. This means you'll need to set up a control group.

Collecting Data

After designing your investigation to perfection, you'll need to collect some data.

Your Data Should be **Reliable, Accurate** and **Precise**

1) To improve reliability you need to repeat the readings and calculate the mean (average). You need to repeat each reading at least three times.
2) To make sure your results are reliable you can cross check them by taking a second set of readings with another instrument (or a different observer).
3) Checking your results match with secondary sources, e.g. other studies, also increases the reliability of your data.
4) Your data also needs to be ACCURATE. Really accurate results are those that are really close to the true answer.
5) Your data also needs to be PRECISE. Precise results are ones where the data is all really close to the mean (i.e. not spread out).

Repeat	Data set 1	Data set 2
1	12	11
2	14	17
3	13	14
Mean	13	14

Data set 1 is more precise than data set 2.

Your **Equipment** has to be **Right for the Job**

1) The measuring equipment you use has to be sensitive enough to measure the changes you're looking for. For example, if you need to measure changes of 1 ml you need to use a measuring cylinder that can measure in 1 ml steps — it'd be no good trying with one that only measures 10 ml steps.
2) The smallest change a measuring instrument can detect is called its RESOLUTION. E.g. some mass balances have a resolution of 1 g, some have a resolution of 0.1 g, and some are even more sensitive.
3) Also, equipment needs to be calibrated so that your data is more accurate. E.g. mass balances need to be set to zero before you start weighing things.

Reliability is really important in science...

Weirdly, data can be really precise but not very accurate, e.g. a fancy piece of lab equipment might give results that are precise, but if it's not calibrated properly those results won't be accurate.

Collecting Data

Errors and anomalous results can turn up in your data — and this is what this page is all about.

You Need to Look out for **Errors** and **Anomalous Results**

1) The results of your experiment will always vary a bit because of random errors — tiny differences caused by things like human errors in measuring.
2) You can reduce their effect by taking many readings and calculating the mean.

3) If the same error is made every time, it's called a SYSTEMATIC ERROR. For example, if you measured from the very end of your ruler instead of from the 0 cm mark every time, all your measurements would be a bit small.

Repeating the experiment in the exact same way and calculating an average won't correct a systematic error.

4) Just to make things more complicated, if a systematic error is caused by using equipment that isn't calibrated properly it's called a ZERO ERROR. For example, if a mass balance always reads 1 gram before you put anything on it, all your measurements will be 1 gram too heavy.

5) You can compensate for some systematic errors if you know about them though, e.g. if your mass balance always reads 1 gram before you put anything on it you can subtract 1 gram from all your results.

6) Sometimes you get a result that doesn't seem to fit in with the rest at all.

Park	Number of starlings	Number of bird feeders
A	28	4
B	42	8
C	1127	1

7) These results are called ANOMALOUS RESULTS.
8) You should investigate them and try to work out what happened. If you can work out what happened (e.g. you measured something totally wrong) you can ignore them when processing your results.

An anomalous result should stick out like a sore thumb...

There are some errors that you just can't stop happening — they're the random errors. However, errors like zero errors can be avoided by making sure your equipment is set up properly to start with.

Processing and Presenting Data

After you've collected your data you'll have lots of info that you have to make some kind of sense of. You need to process and present it so you can look for patterns and relationships in it.

Data Needs to be Organised

1) Tables are really useful for organising data.
2) When you draw a table use a ruler, make sure each column has a heading (including the units) and keep it neat and tidy.
3) Annoyingly, tables are about as useful as a chocolate teapot for showing patterns or relationships in data. You need to use some kind of graph for that.

You Might Have to Process Your Data

1) When you've done repeats of an experiment you should always calculate the mean (average). To do this ADD TOGETHER all the data values and DIVIDE by the total number of values in the sample.
2) You might also need to calculate the range (how spread out the data is). To do this find the LARGEST number and SUBTRACT the SMALLEST number from it.

EXAMPLE

Ignore anomalous results when calculating means and ranges.

Test tube	Repeat 1 (g)	Repeat 2 (g)	Repeat 3 (g)	Mean (g)	Range (g)
A	28	37	32	(28 + 37 + 32) ÷ 3 = 32.3	37 – 28 = 9
B	47	51	60	(47 + 51 + 60) ÷ 3 = 52.7	60 – 47 = 13
C	68	72	70	(68 + 72 + 70) ÷ 3 = 70.0	72 – 68 = 4

If Your Data Comes in Categories, Present It in a Bar Chart

1) If the independent variable is categoric (comes in distinct categories, e.g. blood types, metals) you should use a bar chart to display the data.
2) You also use them if the independent variable is discrete (the data can be counted in chunks, where there's no in-between value, e.g. number of people is discrete because you can't have half a person).
3) There are some golden rules you need to follow for drawing bar charts:

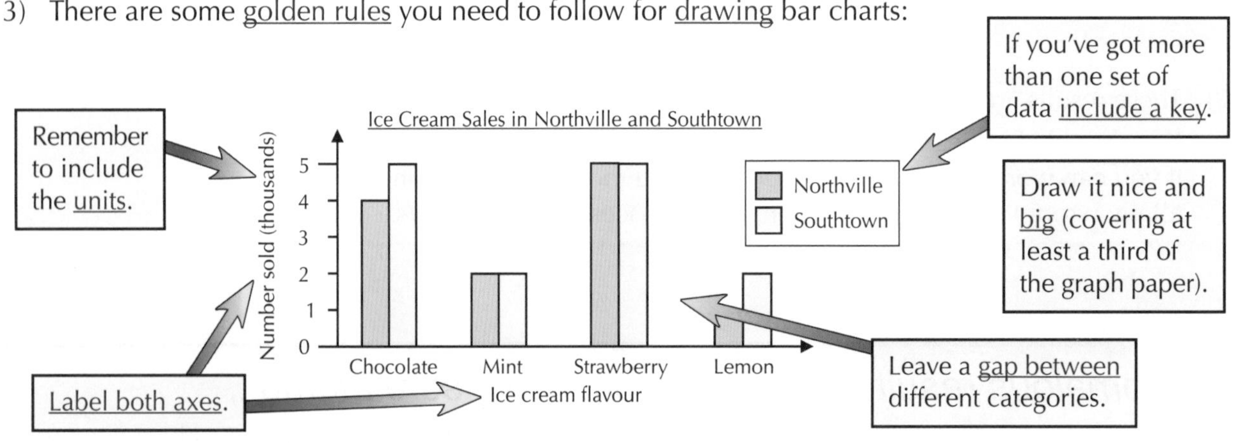

Presenting Data

Scientists love to present data as line graphs...

If Your Data is Continuous, Plot a Line Graph

1) If the independent variable is continuous (numerical data that can have any value within a range, e.g. length, volume, temperature) you should use a line graph to display the data.
2) Here are the rules for drawing line graphs:

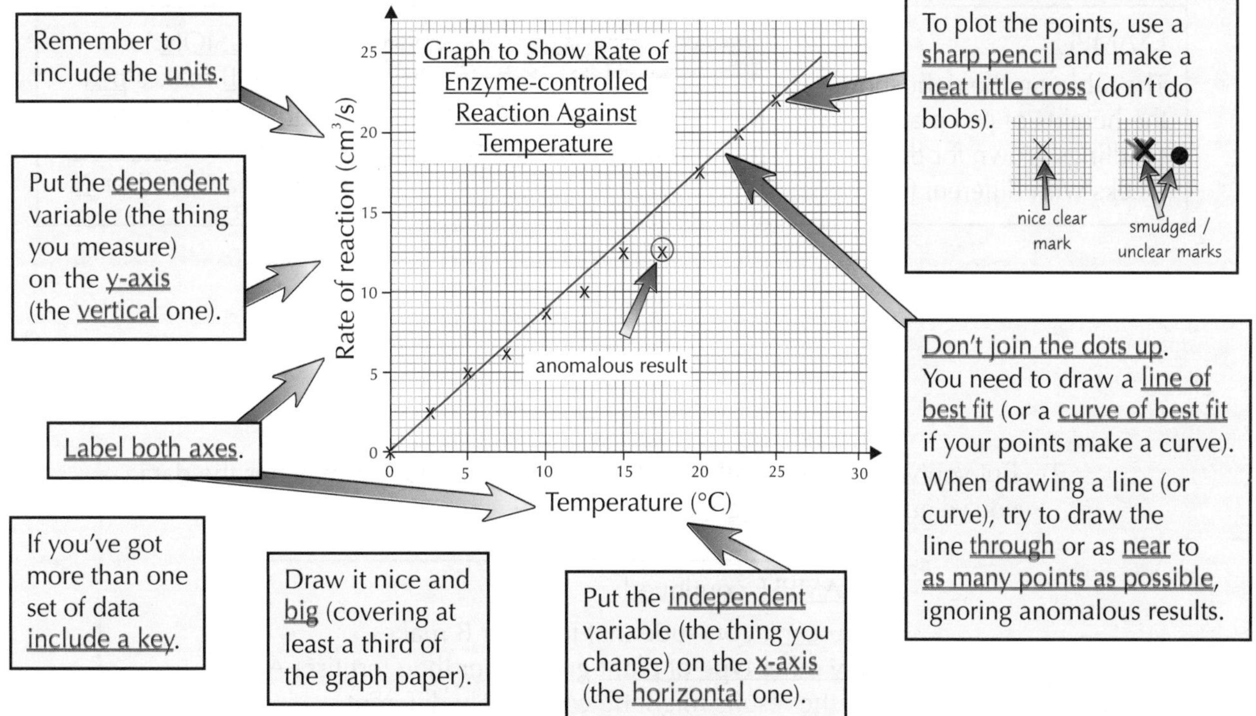

3) Line graphs are used to show the relationship between two variables (just like other graphs).
4) Data can show three different types of correlation (relationship):

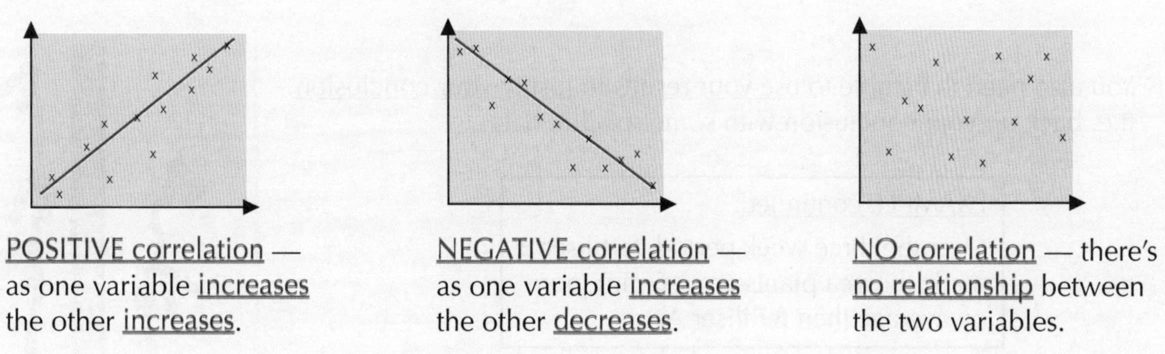

POSITIVE correlation — as one variable increases the other increases.
NEGATIVE correlation — as one variable increases the other decreases.
NO correlation — there's no relationship between the two variables.

5) You need to be able to describe the following relationships on line graphs too:

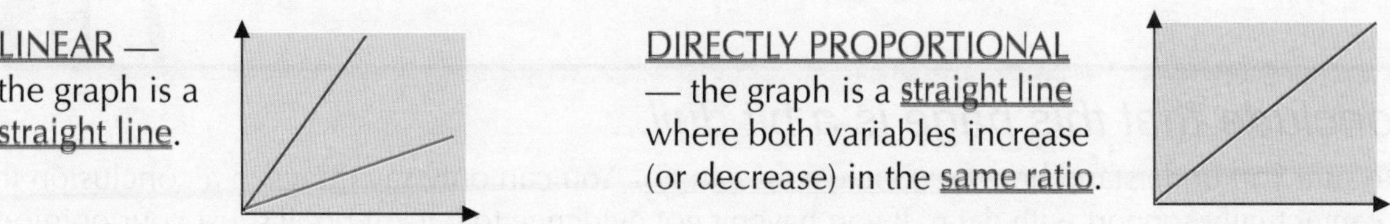

LINEAR — the graph is a straight line.
DIRECTLY PROPORTIONAL — the graph is a straight line where both variables increase (or decrease) in the same ratio.

Drawing Conclusions

The final step of an investigation is to draw a conclusion. Here's what you need to do...

*You Can **Only Conclude** What the Data Shows and **No More***

1) Drawing conclusions might seem pretty straightforward — you just look at your data and say what pattern or relationship you see between the dependent and independent variables.

EXAMPLE:
The table on the right shows the heights of pea plant seedlings grown for three weeks with different fertilisers.

Fertiliser	Mean growth (mm)
A	13.5
B	19.5
No fertiliser	5.5

CONCLUSION:
Fertiliser B makes pea plant seedlings grow taller over a three week period than fertiliser A.

2) But you've got to be really careful that your conclusion matches the data you've got and doesn't go any further.

EXAMPLE continued:
You can't conclude that fertiliser B makes any other type of plant grow taller than fertiliser A — the results might be completely different.

3) You also need to be able to use your results to justify your conclusion (i.e. back up your conclusion with some specific data).

EXAMPLE continued:
Over the three week period, fertiliser B made the pea plants grow 6 mm more on average than fertiliser A.

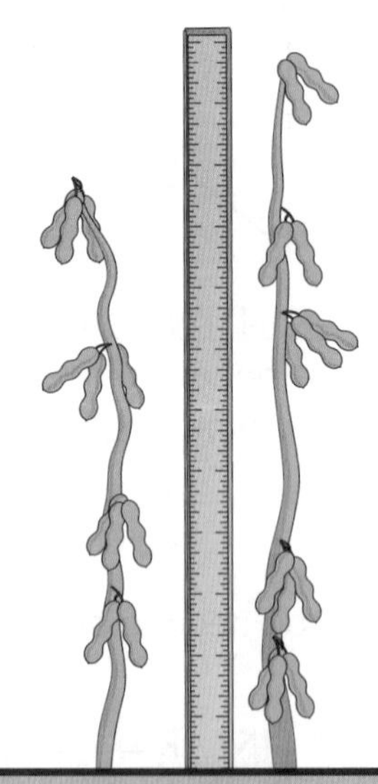

I conclude that this page is a bit dull...

Make sure you understand how far conclusions can go. You can only say things in a conclusion that you can actually support with data. If you haven't got evidence to back it up, it's just your opinion. Correlation and cause are also important in conclusions — luckily that's what the next page is about.

Drawing Conclusions

It's important that you understand the difference between correlation and cause. Take a bit of time to read over this page so that you don't make any mistakes when you're drawing conclusions.

Correlation DOES NOT mean Cause

1) If two things are correlated (i.e. there's a relationship between them) it doesn't necessarily mean that a change in one variable is causing the change in the other — this is REALLY IMPORTANT, don't forget it.
2) There are three possible reasons for a correlation:

1) Chance

1) Even though it might seem a bit weird, it's possible that two things show a correlation in a study purely because of chance.
2) For example, one study might find a correlation between people's hair colour and how good they are at frisbee. But other scientists don't get a correlation when they investigate it — the results of the first study are just a fluke.

2) Linked by a 3rd Variable

1) A lot of the time it may look as if a change in one variable is causing a change in the other, but it isn't — a third variable links the two things.
2) For example, there's a correlation between water temperature and shark attacks. This obviously isn't because warmer water makes sharks crazy. Instead, they're linked by a third variable — the number of people swimming (more people swim when the water's hotter, and with more people in the water you get more shark attacks).

3) Cause

1) Sometimes a change in one variable does cause a change in the other.
2) For example, there's a correlation between smoking and lung cancer. This is because chemicals in tobacco smoke cause lung cancer.
3) You can only conclude that a correlation is due to cause when you've controlled all the variables that could, just could, be affecting the result. (For the smoking example above this would include things like age and exposure to other things that cause cancer.)

One more time — correlation doesn't always mean cause...

If you've understood this page, you'll know that cause is only one of the reasons for a correlation in your results. If you didn't know that, you'd better go back and read the page again.

Controlled Assessment — Section One

Controlled Assessment involves doing an experiment and answering two question papers on it under exam conditions. The next two pages tell you all about the two question papers.

*There are **Two Sections** in the **Controlled Assessment***

1) Planning

The Section 1 question paper is all about planning your experiment.

Before you sit down to do it you'll be given some information about a topic and some time to develop a hypothesis/prediction and plan the experiment. You could get questions on any of the following things, so make sure you know them:

1) What your hypothesis/prediction is.
2) What variables you're going to control (and how you're going to control them).
3) What measurements you're going to take.
4) What range and interval of values you will use for the independent variable.
5) How you'd figure out the range and interval using a trial run (sometimes called a 'preliminary investigation' in the question papers). See page 8 for more.
6) How many times you're going to repeat the experiment — a minimum of three is a good idea.
7) What equipment you're going to use (and why that equipment is right for the job).
8) How to carry out the experiment, i.e. what you do first, what you do second...
9) What hazards are involved in doing the experiment, and how to reduce them.
10) What table you'll draw to put your results in. See page 12 for more on tables.

There's lots of help on all of these things on pages 7-15.

When you've done the planning and completed the first question paper you'll actually do the experiment. Then you'll have to present your data.

Make sure you use the right type of graph, and you draw it properly — see pages 12-13 for help. After that it's onto the second question paper, which covers Section 2...

Read all this through and you'll be ready to face Section 1...

That might be a long list of stuff, but it's all important. No need to panic at the sight of it though — as long as you've learnt everything on the previous few pages, you should be fine.

Controlled Assessment — Section Two

One paper down. On to the second paper...

2) *Drawing Conclusions* and *Evaluating*

For the Section 2 question paper you have to do these things for your experiment:

1) Draw conclusions from your results. For this you need to:
   - Describe the relationship between the variables in detail — see page 14 for how to do this. E.g. 'I found that there is a relationship between picking your nose and having spots. The more often you pick your nose the more spots you'll have. For example, my results showed...'.
   - Refer to the results other people in your group got (which you'll be given). E.g. 'My conclusion is supported by most of the results other people got. They also found that people who pick their nose more have more spots.'

2) Say whether your results back up the hypothesis/prediction, and give reasons why or why not. E.g. 'My results did not back up the prediction. The prediction was that picking your nose more has no effect on the number of spots you have. But I found the opposite to be true in my investigation'.

3) Evaluate your experiment.
   For this you need to suggest ways you could improve your experiment.

   - Comment on your equipment and method, e.g. could you have used more accurate equipment?
   - Make sure you explain how the improvements would give you better data next time.
   - Refer to your results. E.g. 'My data wasn't accurate enough because the mass balance I used only measured in 1 g steps. I could use a more sensitive one next time (e.g. a mass balance that measures in 0.5 g steps) to get more accurate data'.

You'll also be given some data from a different experiment and asked to analyse it. This just involves doing what you did for your data with someone else's data, e.g. draw conclusions from it.

And that's it for the controlled assessment...

This page and the previous page are here to be useful when you're figuring out what you'll need to do in the two stages of your controlled assessment. So, make sure you've read them through at least a couple of times — then you'll be familiar with what to expect in the papers.

Diet and Metabolic Rate

The first thing on the GCSE AQA Biology menu is food. It's where you get your energy from, to do all sorts of things like talking, partying and maybe a bit of revision.

A Balanced Diet Does a Lot to Keep You Healthy

1) For good health, your diet must provide the energy you need (but not more) — see the next page.
2) But that's not all. Because the different food groups have different uses in the body, you need to have the right balance of foods as well. So you need:

   ...enough CARBOHYDRATES to release energy,

   ...enough FATS to keep warm and release energy,

   ...enough PROTEIN for growth, cell repair and cell replacement,

   ...enough FIBRE to keep everything moving smoothly through your digestive system,

   ...and tiny amounts of various VITAMINS and MINERAL IONS to keep your skin, bones, blood and everything else generally healthy.

People's Energy Needs Vary Because of Who They Are...

1) You need energy to fuel the chemical reactions in the body that keep you alive. These reactions are called your metabolism, and the speed at which they occur is your metabolic rate.
2) There are slight variations in the resting metabolic rate of different people. For example, muscle needs more energy than fatty tissue, which means (all other things being equal) people with a higher proportion of muscle to fat in their bodies will have a higher metabolic rate.
3) However, physically bigger people are likely to have a higher metabolic rate than smaller people — the bigger you are, the more energy your body needs to be supplied with (because you have more cells).
4) Men tend to have a slightly higher rate than women — they're slightly bigger and have a larger proportion of muscle. Other genetic factors may also have some effect.
5) And regular exercise can boost your resting metabolic rate because it builds muscle.

...and Because of What They Do

1) When you exercise, you obviously need more energy — so your metabolic rate goes up during exercise and stays high for some time after you finish (particularly if the exercise is strenuous).
2) So people who have more active jobs need more energy on a daily basis — builders require more energy per day than office workers, for instance. The table shows the average kilojoules burned per minute when doing different activities.
3) This means your activity level affects the amount of energy your diet should contain. If you do little exercise, you're going to need less energy, so less fat and carbohydrate in your diet, than if you're constantly on the go.

Activity	kJ/min
Sleeping	4.5
Watching TV	7
Cycling (5 mph)	21
Jogging (5 mph)	40
Climbing stairs	77
Swimming	35
Rowing	58
Slow walking	14

Factors Affecting Health

Being healthy isn't just about being the right weight — it means being free of any diseases too.

Your **Health** is Affected by Having an **Unbalanced Diet**

1) People whose diet is badly out of balance are said to be malnourished.
2) Malnourished people can be fat or thin, or unhealthy in other ways:

Malnourishment is different from starvation, which is not getting enough food of any sort.

Eating **Too Much** Can Lead to **Obesity**...

1) Excess carbohydrate or fat in the diet can lead to obesity.
2) Obesity is a common disorder in developed countries — it's defined as being 20% (or more) over maximum recommended body mass.
3) Hormonal problems can lead to obesity, though the usual cause is a bad diet, overeating and a lack of exercise.
4) Health problems that can arise as a result of obesity include: arthritis (inflammation of the joints), type 2 diabetes (inability to control blood sugar level), high blood pressure and heart disease. It's also a risk factor for some kinds of cancer.

...and Other **Health Problems**

1) Too much saturated fat in your diet can increase your blood cholesterol level (see page 20).
2) Eating too much salt can cause high blood pressure and heart problems.

Eating **Too Little** Can Also Cause Problems

1) Some people suffer from lack of food, particularly in developing countries.
2) The effects of malnutrition vary depending on what foods are missing from the diet. But problems commonly include slow growth (in children), fatigue, poor resistance to infection, and irregular periods in women.
3) Deficiency diseases are caused by a lack of vitamins or minerals. For example, a lack of vitamin C can cause scurvy, a deficiency disease that causes problems with the skin, joints and gums.

Obesity is a really big issue nowadays...

Your health can really suffer if you regularly eat too much, too little, or if you miss out on vital nutrients. Being overweight can cause problems with your heart and your joints. And even if you eat a good amount of food, you can still end up being malnourished if you're missing key vitamins or minerals.

Factors Affecting Health

What you eat isn't the only thing that affects your health. You also need to keep healthy by exercising regularly. And sometimes your genes can affect your health too.

Getting **Regular Exercise** Can Help You to Stay **Healthy**

1) Exercise is important as well as diet — people who exercise regularly are usually healthier than those who don't.

2) Exercise increases the amount of energy used by the body and decreases the amount stored as fat. It also builds muscle so it helps to boost your metabolic rate (see page 18).

3) That means people who exercise are less likely to suffer from health problems such as obesity.

However, sometimes people can be fit but not healthy — e.g. you can be physically fit and slim, but malnourished at the same time because your diet isn't balanced.

Inherited Factors Can Affect Your Health Too

1) It's not just about what you eat and how much exercise you do — your health can depend on inherited factors too.

2) Some people may inherit factors that affect their metabolic rate.

   For example, some inherited factors cause an underactive thyroid gland, which can lower the metabolic rate and cause obesity.

3) Other people may inherit factors that affect their blood cholesterol level.

   Cholesterol is a fatty substance that's essential for good health — it's found in every cell in the body. Some inherited factors increase blood cholesterol level, which increases the risk of heart disease.

To be healthy you need to eat sensibly and exercise...

If you've got any inherited factors that make you more likely to suffer from obesity or heart disease, it doesn't mean that you can't stay healthy. It just means that it's even more important that you keep a close eye on what you eat and make sure that you stay active.

Evaluating Food, Lifestyle and Diet

Sometimes you've got to be a bit clever when working out which is the healthiest food product to eat.

You Need to be Able to Evaluate Information on Food...

In the exam, you may get asked to evaluate information about how food affects health.
Don't panic though — just take a look at the examples of food labels below:

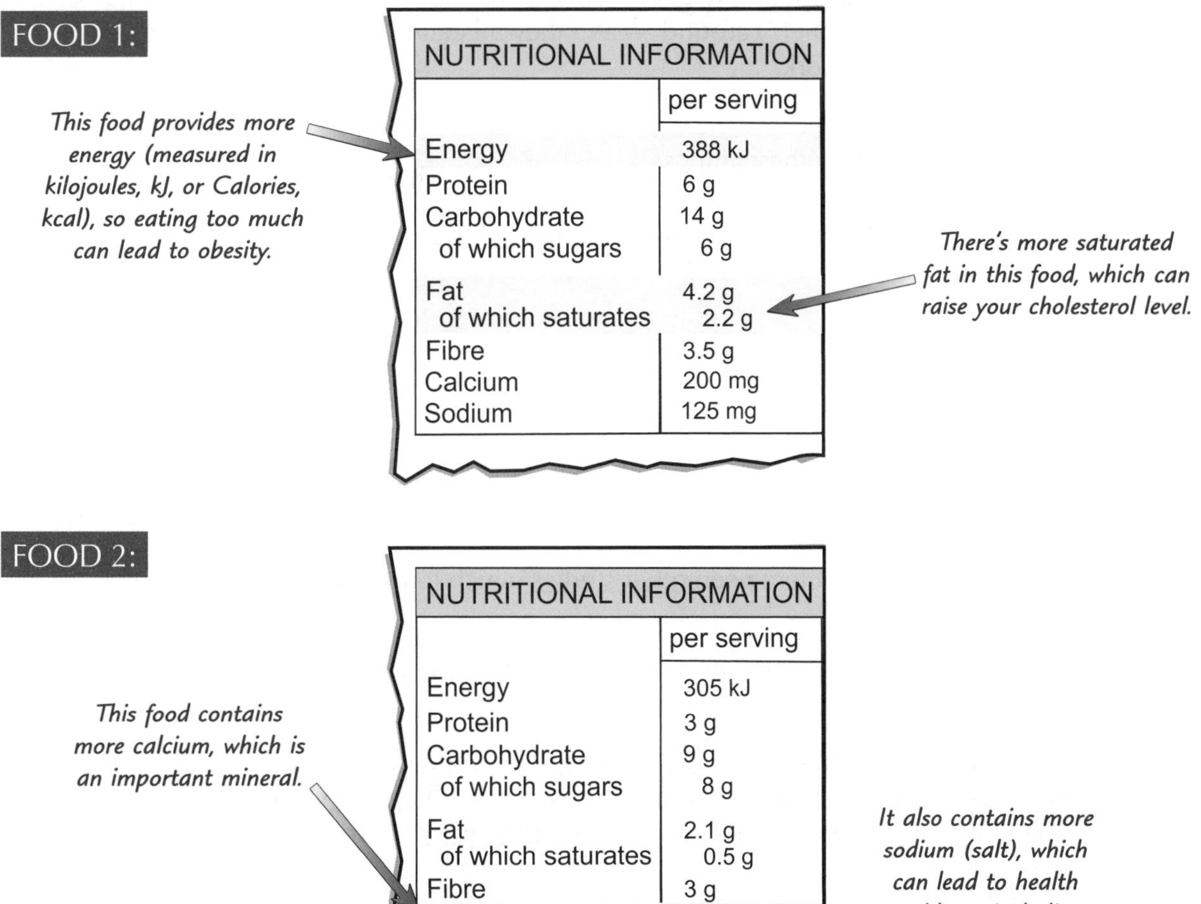

FOOD 1:
This food provides more energy (measured in kilojoules, kJ, or Calories, kcal), so eating too much can lead to obesity.
There's more saturated fat in this food, which can raise your cholesterol level.
FOOD 2:
This food contains more calcium, which is an important mineral.
It also contains more sodium (salt), which can lead to health problems, including high blood pressure.

FOOD 1: NUTRITIONAL INFORMATION

	per serving
Energy	388 kJ
Protein	6 g
Carbohydrate	14 g
of which sugars	6 g
Fat	4.2 g
of which saturates	2.2 g
Fibre	3.5 g
Calcium	200 mg
Sodium	125 mg

FOOD 2: NUTRITIONAL INFORMATION

	per serving
Energy	305 kJ
Protein	3 g
Carbohydrate	9 g
of which sugars	8 g
Fat	2.1 g
of which saturates	0.5 g
Fibre	3 g
Calcium	500 mg
Sodium	250 mg

...and Information on Lifestyle

1) You might also get asked to evaluate information about how lifestyle affects health.
2) Your lifestyle includes what you eat and what you do. E.g. a person who eats too much fat or carbohydrate and doesn't do much exercise will increase their risk of obesity.
3) Remember, you'll need to use your knowledge of how diet and exercise affect health to answer exam questions — make sure all the facts on the previous three pages are well lodged in your memory.

So many food labels, so little time...

Having a healthy diet is all about having a balanced diet. It's no good saying that a food is healthy just because it contains plenty of fibre and vitamins — if it's got lots of fat and sugar in it too, it won't do you much good. That's why it's important that you know how to read and understand food labels.

Evaluating Slimming Claims

Losing weight can be pretty difficult. If you're trying to lose weight, there are plenty of slimming products and programmes out there. But knowing if they'll work or not, now that's another thing. And that's where this page comes in...

Watch Out for **Slimming Claims** that Aren't **Scientifically Proven**

1) There are loads of slimming products (e.g. diet pills, slimming milkshakes) and slimming programmes (e.g. the Atkins Diet™) around — and they all claim they'll help you lose weight. But how do you know they work...

2) It's a good idea to look out for these things:

- Is the report a scientific study, published in a reputable journal?
- Was it written by a qualified person (not connected with the people selling it)?
- Was the sample of people asked/tested large enough to give reliable results?
- Have there been other studies which found similar results?

A "yes" to one or more of these is a good sign.

E.g. a common way to promote a new diet is to say, "Celebrity A has lost x pounds using it". But effectiveness in one person doesn't mean much. Only a large survey can tell if a diet is more or less effective than just eating less and exercising more — and these aren't done often.

3) Really, all you need to do to lose weight is to take in less energy than you use. So diets and slimming products will only work if you...

- eat less fat or carbohydrate (so that you take in less energy), or
- do more exercise (so that you use more energy).

4) Some claims may be true but a little misleading.

For example, low-fat bars might be low in fat, but eating them without changing the rest of your diet doesn't necessarily mean you'll lose weight — you could still be taking in too much energy.

I'm afraid I'm going to need proper scientific proof...

Learn what to look out for before you put too much faith in what you read. You can only trust a report if the study was carried out properly by someone independent from the company selling the product. Otherwise it probably won't tell you that much about how good that product really is.

Warm-Up and Exam Questions

By the time the big day comes you need to know all the facts in these warm-up questions and exam questions like the back of your hand. It's not a barrel of laughs, but it's the only way to get good marks.

Warm-Up Questions

1) Why is it important to eat carbohydrates as part of a balanced diet?
2) Name a health problem that eating too much salt can cause.
3) Give three possible effects of eating too little.
4) Does exercising regularly increase or decrease your metabolic rate?
5) Why is having a high blood cholesterol level a health risk?
6) Name one thing to look out for when evaluating a claim about a slimming product.

Exam Questions

1 The right amount of carbohydrates and vitamins are needed for a healthy, balanced diet.

(a) Name **one** other food group that is needed for a healthy, balanced diet.

(1 mark)

(b) Some people are said to be malnourished. Define the term 'malnourished'.

(1 mark)

(c) Obesity increases the risk of various health problems. Name **one** such problem.

(1 mark)

2 The labels below show some basic nutritional information from two food packets.

(a) Calculate how much energy a 40 g serving of **Food A** contains. Show your working.

(2 marks)

(b) Which of the two foods, A or B, is healthier? Explain your answer.

(3 marks)

FOOD A

NUTRITIONAL INFORMATION	per 100 g
Energy	512 kcal
Protein	6.9 g
Carbohydrate	49 g
Fat	5.2 g
Iron	0.5 mg

FOOD B

NUTRITIONAL INFORMATION	per 100 g
Energy	307 kcal
Protein	7.4 g
Carbohydrate	25 g
Fat	4.7 g
Iron	3 mg

3 To stay healthy you need to keep active.

(a) John and Dave are twins. John is a receptionist and Dave is a builder. Copy and complete the following sentence about John and Dave:

.... has the most active job, so he will need the most .... per day.

(2 marks)

(b) Explain why taking regular exercise decreases your risk of becoming obese.

(3 marks)

(c) Dave takes regular exercise and is fit, but his doctor tells him that he is at high risk of becoming obese.
Give **one** reason why Dave might be at risk of becoming obese despite being fit.

(1 mark)

Pathogens

Microorganisms that enter the body and cause disease are called pathogens.
Pathogens cause infectious diseases — diseases that can easily spread.

There Are Two Main Types of Pathogen: Bacteria and Viruses

1) Bacteria Are Very Small Living Cells

1) Bacteria are very small cells (about 1/100th the size of your body cells), which can reproduce rapidly inside your body.

2) They make you feel ill by doing two things:

a) damaging your cells

b) producing toxins (poisons)

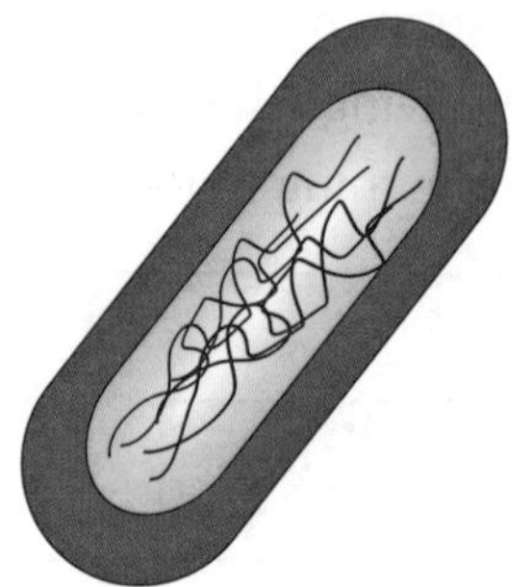

2) Viruses Are Not Cells — They're Much Smaller

1) Viruses are not cells. They're tiny, about 1/100th the size of a bacterium.

2) They replicate themselves by invading your cells and using the cells' machinery to produce many copies of themselves.

3) The cell will usually then burst, releasing all the new viruses.

4) This cell damage is what makes you feel ill.

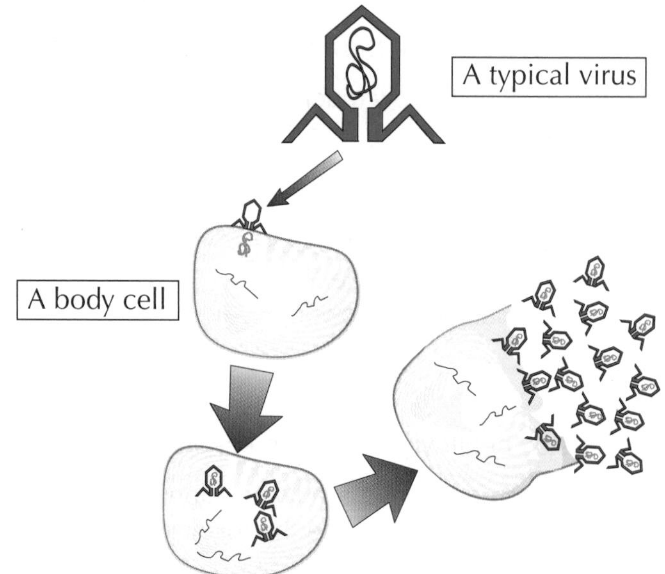

Trillions of bacteria call your digestive system home...

It's strange to think that such small things can have such massive effects on your body. But bacteria and viruses can multiply extremely quickly and make you feel ill by cell damage (bacteria and viruses) or by producing toxins (bacteria). It's a good job our bodies have ways of attacking them...

Fighting Disease

Your body is constantly fighting off attack from all sorts of bugs — yep, things really are out to get you. The body has lots of ways to stop pathogens causing disease.

Your Body Has a Pretty Sophisticated ***Defence System***

1) Your skin, plus hairs and mucus in your respiratory tract (breathing pipework), stop a lot of microorganisms getting inside your body.

2) And to try and prevent microorganisms getting into the body through cuts, small fragments of cells (called platelets) help blood clot quickly to seal wounds. If the blood contains low numbers of platelets then it will clot more slowly.

3) But if something does make it through, your immune system kicks in. The most important part is the white blood cells. They travel around in your blood and crawl into every part of you, constantly patrolling for microbes. When they come across an invading microbe they have three lines of attack.

1) ***Consuming*** *Them*

White blood cells can engulf foreign cells and digest them.

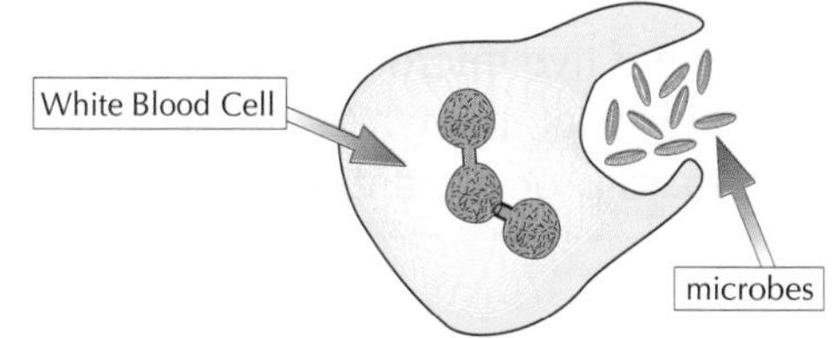

2) Producing ***Antibodies***

1) Every invading cell has unique molecules (called antigens) on its surface.

2) When your white blood cells come across a foreign antigen (i.e. one it doesn't recognise), they will start to produce proteins called antibodies to lock on to and kill the invading cells. The antibodies produced are specific to that type of antigen — they won't lock on to any others.

New microbe

Antibodies produced

White blood cell

New microbes attacked by new antibodies

3) Antibodies are then produced rapidly and carried around the body to kill all similar bacteria or viruses.

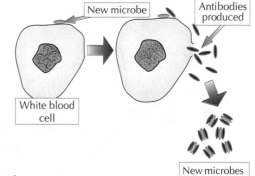

4) If the person is infected with the same pathogen again the white blood cells will rapidly produce the antibodies to kill it — the person is naturally immune to that pathogen and won't get ill.

3) Producing ***Antitoxins***

These counter toxins produced by the invading bacteria.

White blood cells protect our bodies from pathogens

So by now you might have worked out that if you have a low level of white blood cells you'll be more susceptible to infections. In fact, HIV/AIDS doesn't kill people directly, it just makes it easier for something else to by attacking white blood cells and weakening the immune system. However, other diseases (e.g. leukaemia) can increase the number of white blood cells — and that's no good either.

Fighting Disease — Vaccination

Vaccinations have changed the way we fight disease. We don't always have to deal with the problem once it's happened — we can prevent it happening in the first place.

Vaccination — Protects from Future Infections

1) When you're infected with a new microorganism, it takes your white blood cells a few days to learn how to deal with it. But by that time, you can be pretty ill.

2) Vaccinations involve injecting small amounts of dead or inactive microorganisms. These carry antigens, which cause your body to produce antibodies to attack them — even though the microorganism is harmless (since it's dead or inactive). For example, the MMR vaccine contains weakened versions of the viruses that cause measles, mumps and rubella (German measles) all in one vaccine.

3) But if live microorganisms of the same type appear after that, the white blood cells can rapidly mass-produce antibodies to kill off the pathogen.

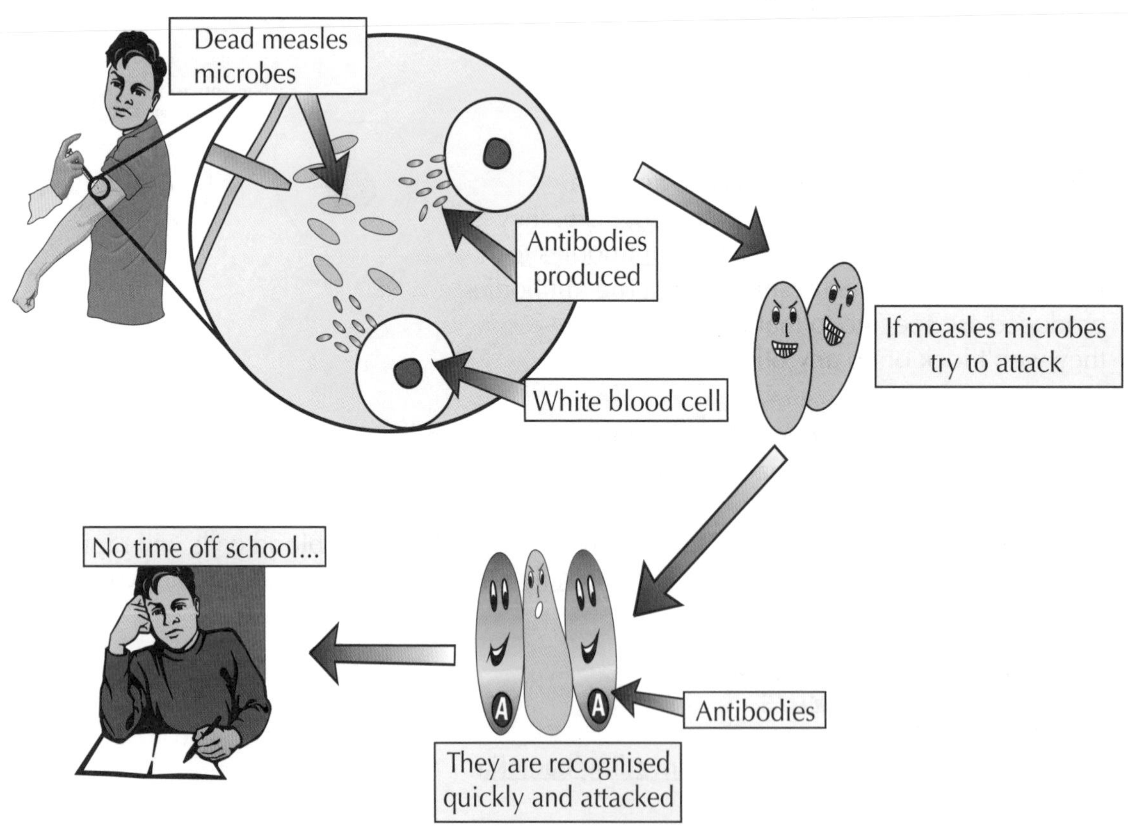

4) Some vaccinations "wear off" over time. So booster injections may need to be given to increase levels of antibodies again.

Fighting Disease — Vaccination

Having a whole range of vaccinations is pretty much standard now, so children today are much less likely to catch the kind of diseases that they might have in the past. That doesn't mean that vaccination is without its problems though...

There are **Pros** and **Cons** of **Vaccination**

You need to have an idea of the advantages that vaccination has. And you need to know about its disadvantages too. Read on...

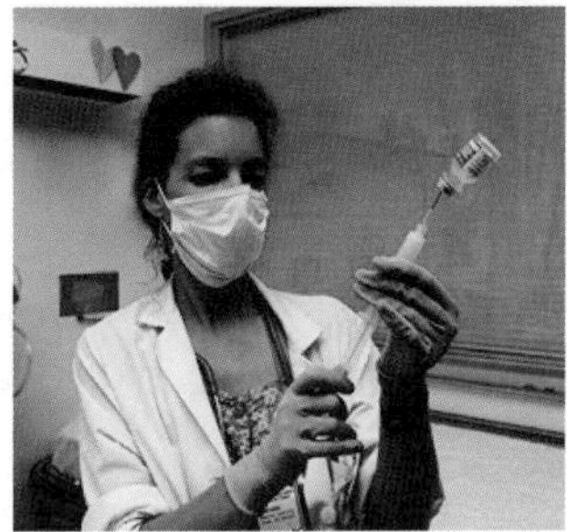

Pros:

1) Vaccines have helped control lots of infectious diseases that were once common in the UK (e.g. polio, measles, whooping cough, rubella, mumps, tetanus...). Smallpox no longer occurs at all, and polio infections have fallen by 99%.

2) Big outbreaks of disease — called epidemics — can be prevented if a large percentage of the population is vaccinated. That way, even the people who aren't vaccinated are unlikely to catch the disease because there are fewer people able to pass it on. But if a significant number of people aren't vaccinated, the disease can spread quickly through them and lots of people will be ill at the same time.

Cons:

1) Vaccines don't always work — sometimes they don't give you immunity.

2) You can sometimes have a bad reaction to a vaccine (e.g. swelling, or maybe something more serious like a fever or seizures). But bad reactions are very rare.

Prevention is better than cure...

Deciding whether to have a vaccination means balancing risks — the risk of catching the disease if you don't have a vaccine, against the risk of having a bad reaction if you do. As always, you need to look at the evidence. For example, if you get measles (the disease), there's about a 1 in 15 chance that you'll get complications (e.g. pneumonia) — and about 1 in 500 people who get measles actually die. However, the number of people who have a problem with the vaccine is more like 1 in 1 000 000.

Fighting Disease — Drugs

You've probably had to take some sort of medicine if you've been ill, e.g. cough remedies, painkillers. And you're about to find out why it's important to only take antibiotics when you really need them.

Some Drugs Just **Relieve Symptoms** — Others **Cure** the Problem

1) Painkillers (e.g. aspirin) are drugs that relieve pain. However, they don't actually tackle the cause of the disease, they just help to reduce the symptoms.

2) Other drugs do a similar kind of thing — reduce the symptoms without tackling the underlying cause. For example, lots of "cold remedies" don't actually cure colds.

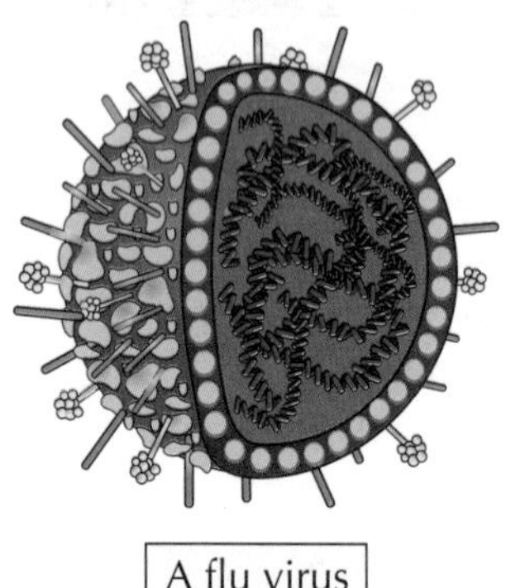

A flu virus

3) Antibiotics (e.g. penicillin) work differently — they actually kill (or prevent the growth of) the bacteria causing the problem without killing your own body cells. Different antibiotics kill different types of bacteria, so it's important to be treated with the right one.

4) But antibiotics don't destroy viruses (e.g. flu or cold viruses). Viruses reproduce using your own body cells, which makes it very difficult to develop drugs that destroy just the virus without killing the body's cells.

Bacteria Can Become **Resistant** to **Antibiotics**

1) Bacteria can mutate — sometimes the mutations cause them to be resistant to (not killed by) an antibiotic.

2) If you have an infection, some of the bacteria might be resistant to antibiotics.

3) This means that when you treat the infection, only the non-resistant strains of bacteria will be killed.

4) The individual resistant bacteria will survive and reproduce, and the population of the resistant strain will increase. This is an example of natural selection (see page 76).

5) This resistant strain could cause a serious infection that can't be treated by antibiotics. E.g. MRSA (methicillin-resistant *Staphylococcus aureus*) causes serious wound infectious and is resistant to the powerful antibiotic methicillin.

6) To slow down the rate of development of resistant strains, it's important for doctors to avoid over-prescribing antibiotics. So you won't get them for a sore throat, only for something more serious.

Antibiotic resistance is inevitable...

Antibiotic resistance is scary. Bacteria reproduce quickly, and so are pretty fast at evolving to deal with threats (e.g. antibiotics). If we were back in the situation where we had no way to treat bacterial infections, we'd have a nightmare. So do your bit, and finish your courses of antibiotics.

Fighting Disease — Drugs

Microorganisms can be grown in a lab, but they need certain conditions to flourish.
Also, precautions must be taken to stop unwanted microorganisms growing as well.

You can *Investigate Antibiotics* by *Growing Microorganisms*

You can test the action of antibiotics or disinfectants by growing cultures of microorganisms:

1) Microorganisms are grown (cultured) in a "culture medium". This is usually agar jelly containing the carbohydrates, minerals, proteins and vitamins they need to grow.
2) Hot agar jelly is poured into shallow round plastic dishes called Petri dishes.
3) When the jelly's cooled and set, inoculating loops (wire loops) are used to transfer microorganisms to the culture medium. The microorganisms then multiply.

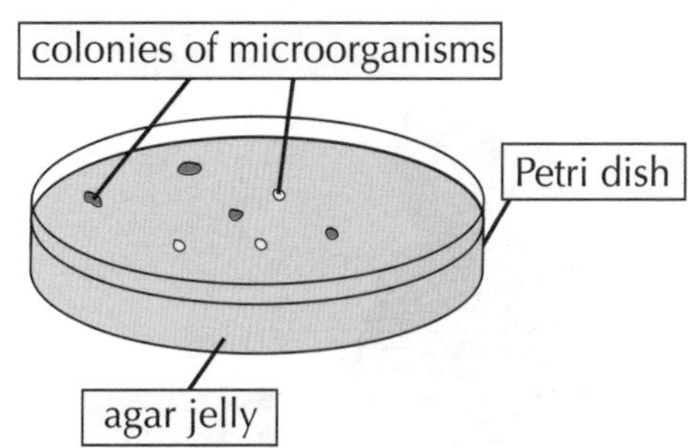

4) Paper discs are soaked in different types of antibiotics and placed on the jelly. Antibiotic-resistant bacteria will continue to grow around them but non-resistant strains will die.

Equipment is *Sterilised* to Prevent *Contamination*

1) If equipment isn't sterilised, unwanted microorganisms in the culture medium will grow and affect the result.
2) The Petri dishes, culture medium and inoculating loops must be sterilised before use.
3) The inoculating loops are sterilised by passing them through a flame.
4) The Petri dish must also have a lid to stop any microorganisms in the air contaminating the culture. The lid should be taped on.

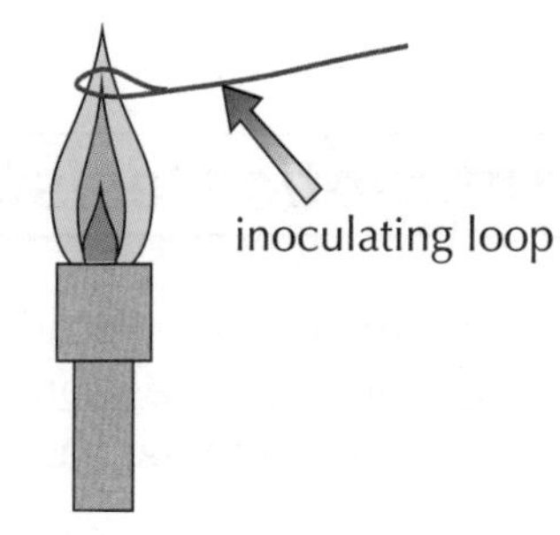

The *Temperature* Must be Kept *Fairly Low* in *School Labs*

In the lab at school, cultures of microorganisms are kept at about 25 °C. Harmful pathogens aren't likely to grow at this temperature.

In industrial conditions, cultures are incubated at higher temperatures so that they can grow a lot faster.

Microorganisms need carbohydrates and other nutrients to grow

Culture medium is just the liquid or jelly that the microorganisms are grown in. When you're growing microorganisms it's really important to keep all your equipment (like inoculating loops and Petri dishes) sterile. Otherwise who knows what kind of horrible bacteria you might be growing by accident...

Fighting Disease — Past and Future

The treatment of disease has changed somewhat over the last 200 years or so.
Which is just as well really, when you think about what medicine used to be like...

Semmelweis Cut Deaths by Using Antiseptics

1) While Ignaz Semmelweis was working in Vienna General Hospital in the 1840s, he saw that women were dying in huge numbers after childbirth from a disease called puerperal fever.

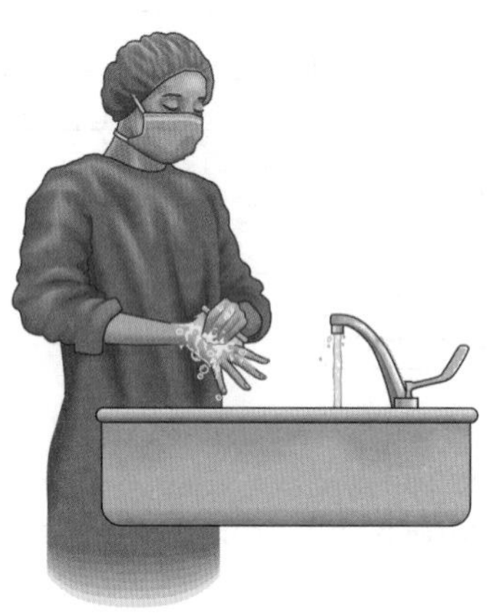

2) He believed that doctors were spreading the disease on their unwashed hands. By telling doctors entering his ward to wash their hands in an antiseptic solution, he cut the death rate from 12% to 2%.

3) The antiseptic solution killed bacteria on doctors' hands, though Semmelweis didn't know this (the existence of bacteria and their part in causing disease wasn't discovered for another 20 years).

4) So Semmelweis couldn't prove why his idea worked, and his methods were dropped when he left the hospital (allowing death rates to rise once again).

5) Nowadays we know that basic hygiene is essential in controlling disease (though recent reports have found that a lack of it in some modern hospitals has helped the disease MRSA spread).

Antibiotic Resistance is Becoming More Common

1) For the last few decades, we've been able to deal with bacterial infections pretty easily using antibiotics. The death rate from infectious bacterial diseases (e.g. pneumonia) has fallen dramatically.

2) But bacteria evolve antibiotic resistance, e.g MRSA bacteria are already resistant to certain antibiotics.

3) And overuse of antibiotics has made this problem worse — by increasing the likelihood of people being infected by antibiotic-resistant strains (see page 28).

4) People who become infected with these bacteria can't easily get rid of them (because antibiotics don't work) and may pass on the infection to others.

5) So antibiotic resistance is a big problem and it's encouraged drug companies to work on developing new antibiotics that are effective against these resistant strains.

6) Meanwhile, bacteria that are resistant to most known antibiotics ('superbugs') are becoming more common.

Remember, antibiotics kill bacteria (see page 28).

Fighting Disease — Past and Future

We've got used to having powerful drugs, like antibiotics, around to treat us when we get sick. But that doesn't mean that we'll always be able to treat every illness we come across.

We Face **New** and **Scary Dangers** All the Time

Bacteria and viruses are pretty fast at evolving to deal with threats. And that could mean big problems for us in the future...

Bacteria

1) As you know, bacteria can mutate to produce new strains (see page 28).
2) A new strain could be antibiotic-resistant, so current treatments would no longer clear an infection.
3) Or a new strain could be one that we've not encountered before, so no-one would be immune to it.
4) This means a new strain of bacteria could spread rapidly in a population of people and could even cause an epidemic — a big outbreak of disease.

Viruses

1) Viruses also tend to mutate often. This makes it hard to develop vaccines against them because the changes to their DNA can lead to them having different antigens.
2) There'd be a real problem if a virus evolved so that it was both deadly and very infectious. (Flu viruses, for example, evolve quickly so this is quite possible.)
3) If this happened, precautions could be taken to stop the virus spreading in the first place (though this is hard nowadays — millions of people travel by plane every day). And vaccines and antiviral drugs could be developed (though these take time to mass produce).
4) But in the worst-case scenario, a flu pandemic could kill billions of people all over the world.

A pandemic is when a disease spreads all over the world.

New strains of bacteria and viruses can spread incredibly fast

Microorganisms that are resistant to all our drugs are a worrying thought. It'll be like going back in time to before antibiotics were invented. So far new drugs have kept us one step ahead, but some people think it's only a matter of time until the options run out.

Warm-Up and Exam Questions

It's easy to think you've learnt everything in the section until you try the warm-up questions. Don't panic if there's a bit you've forgotten, just go back over that bit until it's firmly fixed in your brain.

Warm-Up Questions

1) What is a pathogen?
2) Explain how viruses replicate within your body.
3) What are antigens?
4) What are antibiotics designed to do?
5) Why are cultures of microorganisms grown at temperatures no higher than 25 °C in school laboratories?
6) What is an epidemic?
7) What is a pandemic?

Exam Questions

1 Antibiotics can be used to treat certain illnesses.

(a) Why would a course of antibiotics not be suitable for treatment of flu?

(2 marks)

(b) What might the inappropriate use of antibiotics lead to?

(1 mark)

2 Describe **three** ways that white blood cells fight pathogens.

(3 marks)

3 Read the following passage.

Typhoid is an infectious bacterial disease. The typhoid bacterium is often found in food and water where there is poor sanitation. The bacterium causes fever and severe diarrhoea. Typhoid can be fatal but can be treated using antibiotics. Fortunately, the spread of the disease can be reduced by vaccination.

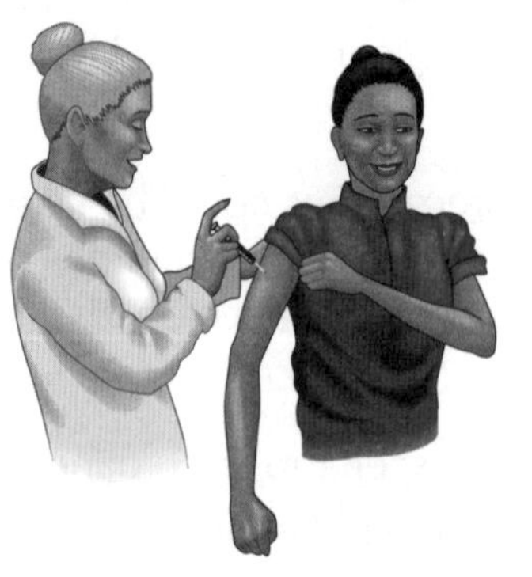

Explain what vaccination involves and how being vaccinated against typhoid can prevent a person from catching the disease.

(4 marks)

The Nervous System

The nervous system allows you to react to what goes on around you — you'd find life tough without it.

Sense Organs Detect Stimuli

A stimulus is a change in your environment which you may need to react to (e.g. a grizzly bear looking at you). You need to be constantly monitoring what's going on so you can respond if you need to.

1) You have five different sense organs — eyes, ears, nose, tongue and skin.
2) They all contain different receptors. Receptors are groups of cells which are sensitive to a stimulus. They change stimulus energy (e.g. light energy) into electrical impulses.
3) A stimulus can be light, sound, touch, pressure, chemical, or a change in position or temperature.

Sense organs and Receptors
Don't get them mixed up:

The eye is a sense organ — it contains light receptors.

The ear is a sense organ — it contains sound receptors.

The Five Sense Organs and the receptors that each contains:

1) Eyes — Light receptors — sensitive to light. These cells have a nucleus, cytoplasm and cell membrane (just like most animal cells).

2) Ears — Sound receptors — sensitive to sound. Also, "balance" receptors — sensitive to changes in position.

3) Nose — Smell receptors — sensitive to chemical stimuli.

4) Tongue — Taste receptors — sensitive to bitter, salt, sweet and sour, plus the taste of savoury things like monosodium glutamate (MSG) — chemical stimuli.

5) Skin — Sensitive to touch, pressure, pain and temperature change.

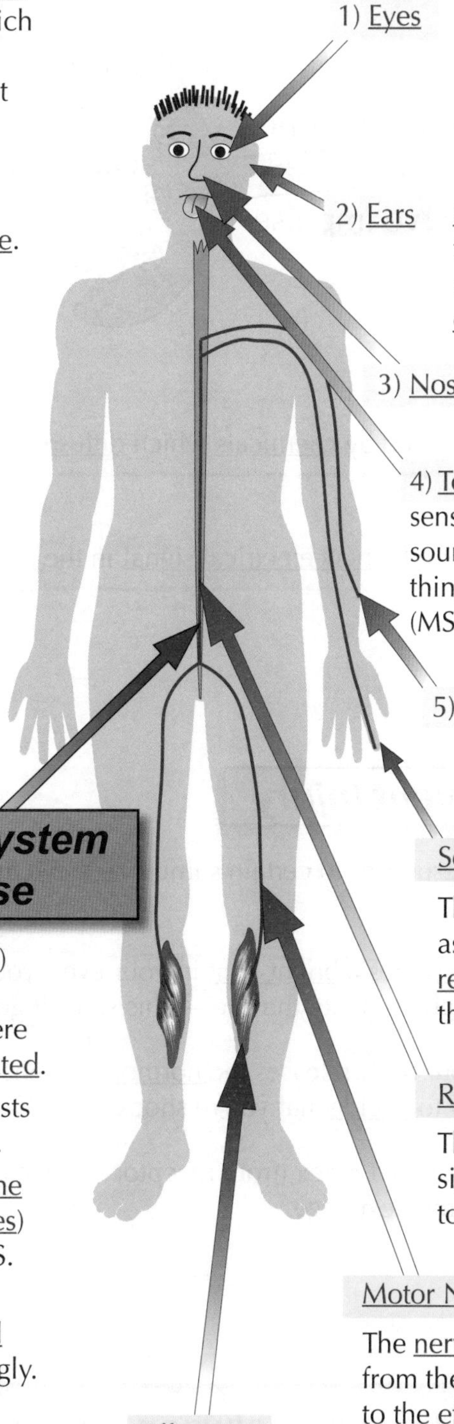

Sensory Neurones

The nerve cells that carry signals as electrical impulses from the receptors in the sense organs to the central nervous system.

Relay Neurones

The nerve cells that carry signals from sensory neurones to motor neurones.

Motor Neurones

The nerve cells that carry signals from the central nervous system to the effector muscles or glands.

Effectors

Muscles and glands are known as effectors — they respond in different ways. Muscles contract in response to a nervous impulse, whereas glands secrete hormones.

The Central Nervous System Coordinates a Response

1) The central nervous system (CNS) is where all the information from the sense organs is sent, and where reflexes and actions are coordinated.

   The central nervous system consists of the brain and spinal cord only.
2) Neurones (nerve cells) transmit the information (as electrical impulses) very quickly to and from the CNS.
3) "Instructions" from the CNS are sent to the effectors (muscles and glands), which respond accordingly.

Synapses and Reflexes

Neurones transmit information very quickly to and from the brain, and your brain quickly decides how to respond to a stimulus. But reflexes are even quicker...

Synapses Connect Neurones

1) The connection between two neurones is called a synapse.

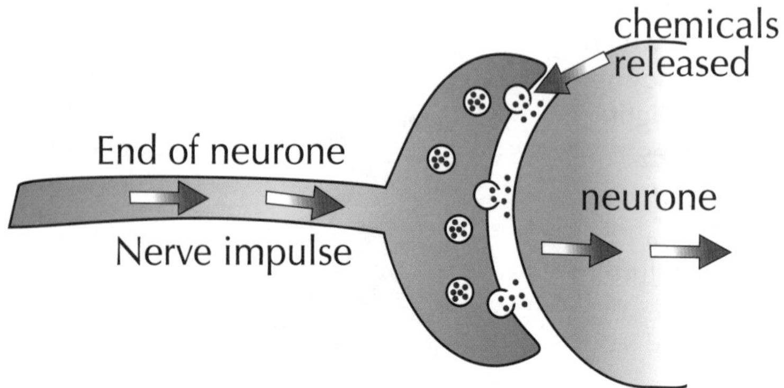

2) The nerve signal is transferred by chemicals which diffuse (move) across the gap.

3) These chemicals then set off a new electrical signal in the next neurone.

Reflexes Help Prevent Injury

1) Reflexes are automatic responses to certain stimuli — they can reduce the chances of being injured.

2) For example, if someone shines a bright light in your eyes, your pupils automatically get smaller so that less light gets into the eye — this stops it getting damaged.

3) Or if you get a shock, your body releases the hormone adrenaline automatically — it doesn't wait for you to decide that you're shocked.

4) The passage of information in a reflex (from receptor to effector) is called a reflex arc — more about these on the next page...

A synapse is just a tiny gap between two neurones

Electrical impulses travel from neurone to neurone really fast. That's important, because it gives you a chance of being able to respond quickly to things that happen around you. If you need an even quicker response though, a reflex kicks in so you don't even have to think about what to do. There's more about reflexes coming up on the next page, so make sure you understand all this before you move on.

The Reflex Arc

Reflexes are really handy reactions because they stop you from getting hurt.

The **Reflex Arc** Goes **Through** the **Central Nervous System**

1) The neurones in reflex arcs go through the spinal cord or through an unconscious part of the brain.
2) When a stimulus (e.g. a painful bee sting) is detected by receptors, impulses are sent along a sensory neurone to the CNS.
3) When the impulses reach a synapse between the sensory neurone and a relay neurone, they trigger chemicals to be released (see p.34). These chemicals cause impulses to be sent along the relay neurone.
4) When the impulses reach a synapse between the relay neurone and a motor neurone, the same thing happens. Chemicals are released and cause impulses to be sent along the motor neurone.

1. Bee stings finger.
2. Stimulation of pain receptors.
3. Message travels along a sensory neurone.
4. Message is passed along a relay neurone.
5. Message travels along a motor neurone.
6. When message reaches muscle, it contracts.

5) The impulses then travel along the motor neurone to the effector (in this example it's a muscle).
6) The muscle then contracts and moves your hand away from the bee.
7) Because you don't have to think about the response (which takes time) it's quicker than normal responses.

Stimulus, Receptor, Neurones, Effector, Response

Here's a block diagram of a reflex arc — it shows what happens, from stimulus to response.

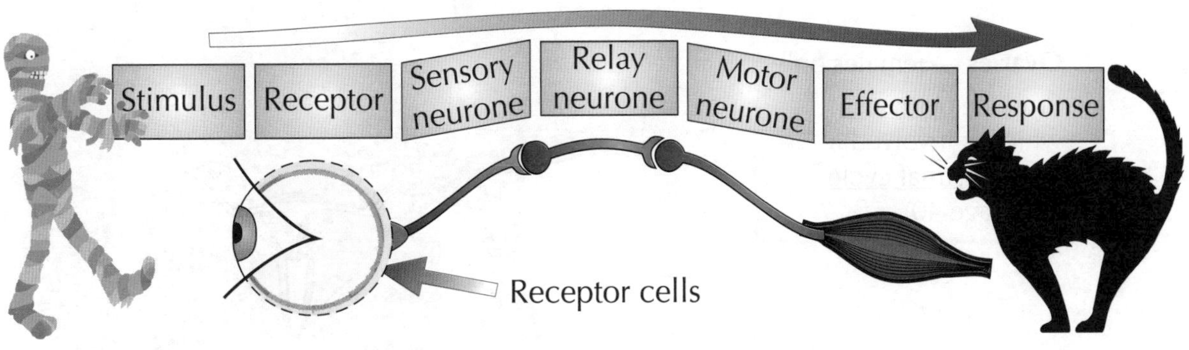

Don't get all twitchy — just learn it...

Reflexes bypass your conscious brain completely when a quick response is essential — your body just gets on with things. Reflex actions can be used to assess the condition of unconscious casualties or those with spinal injuries. So... if you're asked which bodily system doctors are examining when they tap your knee with a hammer and check that you kick, just work it out.

Hormones

The other way to send information around the body (apart from along nerves) is by using hormones.

Hormones Are Chemical Messengers Sent in the Blood

1) Hormones are chemicals released directly into the blood.
2) They are carried in the blood plasma to other parts of the body, but only affect particular cells (called target cells) in particular places. Hormones control things in organs and cells that need constant adjustment.
3) Hormones are produced in (and secreted by) various glands, as shown on the diagram. They travel through your body at "the speed of blood".
4) Hormones tend to have relatively long-lasting effects.

> Learn this definition:
> HORMONES are chemical messengers which travel in the blood to activate target cells.

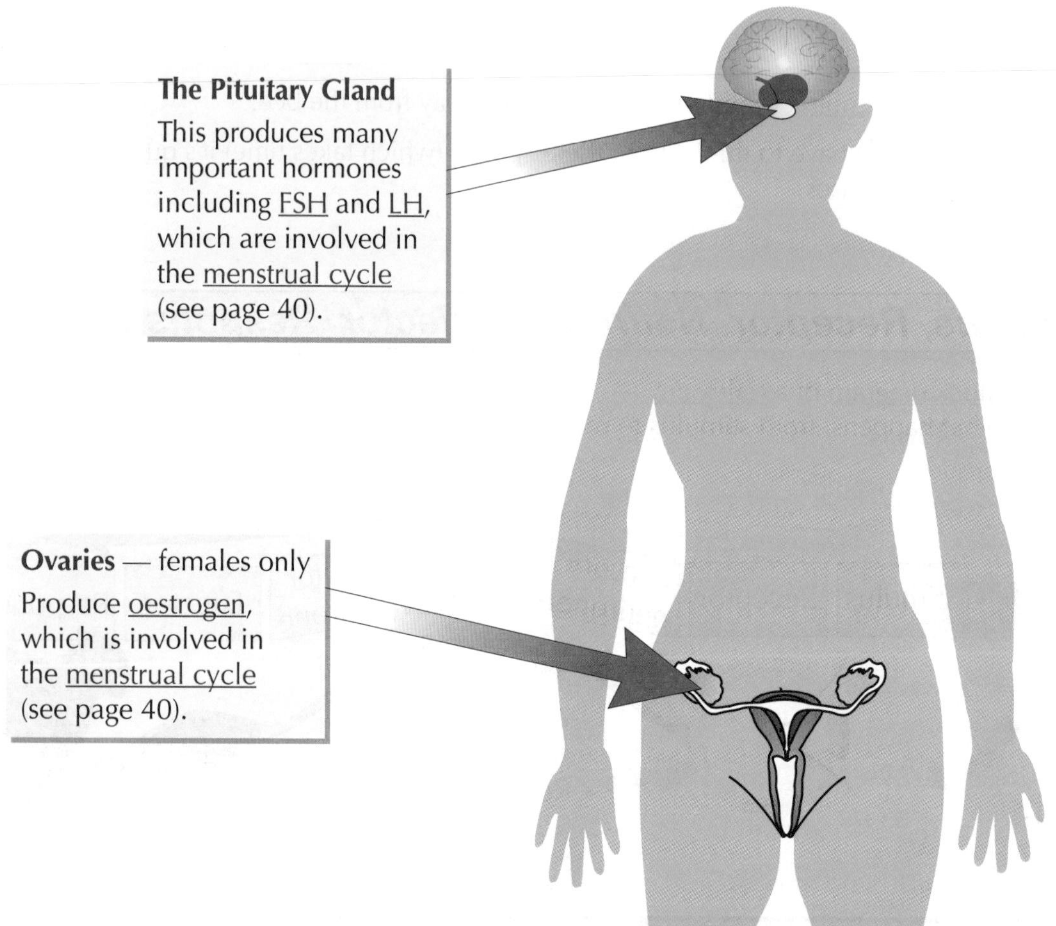

The Pituitary Gland
This produces many important hormones including FSH and LH, which are involved in the menstrual cycle (see page 40).
Ovaries — females only
Produce oestrogen, which is involved in the menstrual cycle (see page 40).

These are just examples — there are lots more, each doing its own thing.

Hormones

Now you know that there are <u>two</u> ways information can be sent round the body — via the <u>nervous</u> or <u>hormonal</u> systems — here's a recap of the differences between them...

Hormones *and* ***Nerves*** *Carry* ***Messages*** *in* ***Different Ways***

<u>Hormones</u> and <u>nerves</u> do similar jobs — they both <u>carry information</u> and <u>instructions</u> about the body. But there are some important <u>differences</u> between them that you need to know too:

Nerves

1) Very <u>FAST</u> message.
2) Act for a very <u>SHORT TIME</u>.
3) Act on a very <u>PRECISE AREA</u>.

Hormones

1) <u>SLOWER</u> message.
2) Act for a <u>LONG TIME</u>.
3) Act in a more <u>GENERAL</u> way.

If you're not sure whether a response is nervous or hormonal, have a think about the <u>speed</u> of the reaction and <u>how long it lasts</u>.

1) If the Response is ***Really Quick****, It's Probably* ***Nervous***

Some information needs to be passed to effectors <u>really quickly</u> (e.g. <u>pain</u> signals, or information from your eyes telling you about the <u>lion</u> heading your way), so it's no good using hormones to carry the message — they're <u>too slow</u>.

2) But if a Response ***Lasts For a Long Time****, It's Probably* ***Hormonal***

For example, when you get a <u>shock</u>, a hormone called <u>adrenaline</u> is released into the body (causing the fight-or-flight response, where your body is hyped up ready for action). You can tell it's a <u>hormonal response</u> (even though it kicks in pretty quickly) because you feel a bit wobbly for a while <u>afterwards</u>.

Nerves, hormones — no wonder revision makes me tense...

Hormones control various <u>organs</u> and <u>cells</u> in the body, though they tend to control things that aren't <u>immediately</u> life-threatening. For example, they take care of all things to do with sexual development, pregnancy, birth, breast-feeding, blood sugar level, water content... and so on. Pretty amazing really.

Warm-Up and Exam Questions

Welcome to another page of questions. There are quite a few of them I'll admit, but that's because they're pretty important...

Warm-Up Questions

1) What are the five sense organs in the human body?
2) In what form is information transmitted along nerve cells?
3) What are the two different types of effector in the human body?
4) What name is given to the connection between two nerve cells?
5) What are hormones secreted by?
6) Give one difference between a nervous response and a hormonal response.

Exam Questions

1 Gordon accidentally touches a hot object, causing his hand to immediately move away from it. The diagram below shows some of the parts involved in this response.

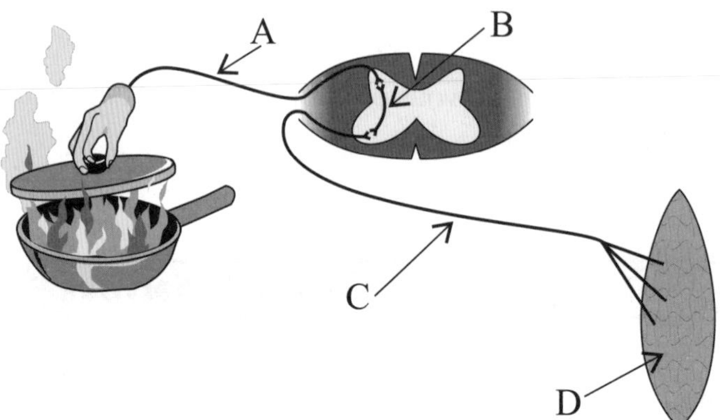

(a) What is the name of this type of automatic response?

(1 mark)

(b) On the diagram:

(i) Which letter points to a relay neurone?

(1 mark)

(ii) Which letter points to an effector?

(1 mark)

(c) Explain how an electrical impulse in one neurone is able to pass to the next neurone.

(2 marks)

(d) Give **one** physiological advantage, to the body, of these automatic responses.

(1 mark)

2 Hormones are chemical messengers that carry information around the body. During the menstrual cycle, the hormone FSH stimulates the production of oestrogen in the ovaries. Describe how this response is carried out.

(3 marks)

The Menstrual Cycle

The monthly release of an egg from a woman's ovaries, and the build-up and breakdown of the protective lining in the uterus (womb), is called the menstrual cycle.

*The **Menstrual Cycle** Has **Four Stages***

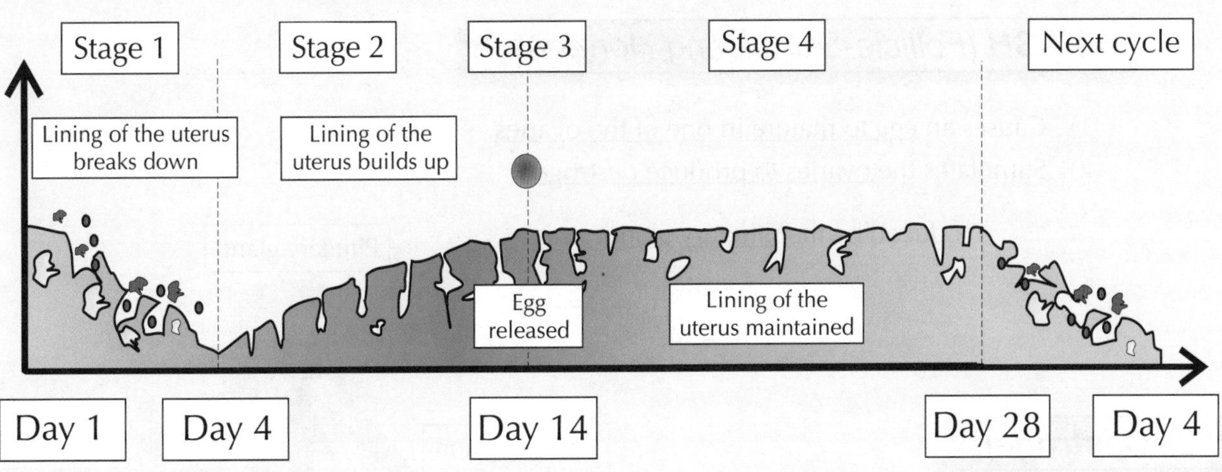

Stage 1

Day 1 is when the bleeding starts.
The uterus lining breaks down for about four days.

Stage 2

The lining of the uterus builds up again, from day 4 to day 14, into a thick spongy layer full of blood vessels, ready to receive a fertilised egg.

Stage 3

An egg is developed and then released from the ovary at day 14.

Stage 4

The wall is then maintained for about 14 days, until day 28. If no fertilised egg has landed on the uterus wall by day 28, the spongy lining starts to break down again and the whole cycle starts again.

The Menstrual Cycle

The menstrual cycle is controlled by hormones — step forward FSH, oestrogen and LH...

Hormones Control the Different Stages

There are three main hormones involved:

1) FSH (Follicle-Stimulating Hormone)

1) Causes an egg to mature in one of the ovaries.
2) Stimulates the ovaries to produce oestrogen.

Produced by the pituitary gland.

2) Oestrogen

1) Causes pituitary to produce LH.
2) Inhibits the further release of FSH.

Produced in the ovaries.

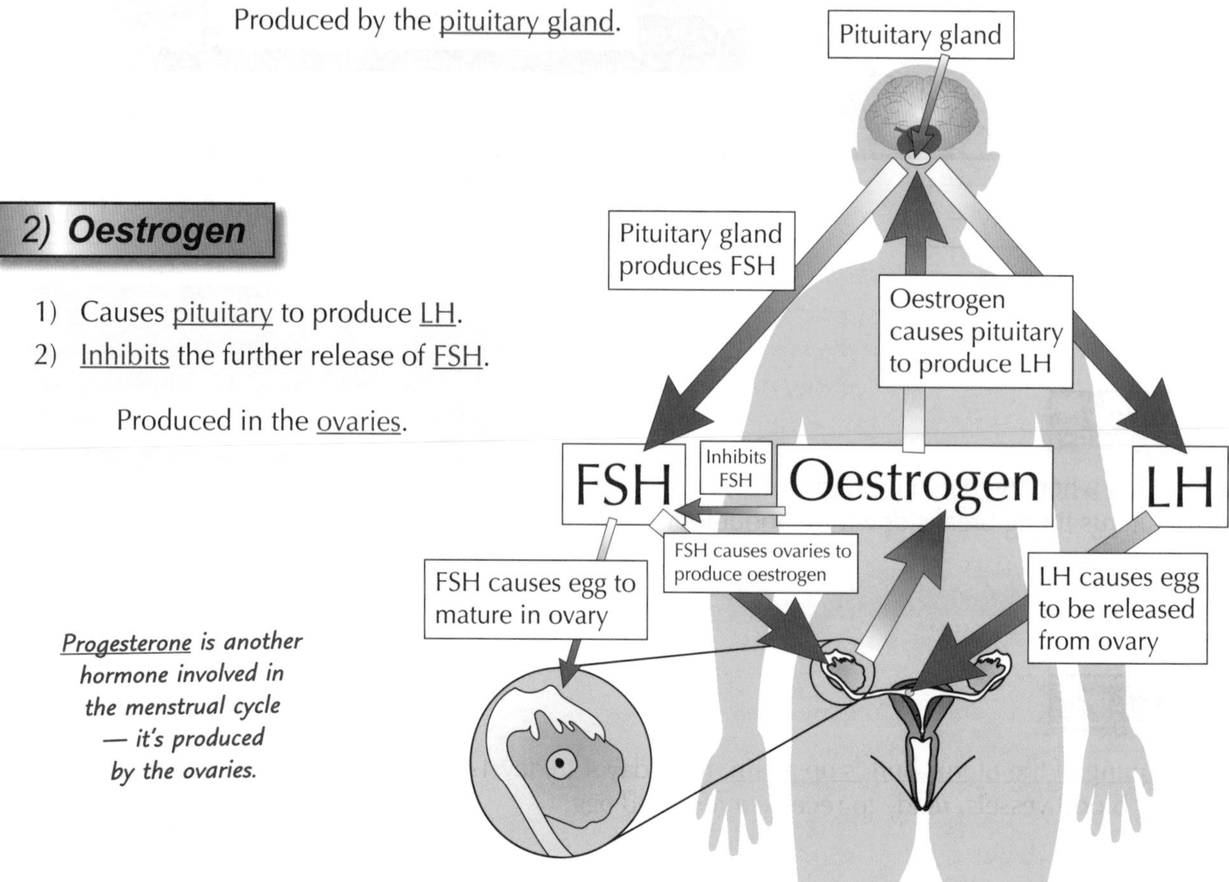

Progesterone is another hormone involved in the menstrual cycle — it's produced by the ovaries.

3) LH (Luteinising Hormone)

Stimulates the release of an egg at around the middle of the menstrual cycle.

Produced by the pituitary gland.

OK, I admit it — this is quite hard to get your head around...

In the exam you could be given a completely new situation and have to answer questions about it. For example, say you're told that certain women with epilepsy suffer more seizures at certain points of the menstrual cycle and you have to suggest a reason why. Sounds scary, but the key is not to panic. You know that during the menstrual cycle, hormone levels change — so maybe it's these hormone changes that are triggering the seizures. There are no guarantees, but that'd be a pretty good answer.

Controlling Fertility

FSH, LH, oestrogen and progesterone can be used to artificially change how fertile a woman is.

Hormones Can Be Used to **Reduce Fertility...**

1) Oestrogen can be used to prevent the release of an egg, so it can be used as a method of contraception.
2) This may seem kind of strange (since naturally oestrogen helps stimulate the release of eggs). But if oestrogen is taken every day to keep the level of it permanently high, it inhibits the production of FSH, and after a while egg development and production stop and stay stopped.
3) Progesterone also reduces fertility e.g. by stimulating the production of thick cervical mucus which prevents any sperm getting through and reaching an egg.
4) The pill is an oral contraceptive. The first version was made in the 1950s and contained high levels of oestrogen and progesterone (known as the combined oral contraceptive pill).
5) But there were concerns about a link between oestrogen in the pill and side effects like blood clots. The pill now contains lower doses of oestrogen so has fewer side effects.

PROS

1) The pill's over 99% effective at preventing pregnancy.
2) It reduces the risk of getting some types of cancer.

CONS

1) It isn't 100% effective — there's still a very slight chance of getting pregnant.
2) It can cause side effects like headaches, nausea, irregular menstrual bleeding, and fluid retention.
3) It doesn't protect against STDs (sexually transmitted diseases).

6) There's also a progesterone-only pill — it has fewer side effects than the pill (but it's not as effective).

...or **Increase It**

1) Some women have levels of FSH (Follicle-Stimulating Hormone) that are too low to cause their eggs to mature. This means that no eggs are released and the women can't get pregnant.
2) The hormones FSH and LH can be injected by these women to stimulate egg release in their ovaries.

PRO

It helps a lot of women to get pregnant when previously they couldn't... pretty obvious.

CONS

1) It doesn't always work — some women may have to do it many times, which can be expensive.
2) Too many eggs could be stimulated, resulting in unexpected multiple pregnancies (twins, triplets etc.).

IVF Can Also Help Couples to **Have Children**

1) IVF ("*in vitro* fertilisation") involves collecting eggs from the woman's ovaries and fertilising them in a lab using the man's sperm. These are then grown into embryos.
2) Once the embryos are tiny balls of cells, one or two of them are transferred to the woman's uterus (womb) to improve the chance of pregnancy.
3) FSH and LH are given before egg collection to stimulate egg production (so more than one egg can be collected).

PRO Fertility treatment can give an infertile couple a child — a pretty obvious benefit.

CONS

1) Some women have a strong reaction to the hormones — e.g. abdominal pain, vomiting, dehydration.
2) There have been some reports of an increased risk of cancer due to the hormonal treatment (though others have reported no such risk — the position isn't really clear at the moment).
3) Multiple births can happen if more than one embryo grows into a baby — these are risky for the mother and babies (there's a higher risk of miscarriage, stillbirth...).

Plant Hormones

You may not have expected plants to turn up in a human biology section... but hey, plants have hormones too. Hormones make sure plants grow in a useful direction (e.g. towards light).

Auxin is a Plant Growth Hormone

1) Auxin is a plant hormone that controls growth near the tips of shoots and roots.

2) It controls the growth of a plant in response to light (PHOTOTROPISM), gravity (GRAVITROPISM or GEOTROPISM) and moisture.

3) Auxin is produced in the tips and moves backwards to stimulate the cell elongation (enlargement) process which occurs in the cells just behind the tips.

4) If the tip of a shoot is removed, no auxin is available and the shoot may stop growing.

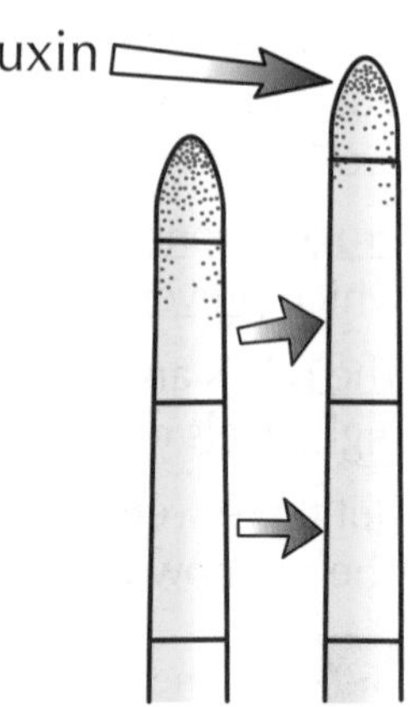

Auxin Promotes Growth in a Plant's Shoots

Shoots Grow Towards Light

1) When a shoot tip is exposed to light, more auxin accumulates on the side that's in the shade than the side that's in the light.
2) This makes the cells grow (elongate) faster on the shaded side, so the shoot bends towards the light.

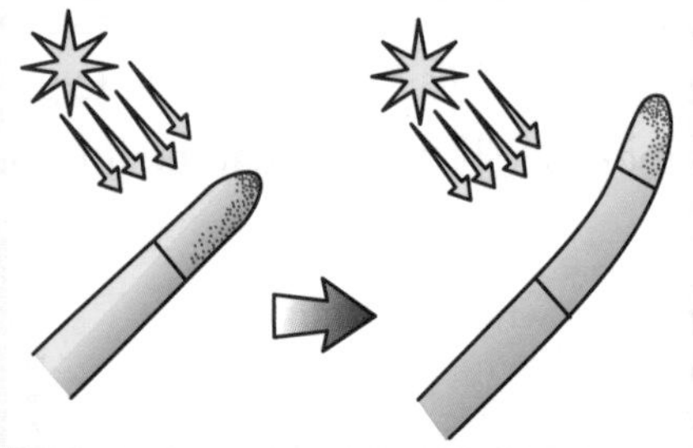

Shoots Grow Away From Gravity

1) When a shoot is growing sideways, gravity produces an unequal distribution of auxin in the tip, with more auxin on the lower side.
2) This causes the lower side to grow faster, bending the shoot upwards.

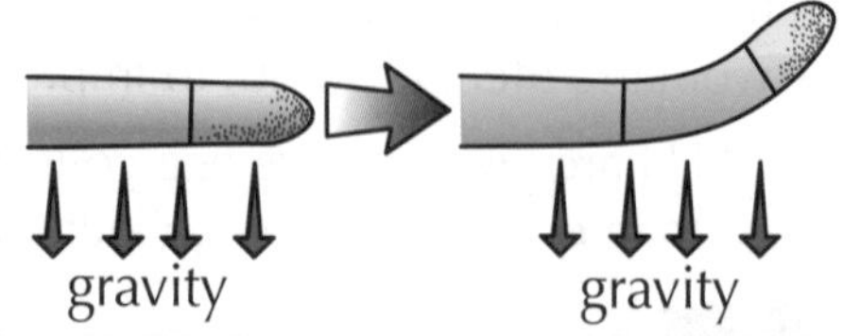

Auxin is a plant hormone that controls growth

If it wasn't for their hormones, plants wouldn't be able to respond to their environment. For starters they wouldn't be able to direct their shoots towards the light — then they'd be dead pretty fast...

Plant Hormones

It isn't only a plant's shoots that respond to auxin — its roots do too...

Auxin Inhibits Growth in a Plant's Roots

Auxin has the opposite effect in shoots to the one it has in roots.
But it still works to control the direction that the roots grow in.

Roots Grow Towards Gravity

1) A root growing sideways will have more auxin on its lower side (because of gravity).
2) But in a root the extra auxin inhibits growth. This means the cells on top elongate faster, and the root bends downwards.

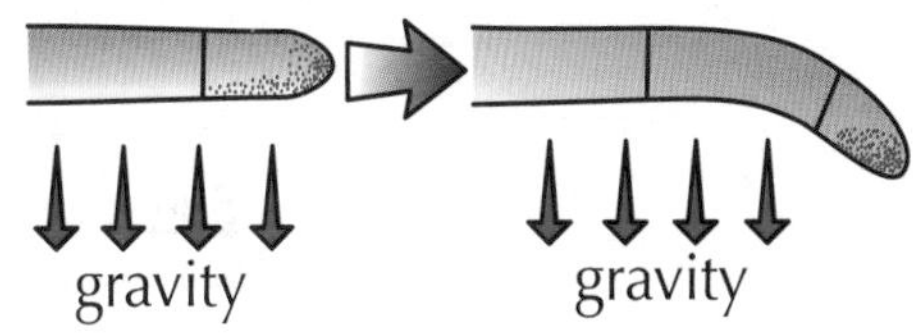

Roots Grow Towards Moisture

1) An uneven amount of moisture either side of a root produces more auxin on the side with more moisture.
2) This inhibits growth on that side, causing the root to bend in that direction, towards the moisture.

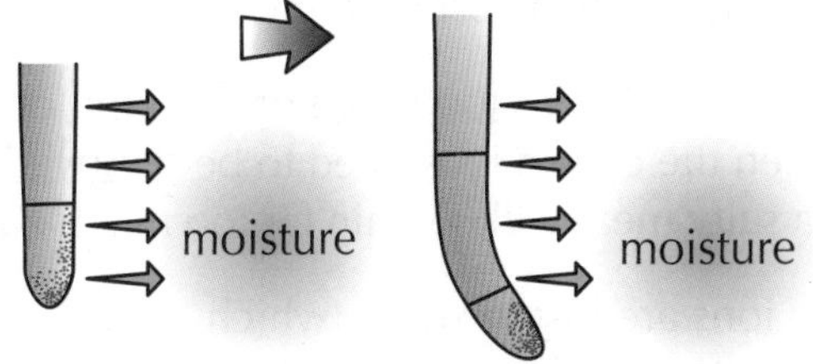

Plant Hormones have Uses in Agriculture

Plant hormones can be extracted and used by people, or artificial versions can be made.

1) Most weeds in crop fields are broad-leaved, unlike grasses and cereals which have very narrow leaves. Selective weedkillers are made of plant growth hormones — they only affect the broad-leaved plants. They disrupt their normal growth patterns, which soon kills them, but leave the crops untouched.

2) Plant cuttings won't always grow in soil. If you add rooting powder, which contains the plant hormone auxin, they'll produce roots rapidly and start growing as new plants. This helps growers to produce lots of clones of a really good plant very quickly.

Plant hormones aren't just useful to plants...

...because if it wasn't for weedkillers and rooting powders, we wouldn't be able to grow so much food.

Homeostasis

Homeostasis is a fancy word, but it covers lots of things, so maybe that's fair enough.
It means all the functions of your body which try to maintain a "constant internal environment".

Your Body Needs Some Things to Be **Kept Constant**

To keep all your cells working properly, certain things must be kept at the right level — not too high, and not too low.

Bodily levels that need to be controlled include:

Ion content

Water content

Sugar content

Temperature

Ion Content Is **Regulated** by the **Kidneys**

1) Ions (e.g. sodium, Na^+) are taken into the body in food, then absorbed into the blood.
2) If the food contains too much of any kind of ion then the excess ions need to be removed. E.g. a salty meal will contain far too much Na^+.
3) Some ions are lost in sweat (which tastes salty, you'll have noticed).
4) The kidneys will remove the excess from the blood — this is then got rid of in urine.

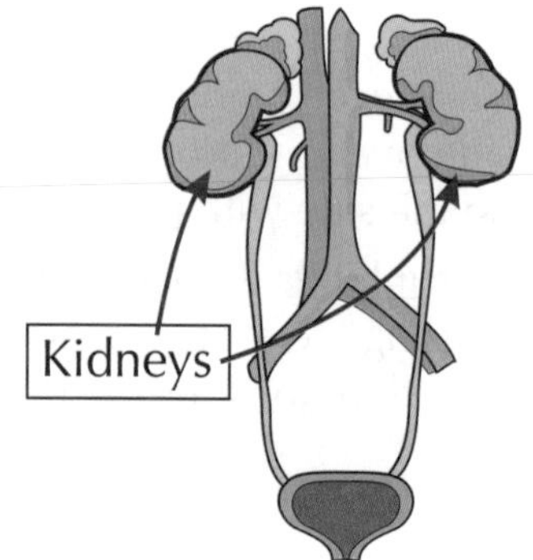

Blood Sugar Level Needs to Be Controlled Too

1) Eating foods containing carbohydrate puts glucose into the blood from the gut.
2) The normal metabolism of cells removes glucose from the blood. But if you do a lot of vigorous exercise, then much more glucose is removed.
3) A hormone called insulin helps to maintain the right level of glucose in your blood, so your cells get a constant supply of energy.

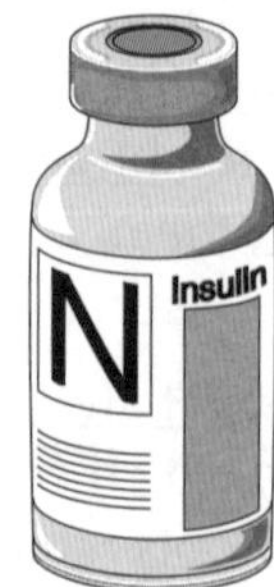

Homeostasis is all about keeping things constant inside your body

It's pretty handy that all of this homeostasis stuff goes on without you even having to think about it. Just imagine if we had to work out how much salt our bodies needed to lose in sweat... we'd probably get it wrong more often then not. Learn this page and test yourself by writing it all down again.

Homeostasis

You also need to know how your body controls water level and temperature.

Water Is Lost from the Body in Various Ways

There's a need for the body to constantly balance the water coming in against the water going out. Water is taken into the body as food and drink and is lost from the body in these ways:

1) through the SKIN as SWEAT...
2) via the LUNGS in BREATH...
3) via the kidneys as URINE.

Some water is also lost in faeces.

The balance between sweat and urine can depend on what you're doing, or what the weather's like...

On a COLD DAY, or when you're NOT EXERCISING, you don't sweat much, so you'll produce more urine, which will be pale (since the waste carried in the urine is more diluted).

On a HOT DAY, or when you're EXERCISING, you sweat a lot, and so you will produce less urine, but this will be more concentrated (and hence a deeper colour). You will also lose more water through your breath when you exercise because you breathe faster.

Body Temperature Is Controlled by the Brain

1) All enzymes work best at a certain temperature. The enzymes within the human body work best at about 37 °C — and so this is the temperature your body tries to maintain.
2) A part of the brain acts as your own personal thermostat. It's sensitive to the blood temperature in the brain, and it receives messages from the skin that provide information about skin temperature.

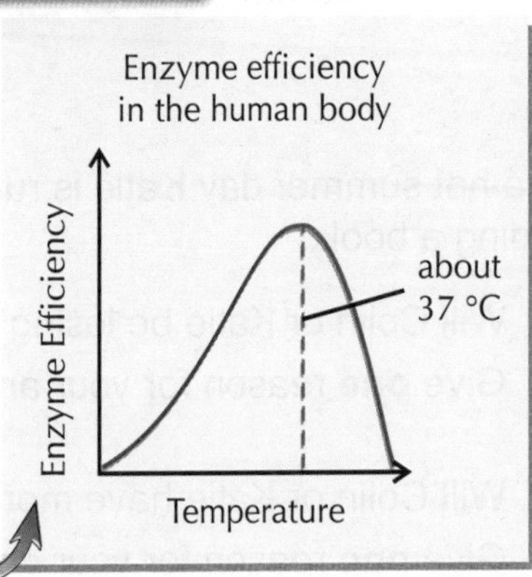

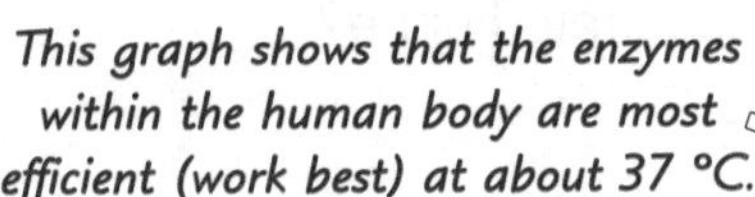

This graph shows that the enzymes within the human body are most efficient (work best) at about 37 °C.

Sweat and urine keep your water level balanced

Sports drinks (which usually contain electrolytes and carbohydrates) can help your body keep things in order. The electrolytes replace salts lost in sweat, while the carbohydrates give you an energy boost.

Warm-Up and Exam Questions

You could skim through this page in a few minutes, but there's no point unless you check over any bits you don't know and make sure you understand everything. It's not quick but it's the only way.

Warm-Up Questions

1) Describe what happens at Day 1 in the menstrual cycle.
2) What is phototropism?
3) Name the plant hormone that controls phototropism.
4) List four things that need to be kept constant within the body.
5) Why is it important that human body temperature is kept at about 37 °C?

Exam Questions

1 The menstrual cycle is controlled by several different hormones.

(a) What effect does oestrogen have on the release of FSH?

(1 mark)

(b) Which hormone causes an egg to mature in an ovary?

(1 mark)

(c) On what day of the menstrual cycle is the egg released?

(1 mark)

2 Oral contraceptive pills used to contain large amounts of oestrogen.

(a) Explain how taking oestrogen can prevent pregnancy.

(2 marks)

(b) Modern contraceptive pills contain a much lower dose of oestrogen.

(i) Give **one** advantage of taking these pills instead of the old high-oestrogen pills.

(1 mark)

(ii) Name **one** other hormone that is often used in contraceptive pills.

(1 mark)

3 On a hot summer day Katie is running in the park, while Colin is sitting still at home reading a book.

(a) Will Colin or Katie be losing more water through their skin?
Give **one** reason for your answer.

(1 mark)

(b) Will Colin or Katie have more concentrated urine?
Give **one** reason for your answer.

(1 mark)

(c) Control of the body's water content is part of **homeostasis**.
Explain what is meant by homeostasis.

(1 mark)

Exam Questions

4 In 1918, a Hungarian scientist called Arpad Paal did experiments to investigate how plants grow. The diagram below shows one experiment that he did.

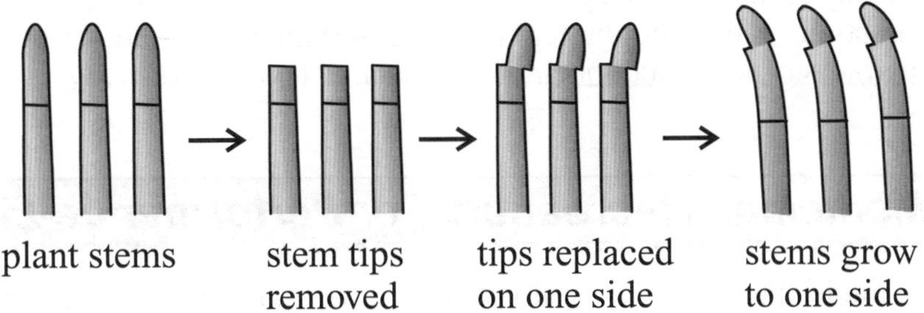

(a) When a stem grows to the left as shown above, which side is growing faster?
(1 mark)

(b) Explain what makes the stems at the final stage grow to the left.
(3 marks)

(c) The stems were kept in the dark after the tips were replaced. Explain why.
(1 mark)

5 Plant hormones have several commercial uses.

(a) Explain why plant growth hormones are used to make selective weedkillers.
(2 marks)

(b) Name **one** other commercial use for plant growth hormones.
(1 mark)

6 To keep cells working properly, the ion content of the body and body temperature must be kept constant.

(a) Which organ is responsible for regulating the ion content of the blood?
(1 mark)

(b) Which organ is responsible for regulating body temperature?
(1 mark)

7 *In this question you will be assessed on the quality of your English, the organisation of your ideas and your use of appropriate specialist vocabulary.*

Hormones can be used to control fertility. Evaluate the use of the contraceptive pill and *in vitro* fertilisation (IVF) to control fertility.
(6 marks)

Drugs

Drugs alter what goes on in your body. Your body's essentially a seething mass of chemical reactions — drugs can interfere with these reactions, sometimes for the better, sometimes not.

Drugs Change Your **Body Chemistry**

Some of the chemical changes caused by drugs can lead to the body becoming addicted to the drug. If the drug isn't taken, an addict can suffer physical withdrawal symptoms — and these are sometimes very unpleasant. E.g. heroin, cocaine, nicotine and caffeine are all very addictive.

Drugs can be **Medicinal**, **Recreational** or **Performance-Enhancing**

1) Medicinal drugs are medically useful, like antibiotics. For some of these drugs you don't need a prescription (e.g. paracetamol), but for others you do (e.g. morphine) because they can be dangerous if misused.
2) Recreational drugs are used for fun. These can be legal or illegal (see page 51).
3) Performance-enhancing drugs can improve a person's performance in sport (see below).

Performance-Enhancing Drugs have **Health** and **Ethical Impacts**

1) Some athletes take performance-enhancing drugs to make them better at sport.
2) There are several different types, including anabolic steroids (that increase muscle size) and stimulants (that increase heart rate).
3) But these drugs can have negative health effects, e.g. steroids can cause high blood pressure.
4) Some of these drugs are banned by law, some are prescription-only, but all are banned by sporting bodies.
5) There are also ethical problems with taking performance-enhancing drugs:

For Drugs:

1) Athletes have the right to make their own decision about whether taking drugs is worth the risk or not.
2) Drug-free sport isn't really fair anyway — different athletes have access to different training facilities, coaches, equipment, etc.

Against Drugs:

1) It's unfair if people gain an advantage by taking drugs, not just through training.
2) Athletes may not be fully informed of the serious health risks of the drugs they take.

Drugs can kill you or cure you (or anything in between)...

Many people take drugs of some kind, e.g. caffeine in coffee, headache tablets, alcohol, hay fever medicine or an inhaler for asthma. Most of these are okay if you're careful with them and don't go mad. It's misuse that can get you into trouble (e.g. a paracetamol overdose can kill you). Read the packet.

Drug Claims

Drug companies and independent teams of scientists spend lots of time and money looking at how drugs affect the body. You need to know how to tell whether their research is reliable or not...

Claims About **Drugs** need to be **Carefully Looked At**

Claims about the effects of drugs (both prescribed and non-prescribed) need to be looked at critically. Here are a couple of examples:

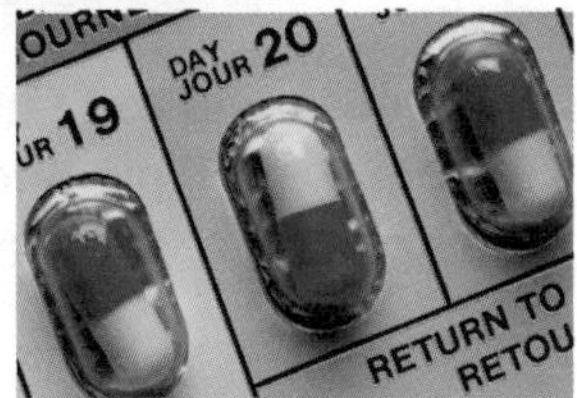

Statins

1) Statins are prescribed drugs used to lower the risk of heart and circulatory disease.
2) There's evidence that statins lower blood cholesterol and significantly lower the risk of heart disease in diabetic patients.
3) The original research was done by government scientists with no connection to the manufacturers. And the sample was big — 6000 patients.
4) It compared two groups of patients — those who had taken statins and those who hadn't. Other studies have since backed up these findings.

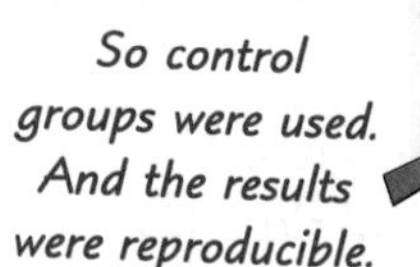
So control groups were used. And the results were reproducible.

But research findings are not always so clear cut...

Cannabis

1) Cannabis is an illegal drug. Scientists have investigated whether the chemicals in cannabis smoke cause mental health problems.
2) The results vary, and are sometimes open to different interpretations.
3) Basically, until more definite scientific evidence is found, no one's sure.

Know the evidence, know the risks...

To know that a drug is safe to take (or that it will actually help you) you need to know that it's been tested properly, on a large sample of people, by scientists with no connection to the manufacturers. If this hasn't been done, then you're taking massive risks with your health by taking it...

Testing Medicinal Drugs

Before new drugs can be given to the public, they have to go through a thorough testing procedure.

There are Three Main Stages in Drug Testing

(1) Drugs are tested on HUMAN CELLS AND TISSUES in the lab.

However, you can't use human cells and tissues to test drugs that affect whole or multiple body systems, e.g. testing a drug for blood pressure must be done on a whole animal because it has an intact circulatory system.

(2) The next step is to test the drug on LIVE ANIMALS.

- This is to see whether the drug works (produces the effect you want), to find out about its toxicity (how harmful it is) and the best dosage (the dose at which it's most effective).
- The law in Britain states that new drugs must be tested on two different live mammals. Some people think it's cruel to test on animals, but others believe this is the safest way to make sure a drug isn't dangerous before it's given to humans.

But some people think that animals are so different from humans that testing on animals is pointless.

(3) If the drug passes the tests on animals then it's tested on human volunteers in a CLINICAL TRIAL.

1) First, the drug is tested on healthy volunteers. This is to make sure that it doesn't have any harmful side effects when the body is working normally. At the start of the trial, a very low dose of the drug is given and this is gradually increased.
2) If the results of the tests on healthy volunteers are good, the drugs can be tested on people suffering from the illness. The optimum dose is found — this is the dose of drug that is the most effective and has few side effects.
3) To test how well the drug works, patients are put into two groups. One is given the new drug, the other is given a placebo (a 'sugar pill' that looks like the real drug but doesn't do anything). This is so the doctor can see the actual difference the drug makes — it allows for the placebo effect (when the patient expects the treatment to work and so feels better, even though the treatment isn't doing anything).
4) Clinical trials are blind — the patient in the study doesn't know whether they're getting the drug or the placebo. In fact, they're often double-blind — neither the patient nor the doctor knows until all the results have been gathered. This is so the doctors monitoring the patients and analysing the results aren't subconsciously influenced by their knowledge.

Things Have Gone Wrong in the Past

An example of what can happen when drugs are not thoroughly tested is the case of thalidomide — a drug developed in the 1950s.

1) Thalidomide was intended as a sleeping pill, and was tested for that use. But later it was also found to be effective in relieving morning sickness in pregnant women.
2) Unfortunately, thalidomide hadn't been tested as a drug for morning sickness, and so it wasn't known that it could pass through the placenta and affect the fetus, causing abnormal limb development. In some cases, babies were born with no arms or legs at all.
3) About 10 000 babies were affected by thalidomide, and only about half of them survived.
4) The drug was banned, and more rigorous testing procedures were introduced.
5) More recently thalidomide has been used in the treatment of leprosy and other diseases, e.g. some cancers.

Recreational Drugs

Not all drugs are used by people with illnesses — some are used for fun. But fun comes with risk...

Recreational Drugs Can Be **Illegal** or **Legal**

1) Illegal drugs are often divided into two main classes — SOFT and HARD. Hard drugs are usually thought of as being seriously addictive and generally more harmful.
2) But the terms "soft" and "hard" are a bit vague — they're not scientific descriptions, and you can certainly have problems with soft drug use. E.g. heroin and ecstasy (hard drugs) and cannabis (a soft drug) can all cause heart and circulatory system problems.

There Are **Various Reasons** Why People Use Recreational Drugs

So if all these recreational drugs are so dangerous, why do so many people use them...

1) When asked why they use cannabis, most users quote either simple enjoyment, relaxation or stress relief. Some say they do it to get stoned or for inspiration.
2) But very often this turns out to be not the whole story. There may be other factors in the user's background or personal life which influence them in choosing to use drugs. It's a personal thing, and often pretty complicated.

And some multiple sclerosis sufferers say cannabis can relieve pain.

Some Studies Link **Cannabis** and **Hard Drug** Use — Others **Don't**

Almost all users of hard drugs have tried cannabis first (though most users of cannabis do not go on to use hard drugs). The link between cannabis and hard drugs isn't clear, but three opinions are common...

Cannabis is a "stepping stone": The effects of cannabis create a desire to try harder drugs.

Cannabis is a "gateway drug": Cannabis use brings people into contact with drug dealers.

It's all down to genetics: Certain people are more likely to take drugs generally, so cannabis users will also try other drugs.

Some **Legal Drugs** have **More** of an **Impact** than **Illegal Drugs**

1) Tobacco and alcohol are legal recreational drugs that have a huge impact on people and society:

SMOKING

1) Smoking causes disease of the heart, blood vessels and lungs.
2) Tobacco smoke causes cancer.
3) Nicotine is the drug found in cigarettes — it's addictive so it's hard to stop smoking.

1) Alcohol affects the nervous system and slows down the body's reactions.
2) Too much alcohol leads to impaired judgement, poor coordination and unconsciousness.
3) Excessive drinking can damage the liver and the brain.
4) Alcohol is also addictive.

2) Tobacco and alcohol have a bigger impact in the UK than illegal drugs, as so many people take them.
3) The National Health Service spends loads on treating people with lung diseases caused by smoking. Add to this the cost to businesses of people missing days from work, and the figures get pretty scary.
4) The same goes for alcohol. The costs to the NHS are huge, but pretty small compared to the costs related to crime (police time, damage to people/property) and the economy (lost working days etc.).
5) And in addition to the financial costs, alcohol and tobacco cause sorrow and anguish to people affected by them, either directly or indirectly.

Drinking and smoking — it's so big and clever...

So legal drugs have the biggest impact on the country, when you take everything into account. Some prescribed drugs can also have an impact on health if they're misused, e.g. addiction to painkillers.

Warm-Up and Exam Questions

There's no point in whizzing through the section and glancing over the questions. Do the warm-up questions and go back over any bits you don't know. Then practise and practise the exam questions.

Warm-Up Questions

1) What is a drug?
2) Why might a patient be prescribed statins?
3) What is a placebo? Why are placebos often used in drug trials?
4) Name two illegal recreational drugs.
5) Name one legal drug to which people may become addicted.

Exam Questions

1 Steroids are a type of drug. Steroid use is banned by sports governing bodies. Athletes found taking steroids are usually banned from future competitions.

(a) Explain why an athlete may choose to take steroids.

(2 marks)

(b) Apart from being banned from future competitions, give **one** reason why an athlete might choose not to take steroids.

(1 mark)

2 In the UK it is illegal to drive if your blood alcohol concentration exceeds 80 mg of alcohol per 100 ml of blood.

(a) Alcohol affects the nervous system, slowing down the body's reactions. Suggest why drinking alcohol increases the risk of having a car accident.

(1 mark)

(b) Alcohol is addictive. What does this mean?

(1 mark)

(c) Other than drink-related driving accidents, give **two** ways in which excessive alcohol consumption has a negative effect on society.

(2 marks)

3 Thalidomide was used to treat morning sickness in pregnant women, but it hadn't been tested for this use.

(a) Describe the effect that thalidomide had on fetuses.

(1 mark)

(b) Name **one** disease that thalidomide is currently used in the treatment of.

(1 mark)

4 A new drug has gone through laboratory tests on human tissues, and animal testing procedures. It is about to be tested on human volunteers in a double-blind clinical trial.

(a) Before beginning the main clinical trial, the new drug is tested on healthy volunteers. Suggest why this step is carried out.

(1 mark)

(b) Explain what is meant by a double-blind clinical trial, including the reason why drug trials are often carried out in this way.

(3 marks)

Revision Summary for Biology 1a

Congratulations, you've made it to the end of the first section. I reckon that section wasn't too bad, there's some pretty interesting stuff there — diets, vaccinations, nerves, drugs, booze... what more could you want? Actually, I know what more you could want, some questions to make sure you know it all.

1) Name all the food groups you should eat to have a balanced diet.
2)* Put these jobs in order of how much energy they would need from their food (from highest to lowest): a) mechanic, b) professional runner, c) secretary.
3) What kind of diseases are caused by a lack of certain vitamins or minerals?
4) In terms of energy, what does a person have to do to lose weight?
5) Briefly describe the defences that your body has to stop microorganisms getting inside it.
6) Which three diseases is the MMR vaccine used to protect children from?
7) Name one type of bacteria that has developed resistance to antibiotics.
8) What practice did Semmelweis introduce in the 1840s? Explain why this reduced death rates on his ward.
9) Viruses can mutate frequently to produce new strains. Why does this make it hard to develop effective vaccines against them?
10) Describe the structure of the central nervous system and explain what it does.
11) What is a receptor? What is an effector?
12) Where would you find the following receptors in a dog: a) smell, b) taste, c) light, d) pressure, e) sound?
13) What is a synapse?
14) Describe the pathway of a reflex arc from stimulus to response.
15) Define "hormone".
16)*Here's a table of data about response times.
   a) Which response (A or B) is carried by nerves?
   b) Which is carried by hormones?

Response	Reaction time (s)	Response duration (s)
A	0.005	0.05
B	2	10

17) Draw a timeline of the 28 day menstrual cycle. Label the four stages of the cycle.
18) Describe two effects of FSH on the body.
19) Briefly describe how IVF is carried out.
20) What is auxin? Explain how auxin causes plant shoots to grow towards light.
21) Water content is kept steady by homeostasis. Describe how the amount and concentration of urine you produce changes on a cold day.
22) Stimulants can be used as a performance-enhancing drug. What effect do stimulants have on the body?
23) Describe how a clinical trial of a new drug works.
24) Describe three opinions about the link between cannabis and hard drug use.
25) Which has the bigger impact on society in the UK, legal or illegal drugs? Explain your answer.

* Answers on page 230.

Adaptations

Animals and plants survive in many different environments — from hot deserts to cold polar regions, and everywhere in between. They can do this because they have adapted to their environment.

Desert Animals Have Adapted to Save Water and Keep Cool

Animals that live in hot, dry conditions need to keep cool and use water efficiently.

Large Surface Area Compared to Volume

This lets desert animals lose more body heat — which helps to stop them overheating.

Efficient with Water

1) Desert animals lose less water by producing small amounts of concentrated urine.
2) They also make very little sweat. Camels are able to do this by tolerating big changes in body temperature, while kangaroo rats live in burrows underground where it's cool.

Good in Hot Conditions

Desert animals have very thin layers of body fat and a thin coat to help them lose body heat. E.g. camels keep nearly all their fat in their humps.

Camouflage

A sandy colour gives good camouflage — to help them avoid predators, or sneak up on prey.

Arctic Animals Have Adapted to Reduce Heat Loss

Animals that live in really cold conditions need to keep warm.

Small Surface Area Compared to Volume

Animals living in cold conditions have a compact (rounded) shape to keep their surface area to a minimum — this reduces heat loss.

Well Insulated

1) They also have a thick layer of blubber for insulation — this also acts as an energy store when food is scarce.
2) Thick hairy coats keep body heat in, and greasy fur sheds water (this prevents cooling due to evaporation).

Camouflage

Arctic animals have white fur to help them avoid predators, or sneak up on prey.

Adaptations

Whether you're an animal or a plant, you have to adapt to your environment — and that includes adapting to deal with other plants and animals...

Desert Plants Have Adapted to Having Little Water

Desert-dwelling plants make best use of what little water is available.

Small Surface Area Compared to Volume

1) Plants lose water vapour from the surface of their leaves. Cacti have spines instead of leaves — to reduce water loss.
2) They also have a small surface area compared to their size (about 1000 times smaller surface area than normal plants), which also reduces water loss.

Water Storage Tissues

For example, a cactus stores water in its thick stem.

Maximising Water Absorption

Some cacti have shallow but extensive roots to absorb water quickly over a large area. Others have deep roots to access underground water.

Some Plants and Animals Are Adapted to Deter Predators

There are various special features used by animals and plants to help protect them against being eaten.

1) Some plants and animals have armour — like roses (thorns), cacti (sharp spines) and tortoises (shells).

2) Others produce poisons — like bees and poison ivy.

3) And some have amazing warning colours to scare off predators — like wasps.

Microorganisms Have a Huge Variety of Adaptations...

...so that they can live in a wide range of environments. For example:

Some microorganisms (e.g. bacteria) are known as extremophiles — they're adapted to live in seriously extreme conditions like super hot volcanic vents, in very salty lakes or at high pressure on the sea bed.

In a nutshell, it's horses for courses...

It's no accident that animals and plants look like they do. So by looking at an animal's characteristics, you should be able to have a pretty good guess at the kind of environment it lives in — or vice versa.

Competition and Environmental Change

It's tough in the wild — there's always competition for food and other resources.

Organisms **Compete** *for* **Resources** *to* **Survive**

Organisms need things from their environment and from other organisms to survive and reproduce:

1) Plants need light, space, water and minerals (nutrients) from the soil.
2) Animals need space (territory), food, water and mates.

Organisms compete with other species (and members of their own species) for the same resources.

E.g. red and grey squirrels live in the same habitat and eat the same food. Competition with greys means there's not enough food for the reds. So the population of red squirrels is decreasing.

Environmental Changes *are Caused by* **Different Factors**

The environment in which plants and animals live changes all the time. These changes are caused by living and non-living factors, such as:

A change could be an increase or a decrease.

LIVING FACTORS:

1) A change in the occurrence of infectious diseases.
2) A change in the number of predators.
3) A change in the number of prey or the availability of food sources.
4) A change in the number or types of competitors.

NON-LIVING FACTORS:

1) A change in average temperature.
2) A change in average rainfall.
3) A change in the level of air or water pollution.

Environmental Changes **Affect Populations** *in* **Different Ways**

Environmental changes can affect animals and plants in these three ways:

1) Population size INCREASES.

   E.g. if the number of prey increases, then there's more food available for predators, so more predators survive and reproduce, and their numbers increase too.

2) Population size DECREASES.

   E.g. the number of bees in the US is falling rapidly.
   Experts aren't sure why but they think it could be because:
   1) Some pesticides may be having a negative effect on bees.
   2) There's less food available — there aren't as many nectar-rich plants around any more.
   3) There's more disease — bees are being killed by new pathogens or parasites.

3) Population DISTRIBUTION CHANGES.

   A change in distribution means a change in where an organism lives. E.g. the distribution of bird species in Germany is changing because of a rise in average temperature — e.g. the European Bee-Eater bird is a Mediterranean species but it's now present in parts of Germany.

Environmental changes affect population numbers and distribution

In the exam you might be given some data and asked about the change in distribution of an organism. Don't panic — just think about what that organism would need to survive and any environmental changes that have occurred. Remember — if things are in limited supply then there'll be competition.

Measuring Environmental Change

It's difficult to measure accurately just how much our environment is changing. But there are some useful indicators that can be used...

You can Measure Environmental Change Using Living Indicators...

1) Some organisms are very sensitive to changes in their environment and so can be studied to see the effect of human activities — these organisms are known as indicator species.

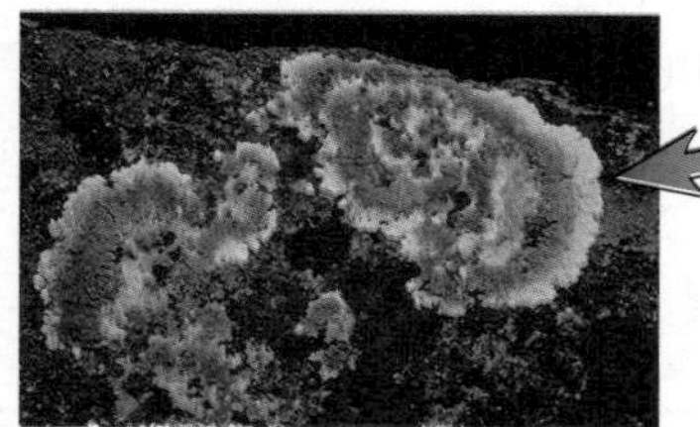

2) For example, air pollution can be monitored by looking at particular types of lichen that are very sensitive to the concentration of sulfur dioxide in the atmosphere (and so can give a good idea about the level of pollution from car exhausts, power stations, etc.). The number and type of lichen at a particular location will indicate how clean the air is (e.g. the air is clean if there are lots of lichen).

3) If raw sewage is released into a river, the bacterial population in the water increases and uses up the oxygen. Some invertebrate animals, like mayfly larvae, are good indicators for water pollution because they're very sensitive to the concentration of dissolved oxygen in the water. If you find mayfly larvae in a river, it indicates that the water is clean.

4) Other invertebrate species have adapted to live in polluted conditions — so if you see a lot of them you know there's a problem. E.g. rat-tailed maggots and sludgeworms indicate a very high level of water pollution.

...and Non-Living Indicators

To find out about environmental change, scientists are busy collecting data about the environment.

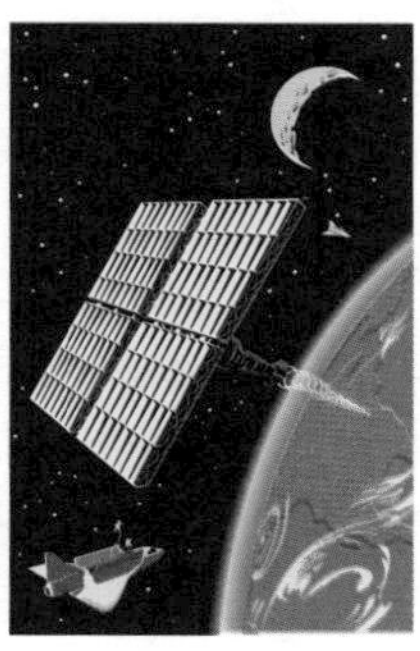

1) They use satellites to measure the temperature of the sea surface and the amount of snow and ice cover. These are modern, accurate instruments and give us a global coverage.

2) Automatic weather stations tell us the atmospheric temperature at various locations. They contain thermometers that are sensitive and accurate — they can measure to very small fractions of a degree.

3) They measure rainfall using rain gauges, to find out how much the average rainfall changes year on year.

4) They use dissolved oxygen meters, which measure the concentration of dissolved oxygen in water, to discover how the level of water pollution is changing.

Lichens and mayfly larvae are both common indicator species

Recording the levels of living and non-living things helps scientists to have a good idea of how our environment is changing. In your exam, you might get given some data about lichen or mayfly larvae as an indirect measure of pollution — and you'll have to figure out what the data means. (Easy — lots of lichen indicates clean air, lots of mayfly larvae indicates clean water. Nothing to it.)

Warm-Up and Exam Questions

Learning facts and practising exam questions is the only recipe for success.
That's what the questions on this page are all about. All you have to do — is do them.

Warm-Up Questions

1) Why is a small body surface area compared to its volume an advantage for an animal living in cold conditions?
2) Name an adaptation that a wasp has developed to help deter predators.
3) Name an organism that can be used as a living indicator of air pollution.
4) Joan finds lots of sludgeworms in a sample of water from a river near her house. What does this tell you about the river?
5) What piece of equipment might a scientist use to measure rainfall?

Exam Questions

1 Arctic animals, like polar bears, are well adapted to their environment.
Explain how each of the following helps the polar bear to survive in the Arctic.

(a) Polar bears have white fur.

(1 mark)

(b) Polar bears have a thick layer of blubber.

(2 marks)

(c) Polar bears have greasy fur.

(2 marks)

2 Explain how the features of a cactus help it to survive in desert conditions.

(3 marks)

3 Species A is a type of small mammal that eats beetles found in woodland areas.

(a) Where is Species A likely to live?

(1 mark)

(b) Species B moves into the same area as Species A.
Species B feeds on the same type of beetle as Species A.

(i) What word is used to describe how Species A and Species B interact with each other?

(1 mark)

(ii) What is likely to happen to the population of Species A after Species B has moved into the area?
Explain your answer.

(3 marks)

Pyramids of Biomass

A trophic level is a feeding level. It comes from the Greek word trophe meaning 'nourishment'.

You Need to Be Able to **Construct Pyramids of Biomass**

There's less energy and less biomass every time you move up a stage (trophic level) in a food chain. There are usually fewer organisms every time you move up a level too.

100 dandelions... feed... 10 rabbits... which feed... one fox.

This isn't always true though — for example, if 500 fleas are feeding on the fox, the number of organisms has increased as you move up that stage in the food chain.

So a better way to look at the food chain is often to think about biomass instead of number of organisms. You can use information about biomass to construct a pyramid of biomass to represent the food chain:

Biomass just means the mass of living material.

1) Each bar on a pyramid of biomass shows the mass of living material at that stage of the food chain — basically how much all the organisms at each level would "weigh" if you put them all together.
2) So the one fox above would have a big biomass and the hundreds of fleas would have a very small biomass. Biomass pyramids are practically always pyramid-shaped (unlike number pyramids).

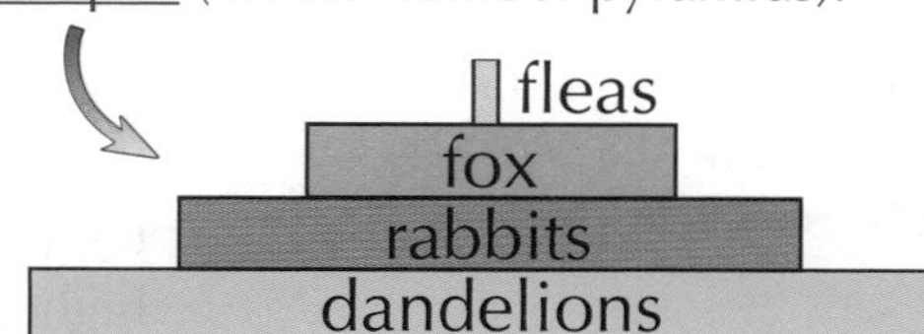

You need to be able to construct pyramids of biomass. Luckily it's pretty simple — they'll give you all the information you need to do it in the exam.

The big bar along the bottom of the pyramid always represents the producer (i.e. a plant). The next bar will be the primary consumer (the animal that eats the plant), then the secondary consumer (the animal that eats the primary consumer) and so on up the food chain.

You Need to be Able to **Interpret Pyramids of Biomass**

You also need to be able to look at pyramids of biomass and explain what they show about the food chain. For example:

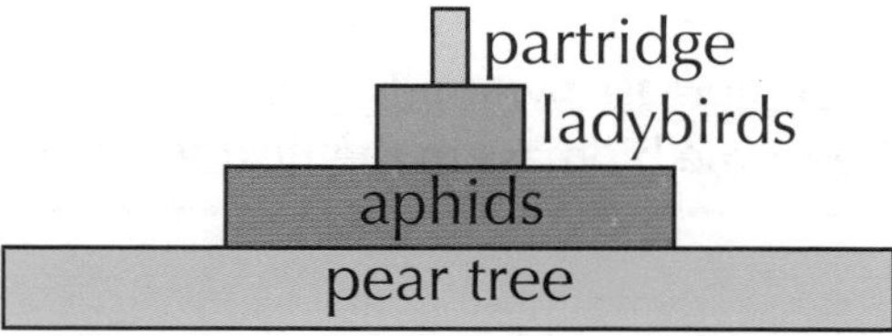

Even if you know nothing about the natural world, you're probably aware that a tree is quite a bit bigger than an aphid. So what's going on here is that lots (probably thousands) of aphids are feeding on a few great big trees. Quite a lot of ladybirds are then eating the aphids, and a few partridges are eating the ladybirds. Biomass and energy are still decreasing as you go up the levels — it's just that one tree can have a very big biomass, and can fix a lot of the Sun's energy using all those leaves.

Energy Transfer

So now you need to learn why there's less energy and biomass each time you move up a trophic level.

All That **Energy** Just **Disappears** Somehow...

1) Energy from the Sun is the source of energy for nearly all life on Earth.

2) Green plants and algae use a small percentage of the light energy from the Sun to make food during photosynthesis. This energy's stored in the substances which make up the cells of plants and algae, and then works its way through the food chain as animals eat them and each other.

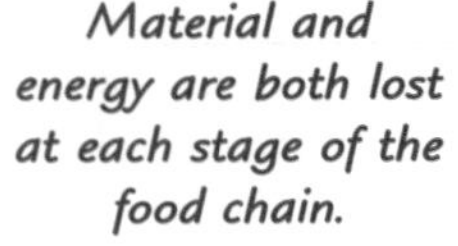
Material and energy are both lost at each stage of the food chain.

HEAT LOSS
MATERIAL IS LOST IN ANIMALS' WASTE

3) Respiration supplies the energy for all life processes, including movement. Most of the energy is eventually lost to the surroundings as heat. This is especially true for mammals and birds, whose bodies must be kept at a constant temperature which is normally higher than their surroundings.

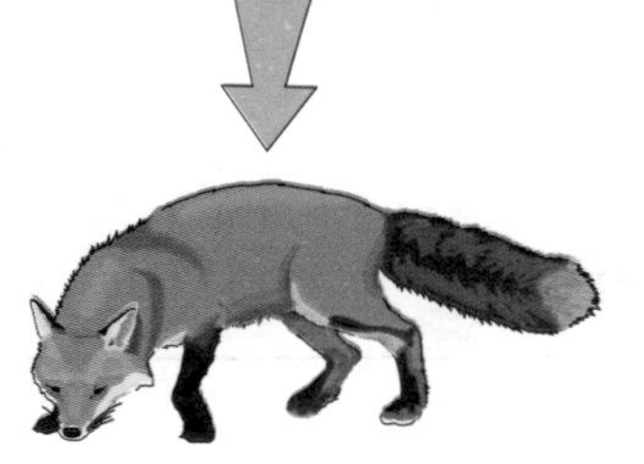

4) Some of the material which makes up plants and animals is inedible (e.g. bone), so it doesn't pass to the next stage of the food chain. Material and energy are also lost from the food chain in the organisms' waste materials.

5) This explains why you get biomass pyramids. Most of the biomass is lost and so does not become biomass in the next level up.

6) It also explains why you hardly ever get food chains with more than about five trophic levels. So much energy is lost at each stage that there's not enough left to support more organisms after four or five stages.

Decay

Decay is the reason why we're not knee-deep in waste material and dead organisms...

Elements are Cycled Back to the Start of the Food Chain by Decay

1) Living things are made of materials they take from the world around them.

2) Plants take elements like carbon, oxygen, hydrogen and nitrogen from the soil or the air. They turn these elements into the complex compounds (carbohydrates, proteins and fats) that make up living organisms, and these then pass through the food chain.

3) These elements are returned to the environment in waste products produced by the organisms, or when the organisms die. These materials decay because they're broken down (digested) by microorganisms — that's how the elements get put back into the soil.

4) Microorganisms work best in warm, moist conditions. Many microorganisms also break down material faster when there's plenty of oxygen available. Compost bins recreate these ideal conditions.

5) All the important elements are thus recycled — they return to the soil, ready to be used by new plants and put back into the food chain again.

6) In a stable community the materials taken out of the soil and used are balanced by those that are put back in. There's a constant cycle happening.

A COMPOST BIN

- Kitchen waste (e.g. food peelings) can be made into compost.
- Compost is decayed remains of animal and plant matter that can be used as fertiliser.
- It recycles nutrients back into the soil — giving you a lovely garden.

Extra decomposers added (compost maker)
Compost maker
Finely shredded waste is best
Mesh sides to let air in
Warmth generated by decompostion helps it all along

What goes around, comes around...

The constant recycling of material by microorganisms is vital to food chains. If this didn't happen, the nutrients that plants need would be locked up in the bodies of organisms and their excrement — plant growth would be next to none and without a producer the rest of the food chain would collapse.

The Carbon Cycle

As you've seen, all the nutrients in our environment are constantly being recycled — there's a nice balance between what goes in and what goes out again. This page is all about the recycling of carbon.

The Carbon Cycle Shows How Carbon is Recycled

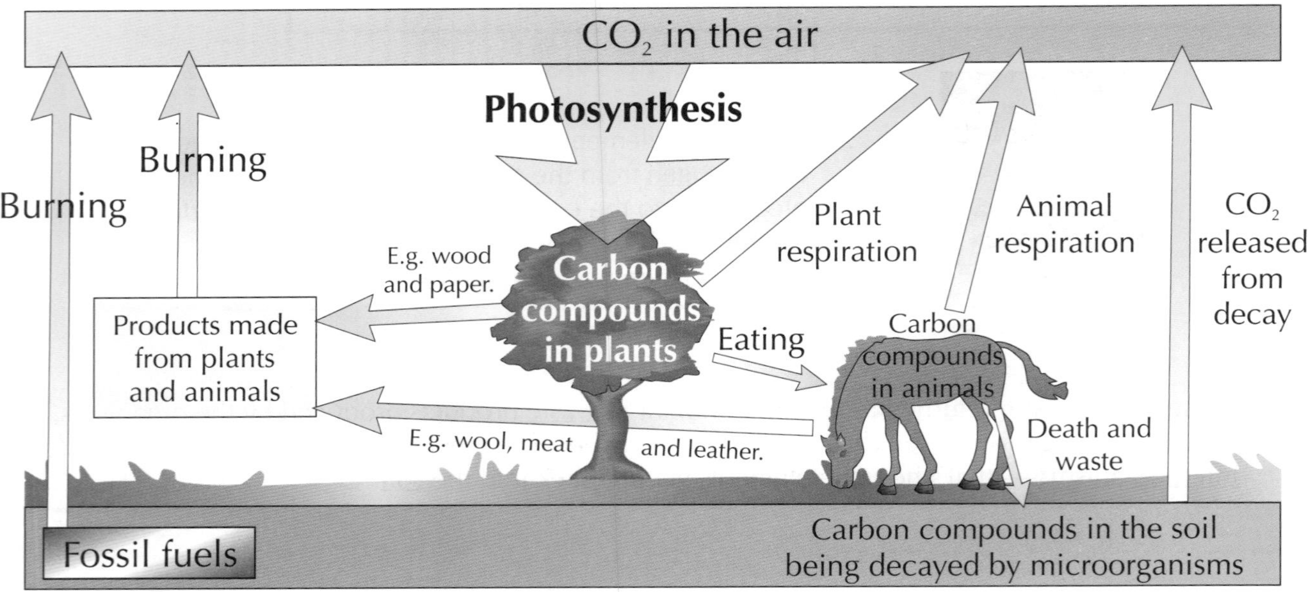

Fossil fuels are made of decayed plant and animal matter.

That can look a bit complicated at first, but it's actually pretty simple.
Learn these important points:

1) There's only one arrow going down from the atmosphere. The whole thing is "powered" by photosynthesis. CO_2 is removed from the atmosphere by green plants and algae, and the carbon is used to make carbohydrates, fats and proteins in the plants and algae.

The energy that green plants and algae get from photosynthesis is transferred up the food chain.

2) Some of the carbon is returned to the atmosphere as CO_2 when the plants and algae respire. Some of the carbon becomes part of the fats and proteins in animals when the plants and algae are eaten. The carbon then moves through the food chain.
3) Some of the carbon is returned to the atmosphere as CO_2 when the animals respire.
4) When plants, algae and animals die, other animals (called detritus feeders) and microorganisms feed on their remains. When these organisms respire, CO_2 is returned to the atmosphere.
5) Animals also produce waste, and this too is broken down by detritus feeders and microorganisms. Compounds in the waste are taken up from the soil by plants as nutrients — they're put back into the food chain again.
6) Some useful plant and animal products, e.g. wood and fossil fuels, are burnt (combustion). This also releases CO_2 back into the air.
7) So the carbon is constantly being cycled — from the air, through food chains and eventually back out into the air again.

Lots of processes release CO_2 — only photosynthesis takes it in

Carbon is very important for living things. It's the basis for all the organic molecules in our bodies — and that includes lots of really important types of molecules like fats, proteins and carbohydrates.

Warm-Up and Exam Questions

Right, now you've got to grips with how energy and material move through a food chain, have a go at these practice questions. If there's anything you're struggling with, go back and read that bit again.

Warm-Up Questions

1) What is a trophic level?
2) What is biomass?
3) Why do most food chains have no more than five trophic levels?
4) What is a stable community?
5) Name the two types of organism that can remove carbon dioxide from the atmosphere using photosynthesis.
6) Name the process that releases carbon dioxide from fossil fuels.

Exam Questions

1 A single robin has a mass of 15 g and eats caterpillars.
Each robin eats 25 caterpillars that each have a mass of 2.5 g.
The caterpillars feed on 10 stinging nettles that together have a mass of 500 g.

(a) Calculate the total mass of the caterpillars eaten by a single robin.

(1 mark)

Study the pyramid diagrams shown then answer the questions that follow.

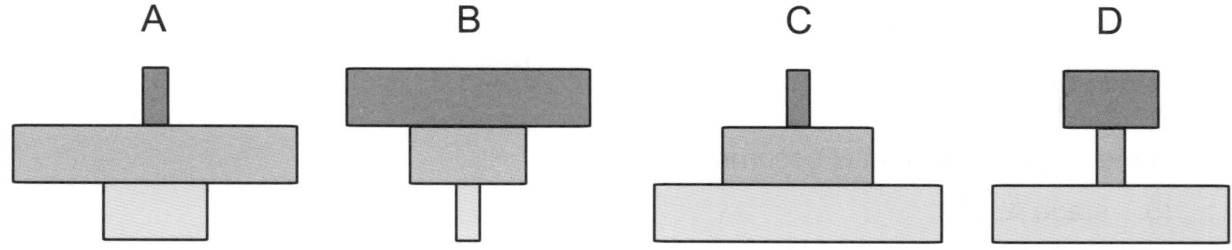

(b) Which diagram is most likely to represent a pyramid of biomass for these organisms? Give a reason for your answer.

(1 mark)

(c) The stinging nettles are the first trophic level.
Where does their energy initially come from?

(1 mark)

Exam Questions

2 All living organisms contain material taken from their surrounding environment. These materials are eventually recycled back into the environment. Some gardeners try to speed up this recycling process by producing compost in a compost bin.

(a) Describe how materials in living organisms are recycled back to the environment.

(3 marks)

(b) Suggest **two** ways in which a compost bin could provide a suitable environment for the decay of materials.

(2 marks)

3 An owl gets the energy that it needs by eating mice.
Not all of the energy taken in by the mice is passed on to the owl.
Explain how energy is lost from this food chain.

(3 marks)

4 The diagram below shows a simplified version of the carbon cycle.

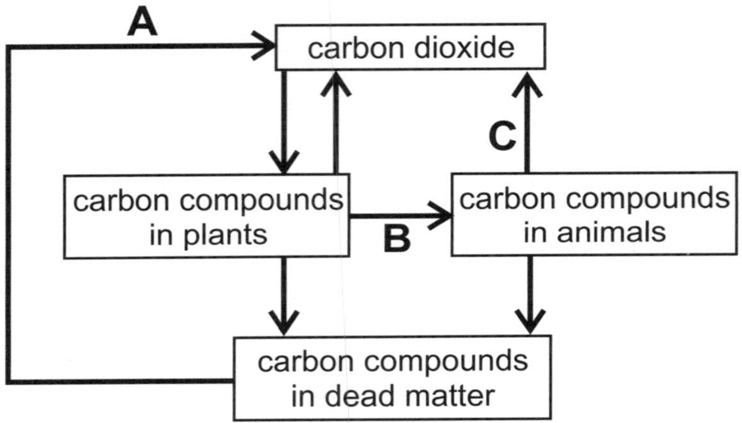

(a) Name the process that is occurring at:

(i) stage A.

(1 mark)

(ii) stage B.

(1 mark)

(iii) stage C.

(1 mark)

(b) Describe the likely effects on the carbon cycle if large areas of forest are cut down.

(1 mark)

(c) Name the only process in the carbon cycle that removes carbon dioxide from the air.

(1 mark)

Variation

You'll probably have noticed that not all people are identical. There are reasons for this.

*Organisms of the **Same Species** Have **Differences***

1) Different species look... well... different — my dog definitely doesn't look like a daisy.
2) But even organisms of the same species will usually look at least slightly different — e.g. in a room full of people you'll see different colour hair, individually shaped noses, a variety of heights etc.
3) These differences are called the variation within a species — and there are two types of variation: genetic variation and environmental variation.

Different Genes Cause Genetic Variation

1) All plants and animals have characteristics that are in some ways similar to their parents'.
2) This is because an organism's characteristics are determined by the genes inherited from their parents. (Genes are the codes inside your cells that control how you're made — more about these on p.66).
3) These genes are passed on in sex cells (gametes), which the offspring develop from (see p.67).
4) Most animals (and quite a lot of plants) get some genes from the mother and some from the father.
5) This combining of genes from two parents causes genetic variation — no two of the species are genetically identical (other than identical twins).
6) Some characteristics are determined only by genes (e.g. violet flower colour). In animals these include: eye colour, blood group and inherited disorders (e.g. haemophilia or cystic fibrosis).

Characteristics are also Influenced by the Environment

1) The environment that organisms live and grow in also causes differences between members of the same species — this is called environmental variation.
2) Environmental variation covers a wide range of differences — from losing your toes in a piranha attack, to getting a suntan, to having yellow leaves, and so on.
3) Basically, any difference that has been caused by the conditions something lives in, is an environmental variation.

A plant grown on a nice sunny windowsill would grow luscious and green.

The same plant grown in darkness would grow tall and spindly and its leaves would turn yellow — these are environmental variations.

Most Characteristics are Due to Genes AND the Environment

1) Most characteristics (e.g. body weight, height, skin colour, condition of teeth, academic or athletic prowess, etc.) are determined by a mixture of genetic and environmental factors.
2) For example, the maximum height that an animal or plant could grow to is determined by its genes. But whether it actually grows that tall depends on its environment (e.g. how much food it gets).

Your environment and your genes affect how you turn out...

So, you are the way you are partly because of the genes you inherited from your parents. But you can't blame it all on them, since your environment then takes over and begins to mould you in all sorts of ways. In fact, it's often really tricky to decide which factor is more influential, your genes or the environment — a good way to study this is with identical twins.

Genes, Chromosomes and DNA

This page is a bit tricky, but it's really important that you get to grips with all the stuff on it — because you're going to hear a lot more about it over the next few pages...

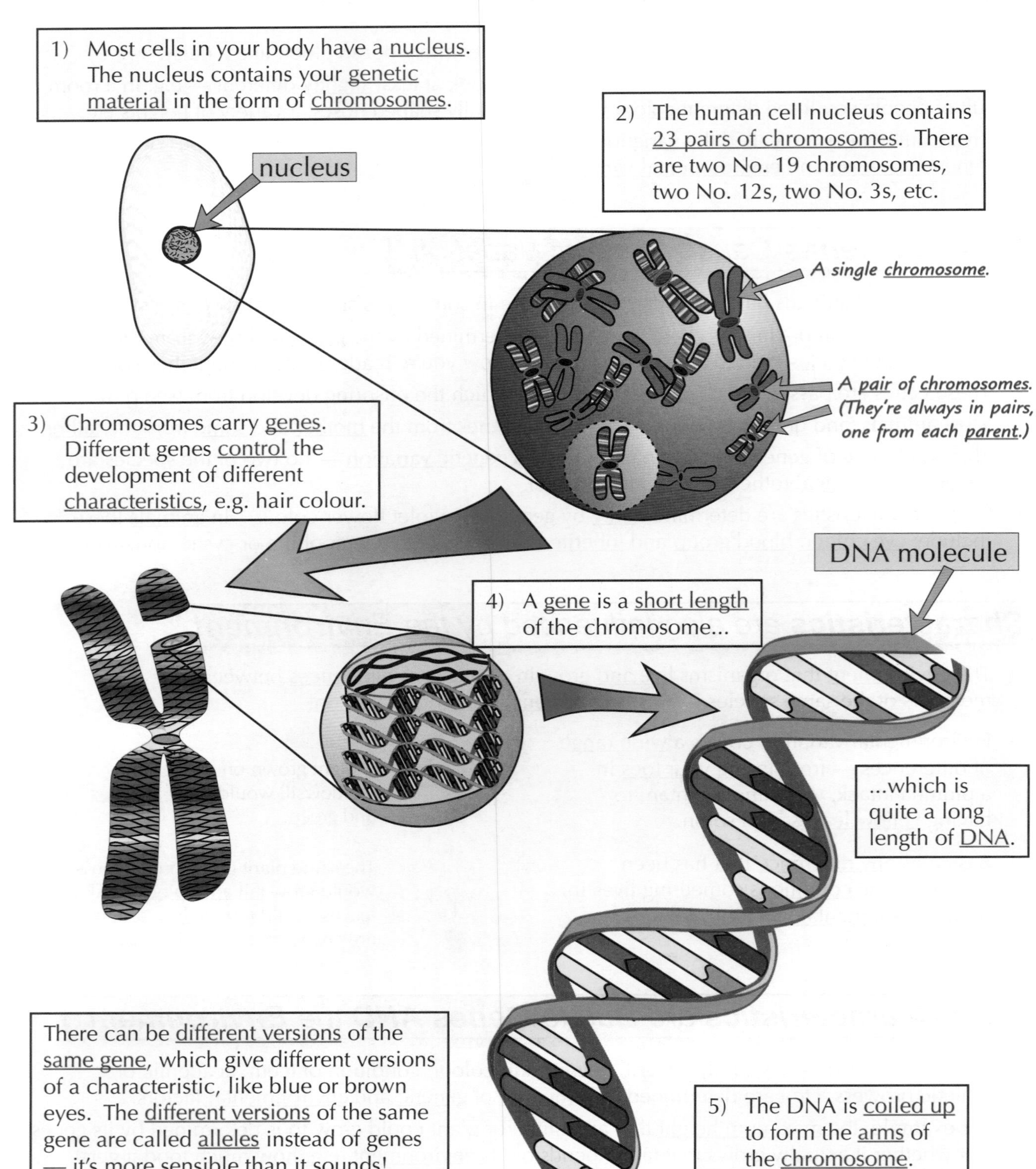

1) Most cells in your body have a nucleus. The nucleus contains your genetic material in the form of chromosomes.
nucleus
2) The human cell nucleus contains 23 pairs of chromosomes. There are two No. 19 chromosomes, two No. 12s, two No. 3s, etc.
A single chromosome.
A pair of chromosomes. (They're always in pairs, one from each parent.)
3) Chromosomes carry genes. Different genes control the development of different characteristics, e.g. hair colour.
DNA molecule
4) A gene is a short length of the chromosome...
...which is quite a long length of DNA.
There can be different versions of the same gene, which give different versions of a characteristic, like blue or brown eyes. The different versions of the same gene are called alleles instead of genes — it's more sensible than it sounds!
5) The DNA is coiled up to form the arms of the chromosome.

It's hard being a DNA molecule, there's so much to remember...

This is the real nuts and bolts of genetics, so you definitely need to understand everything on this page or you'll find the rest of this topic tricky. The best way to get all of these important facts engraved in your mind is to cover the page, scribble down the main points and sketch out the diagrams...

Sexual Reproduction

There are two basic ways that organisms can reproduce. The first one is sexual reproduction.

Sexual Reproduction Produces Genetically Different Cells

1) Sexual reproduction is where genetic information from two organisms (a father and a mother) is combined to produce offspring which are genetically different to either parent.
2) In sexual reproduction the mother and father produce gametes — e.g. egg and sperm cells in animals.
3) In humans, each gamete contains 23 chromosomes — half the number of chromosomes in a normal cell. (Instead of having two of each chromosome, a gamete has just one of each.)
4) The egg (from the mother) and the sperm cell (from the father) then fuse together (fertilisation) to form a cell with the full number of chromosomes (half from the father, half from the mother).

SEXUAL REPRODUCTION involves the fusion of male and female gametes. Because there are TWO parents, the offspring contain a mixture of their parents' genes.

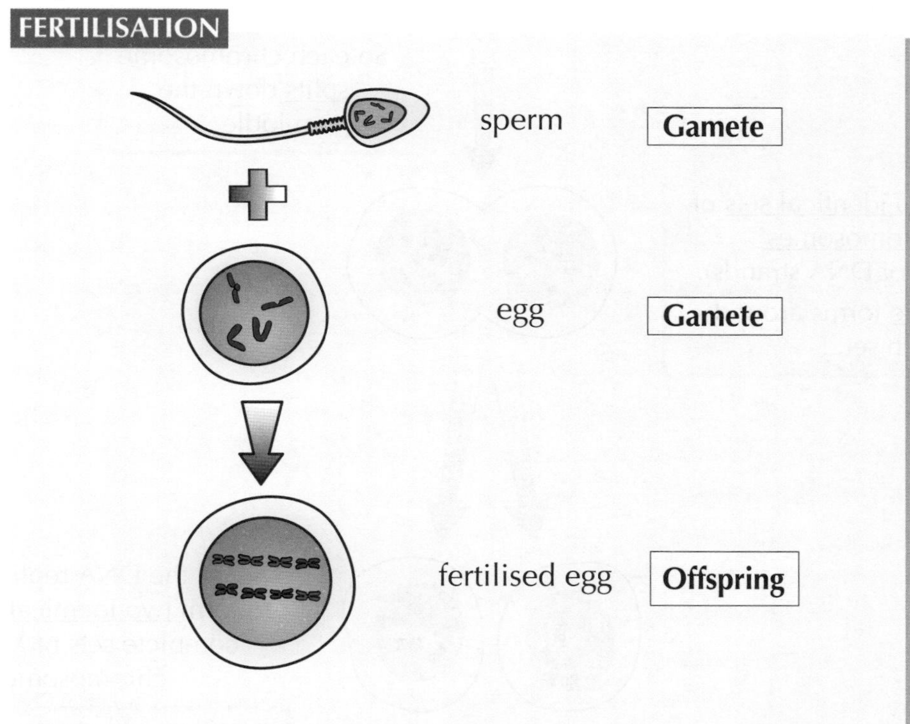

5) This is why the offspring inherits features from both parents — it's received a mixture of chromosomes from its mum and its dad (and it's the chromosomes that decide how you turn out).
6) This mixture of genetic material produces variation in the offspring.

Sexual reproduction creates genetic variation

Sexual reproduction needs two parents and forms cells that are genetically different to the parents, so it creates a lot of variation. Make sure you know this page off by heart before moving onto asexual reproduction, so that you don't get the two types of reproduction mixed up.

Asexual Reproduction

The second way that organisms can reproduce is called asexual reproduction.

Asexual Reproduction Produces **Genetically Identical Cells**

1) An ordinary cell can make a new cell by simply dividing in two. The new cell has exactly the same genetic information (i.e. genes) as the parent cell — this is known as asexual reproduction.

In ASEXUAL REPRODUCTION there's only ONE parent. There's no fusion of gametes, no mixing of chromosomes and no genetic variation between parent and offspring. The offspring are genetically identical to the parent — they're clones.

2) Here's how it works...

X-shaped chromosomes have two identical halves.

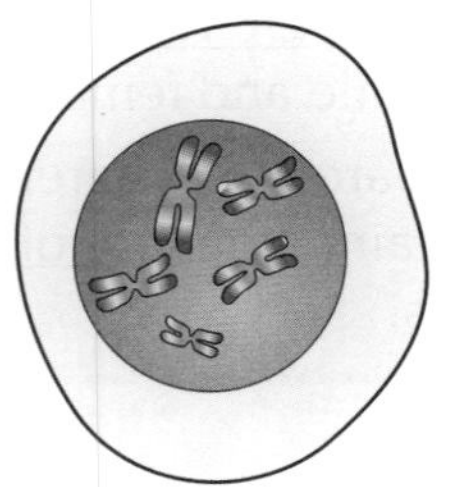

So each chromosome splits down the middle...

...to form two identical sets of 'half-chromosomes' (i.e. two sets of DNA strands).

A membrane forms around each set...

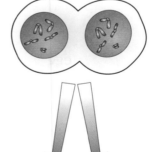

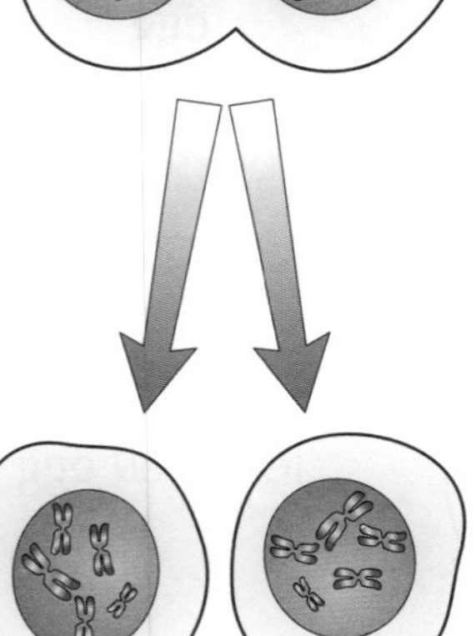

...and the DNA replicates itself to form two identical cells with complete sets of X-shaped chromosomes.

3) This is how all plants and animals grow and produce replacement cells.

4) Some organisms also produce offspring using asexual reproduction, e.g. bacteria and certain plants.

You need to reproduce these facts in the exam...

Asexual reproduction needs just one parent to make genetically identical cells (clones), so there's no genetic variation in the offspring. Have a look back at the previous page and make sure you know the differences between the two types of reproduction — shut the book and try writing them down.

Warm-Up and Exam Questions

Take a deep breath and go through these warm-up questions one by one.
If you don't know these basic facts there's no way you'll cope with the exam questions.

Warm-Up Questions

1) A pair of identical twins have green eyes. Twin A has a scar above her eye. Twin B weighs half a stone more than twin A. Which of these characteristics are due to:
    a) genes only
    b) the environment only
    c) genes and the environment?
2) Where is DNA found in an animal or plant cell?
3) What is a gene?
4) In asexual reproduction, how many parents are there?

Exam Questions

1 (a) What are the male and female human gametes?

(1 mark)

(b) How many chromosomes does a human gamete contain?

(1 mark)

Two human gametes fuse to form a zygote.

(c) How many chromosomes does the zygote contain?

(1 mark)

(d) What fraction of its chromosomes has the zygote inherited from its mother?

(1 mark)

2 This is Ruth, and her little brother Mark.

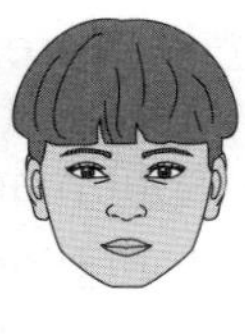

(a) Ruth's eyes are blue.
Mark's eyes are brown.
Why do Ruth and Mark have different colour eyes?

(1 mark)

(b) Explain why sexual reproduction produces variation.

(2 marks)

3 Tulip plants can reproduce asexually by producing bulbs.

Karl plants two tulip bulbs that were produced by the same parent plant.
He plants one in a dry, sunny spot, and the other in a damp, shady area.

(a) Will both new plants have the same colour flowers? Explain your answer.

(3 marks)

(b) Will both new plants be exactly the same height? Explain your answer.

(3 marks)

Cloning

We can use asexual reproduction to clone plants and animals in several different ways...

Plants Can Be Cloned from Cuttings and by Tissue Culture

Cuttings

1) Gardeners can take cuttings from good parent plants, and then plant them to produce genetically identical copies (clones) of the parent plant.
2) These plants can be produced quickly and cheaply.

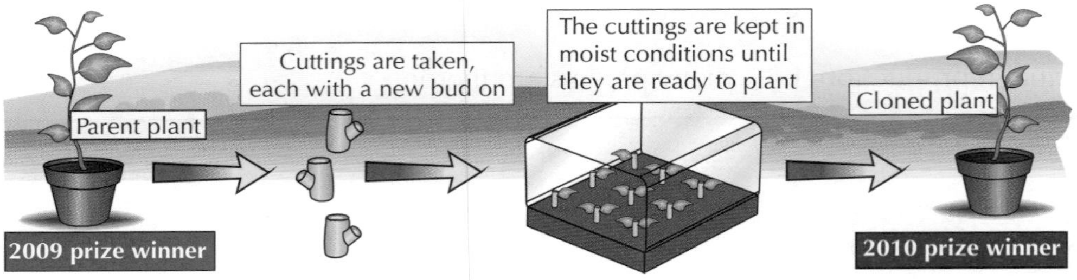
Parent plant
2009 prize winner
Cuttings are taken, each with a new bud on
The cuttings are kept in moist conditions until they are ready to plant
Cloned plant
2010 prize winner

Tissue Culture

1) This is where a few plant cells are put in a growth medium with hormones, and they grow into new plants — clones of the parent plant.
2) These plants can be made very quickly, in very little space, and be grown all year.

You Can Make Animal Clones Using Embryo Transplants

Farmers can produce cloned offspring from their best bull and cow — using embryo transplants.

1) Sperm cells are taken from a prize bull and egg cells are taken from a prize cow. The sperm are then used to artificially fertilise an egg cell. The embryo that develops is then split many times (to form clones) before any cells become specialised.
2) These cloned embryos can then be implanted into lots of other cows where they grow into baby calves (which will all be genetically identical to each other).

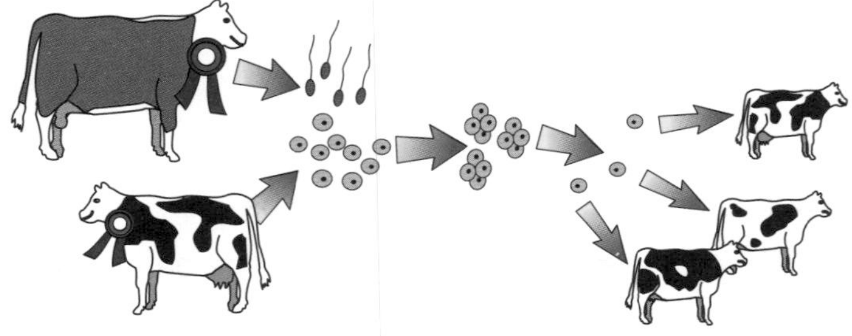

3) Hundreds of "ideal" offspring can be produced every year from the best bull and cow.

Cloning produces genetically identical organisms

Cloning can come in pretty handy if you're a gardener or a farmer. If you've spent ages trying to get an ideal plant or animal (like a prize cow) then you can use cloning to produce plenty more just like it.

Cloning

There's another way to clone animals and it's a bit controversial...

Adult Cell Cloning is Another Way to Make a Clone

1) Adult cell cloning involves taking an unfertilised egg cell and removing its genetic material (the nucleus).

2) A complete set of chromosomes from an adult body cell (e.g. skin cell) is inserted into the 'empty' egg cell.

3) The egg cell is then stimulated by an electric shock — this makes it divide, just like a normal embryo.

4) When the embryo is a ball of cells, it's implanted into an adult female (the surrogate mother) to grow into a genetically identical copy (clone) of the original adult body cell.

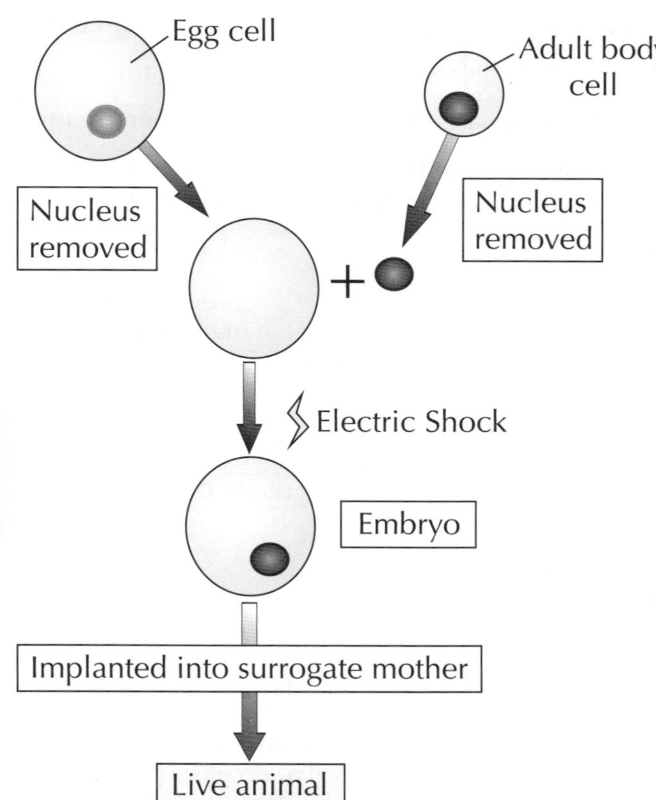

5) This technique was used to create Dolly — the famous cloned sheep.

There are Many Issues Surrounding Cloning

1) Cloning quickly gets you lots of "ideal" offspring. But you also get a "reduced gene pool" — this means there are fewer different alleles in a population. If a population are all closely related and a new disease appears, they could all be wiped out — there may be no allele in the population giving resistance to the disease.
2) But the study of animal clones could lead to greater understanding of the development of the embryo, and of ageing and age-related disorders.
3) Cloning could also be used to help preserve endangered species.
4) It's possible that cloned animals might not be as healthy as normal ones, e.g. Dolly the sheep had arthritis, which tends to occur in older sheep (but the jury's still out on if this was due to cloning).
5) Some people worry that humans might be cloned in the future. If it was allowed, any success may follow many unsuccessful attempts, e.g. children born severely disabled.

Cloning can be a pretty controversial topic...

...especially when it's to do with cloning animals (and especially humans). Is it healthy scientific progress, or are we trying to 'play God'? It's one of those questions science can't answer (see page 6).

Genetic Engineering

Scientists can now change an organism's genes to alter its characteristics. This is a new science with exciting possibilities, but there might be dangers too...

Genetic Engineering Uses Enzymes to Cut and Paste Genes

The basic idea is to copy a useful gene from one organism's chromosome into the cells of another...

1) A useful gene is "cut" from one organism's chromosome using enzymes.
2) Enzymes are then used to cut another organism's chromosome and then to insert the useful gene.
3) Scientists use this method to do all sorts of things — for example, the human insulin gene can be inserted into bacteria to produce human insulin:

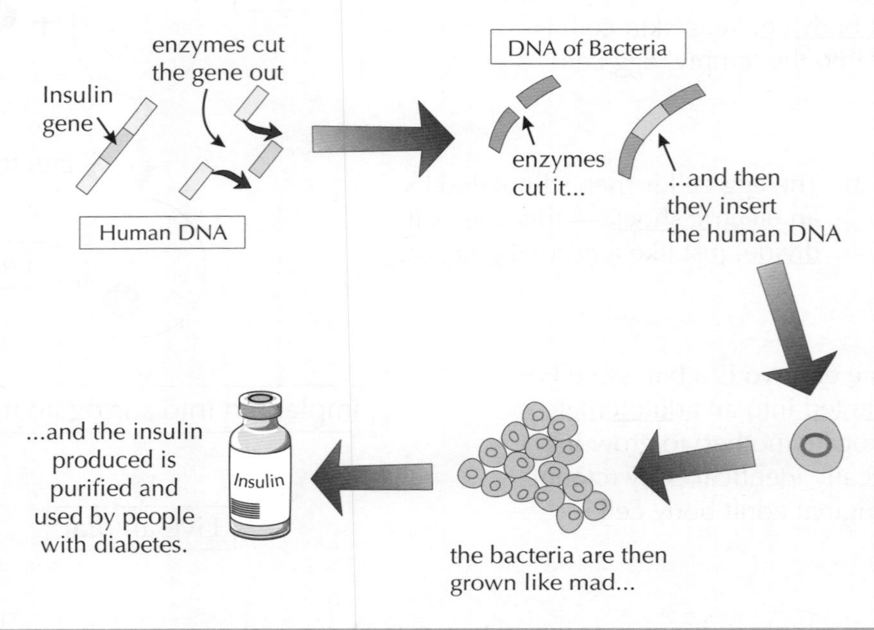

Genes can be Transferred into Animals and Plants

The same method can be used to transfer useful genes into animals and plants at the very early stages of their development (i.e. shortly after fertilisation). This means they'll develop useful characteristics, e.g:

1) Genetically modified (GM) crops have had their genes modified, e.g. to make them resistant to viruses, insects or herbicides (chemicals used to kill weeds).

'Bt corn' contains a gene from a bacterium that protects against some insects.

2) Sheep have been genetically engineered to produce substances, like drugs, in their milk that can be used to treat human diseases.

3) Genetic disorders like cystic fibrosis are caused by faulty genes. Scientists are trying to treat these disorders by inserting working genes into sufferers. This is called gene therapy.

Genetic Engineering

On the face of it, genetic engineering is great.
But like most other things, there are benefits and risks that you need to consider.

Genetic Engineering is a **Controversial Topic...**

1) Genetic engineering is an exciting new area in science which has the potential for solving many of our problems (e.g. treating diseases, more efficient food production etc.) but not everyone thinks it's a great idea.

2) There are worries about the long-term effects of genetic engineering — that changing a person's genes might accidentally create unplanned problems, which could then get passed on to future generations.

It's the Same with **GM Crops** — There Are **Pros** and **Cons...**

Pros:

1) GM crops can increase the yield of a crop, making more food.

2) People living in developing nations often lack nutrients in their diets. GM crops could be engineered to contain the nutrient that's missing. For example, they're testing 'Golden Rice' that contains beta-carotene — lack of this substance causes blindness.

3) GM crops are already being grown elsewhere in the world (not the UK) often without any problems.

Cons:

1) Some people say that growing GM crops will affect the number of weeds and flowers (and so the population of insects) that live in and around the crops — reducing farmland biodiversity.

2) Not everyone is convinced that GM crops are safe. People are worried they may develop allergies to the food — although there's probably no more risk for this than for eating usual foods.

3) A big concern is that transplanted genes may get out into the natural environment. For example, the herbicide resistance gene may be picked up by weeds, creating a new 'superweed' variety.

If only there was a gene to make revision easier...

At the end of the day, it's down to the Government to weigh up all the evidence for the pros and cons before making a decision on how this scientific knowledge is used. All that the scientists can do is make sure the Government has all the information that it needs to make the decision.

Warm-Up and Exam Questions

By doing these warm-up questions, you'll soon find out if you've got the basic facts straight. If not, you'll really struggle, so take the time to go back over the bits you don't know.

Warm-Up Questions

1) Briefly describe how plant clones can be produced using tissue culture.
2) Other than tissue culture, name another way that plant clones can be produced.
3) Give one advantage of cloning using cow embryo transplantation.
4) What is a reduced gene pool?
5) Name one useful product that humans have genetically modified bacteria to produce.

Exam Questions

1 Organisms can be genetically modified.
This means an organism's genes can be altered to alter its characteristics.

(a) Give **two** functions of enzymes used in genetic engineering.
(2 marks)

(b) Suggest **one** useful way that plants can be genetically modified.
(1 mark)

(c) Suggest **one** useful way that animals can be genetically modified.
(1 mark)

(d) Some people think that it is wrong to genetically modify plants.
Give **two** different objections that people might have.
(2 marks)

2 In 1997 scientists at the Roslin Institute announced the birth of Dolly the sheep, the first mammal to be cloned using adult cell cloning.

(a) Explain how a sheep can be cloned using adult cell cloning.
(4 marks)

(b) Dolly was a female sheep. What would have been the gender of the sheep that Dolly was created from? Explain your answer.
(1 mark)

(c) Give **one** potential problem with adult cell cloning.
(1 mark)

Evolution

There are lots of different species around on Earth today. But there wasn't always so much variety...

THE THEORY OF EVOLUTION:

More than 3 billion years ago, life on Earth began as simple organisms from which all the more complex organisms evolved (rather than just popping into existence).

All **Organisms** *are* **Related**... *even if Only* **Distantly**

Looking at the similarities and differences between organisms allows us to classify them into groups.

E.g:
1) Plants make their own food (by photosynthesis) and are fixed in the ground.
2) Animals move about the place and can't make their own food.
3) Microorganisms are different to plants and animals, e.g. bacteria are single-celled.

Studying the similarities and differences between organisms also helps us to understand how all living things are related (evolutionary relationships) and how they interact with each other (ecological relationships):

EVOLUTIONARY RELATIONSHIPS

1) Species with similar characteristics often have similar genes because they share a recent common ancestor, so they're closely related. They often look very alike and tend to live in similar types of habitat, e.g. whales and dolphins.
2) Occasionally, genetically different species might look alike too. E.g. dolphins and sharks look pretty similar because they've both adapted to living in the same habitat. But they're not closely related — they've evolved from different ancestors.
3) Evolutionary trees show common ancestors and relationships between organisms. The more recent the common ancestor, the more closely related the two species.
4) Here's an example of an evolutionary tree:

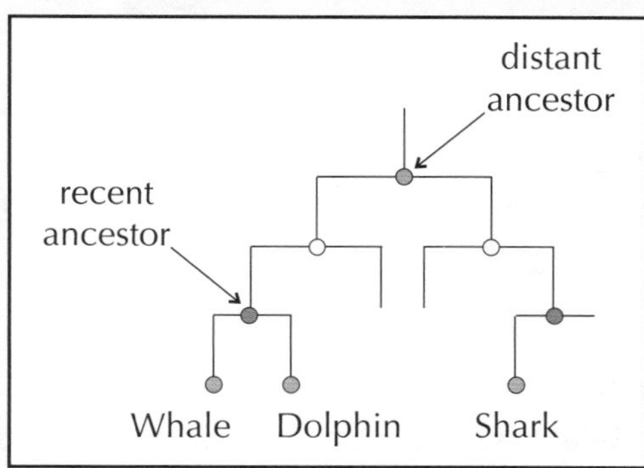

Whales and dolphins have a recent common ancestor so are closely related. They're both more distantly related to sharks.

ECOLOGICAL RELATIONSHIPS

1) If we see organisms in the same environment with similar characteristics (e.g. dolphins and sharks) it suggests they might be in competition (e.g for the same food source).
2) Differences between organisms in the same environment (e.g. dolphins swim in small groups, but herring swim in giant shoals) can show predator-prey relationships (e.g. dolphins hunt herring).

Evolution

Scientists today reckon they have a pretty good understanding of how species evolve.

Natural Selection Explains How Evolution Occurs

Charles Darwin came up with the idea of natural selection. It works like this...

1) Individuals within a species show variation because of the differences in their genes, e.g. some rabbits have big ears and some have small ones.

Genetic differences are caused by sexual reproduction (see page 67) and mutations (see below).

2) Individuals with characteristics that make them better adapted to the environment have a better chance of survival and so are more likely to breed successfully. E.g. big-eared rabbits are more likely to hear a fox sneaking up on them, and so are more likely to live and have millions of babies. Small-eared rabbits are more likely to end up as fox food.

3) So, the genes that are responsible for the useful characteristics are more likely to be passed on to the next generation. E.g. all the baby rabbits are born with big ears.

Evolution can Occur Due To Mutations

1) A mutation is a change in an organism's DNA.

2) Most of the time mutations have no effect, but occasionally they can be beneficial by producing a useful characteristic. This characteristic may give the organism a better chance of surviving and reproducing.

3) If so, the beneficial mutation is more likely to be passed on to future generations by natural selection.

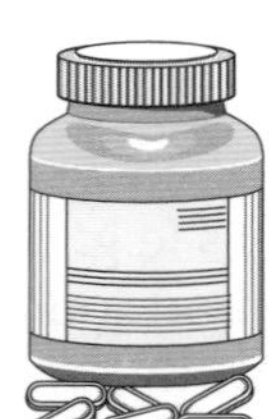

4) Over time, the beneficial mutation will accumulate in a population, e.g. some species of bacteria have become resistant to antibiotics due to a mutation (see page 28).

Natural selection — the fittest pass on their characteristics

Natural selection's all about the organisms with the best characteristics surviving to pass on their genes so that the whole species ends up adapted to its environment. It doesn't happen overnight though.

Evolution

There's a lot of evidence for the theory of evolution by natural selection.
But back in the day, Darwin didn't have half as much evidence to convince people.

Not Everyone Agreed with Darwin...

Darwin's idea was very controversial at the time — for various reasons...

1) It went against common religious beliefs about how life on Earth developed — it was the first plausible explanation for our own existence without the need for a "Creator" (God).
2) Darwin couldn't give a good explanation for why these new, useful characteristics appeared or exactly how individual organisms passed on their beneficial characteristics to their offspring. But then he didn't know anything about genes or mutations — they weren't discovered 'til 50 years after his theory was published.
3) There wasn't enough evidence to convince many scientists, because not many other studies had been done into how organisms change over time.

...and Lamarck had Different Ideas

There were different scientific hypotheses about evolution around at the same time, such as Lamarck's:

1) Lamarck (1744-1829) argued that if a characteristic was used a lot by an organism then it would become more developed during its lifetime. E.g. if a rabbit used its legs to run a lot (to escape predators), then its legs would get longer.
2) Lamarck believed that these acquired characteristics would be passed on to the next generation, e.g. the rabbit's offspring would have longer legs.

Different Hypotheses Can Come from Similar Observations

1) Often scientists come up with different hypotheses to explain similar observations.
2) Scientists might develop different hypotheses because they have different beliefs (e.g. religious) or they have been influenced by different people (e.g. other scientists and their way of thinking)... or they just think differently.
3) The only way to find out whose hypothesis is right is to find evidence to support or disprove each one.
4) For example, Lamarck and Darwin had different hypotheses to explain how evolution happens. In the end...
   - Lamarck's hypothesis was rejected because experiments didn't support it. You can see it for yourself, e.g. if you dye a hamster's fur bright pink (not recommended), its offspring will still be born with the normal fur colour because the new characteristic won't have been passed on.
   - The discovery of genetics supported Darwin's idea because it provided an explanation of how organisms born with beneficial characteristics can pass them on (i.e. via their genes).
5) There's so much evidence for Darwin's idea that it's now an accepted hypothesis (a theory).

There's more about how science works on page 1.

I wonder what exams evolved from...

This is a good example of how scientific hypotheses come about — someone observes something and then tries to explain it. Their hypothesis is then tested by other scientists — if their evidence supports the hypothesis, it gains in credibility. If not, it's rejected. Darwin's theory hasn't been rejected yet.

Warm-Up and Exam Questions

The warm-up questions run quickly over the basic facts you'll need in the exam. The exam questions come later — but unless you've learnt the facts first you'll find the exams tougher than stale bread.

Warm-Up Questions

1) What is the theory of evolution?
2) What two things can genetic differences be caused by?
3) Explain the difference between evolution and natural selection.
4) What is a mutation?
5) Do mutations always produce useful new characteristics? Explain your answer.

Exam Questions

1 Look at the section of an evolutionary tree shown below.

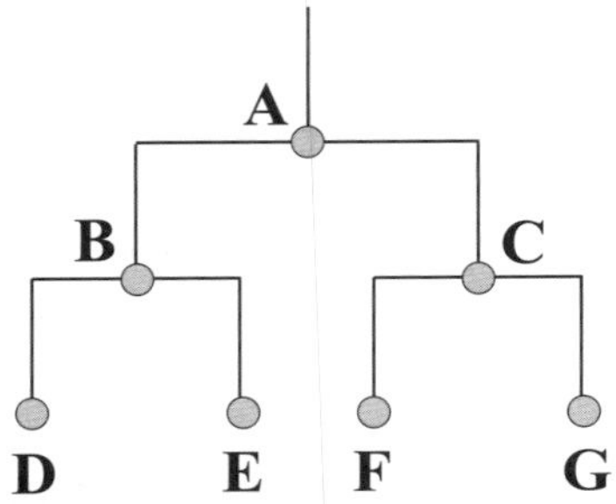

(a) Which species is the most recent common ancestor of Species **F** and Species **G**?

(1 mark)

(b) Would you expect Species **D** to look similar to Species **E**? Give a reason for your answer.

(1 mark)

2 Charles Darwin developed the theory of evolution by natural selection.

(a) According to Darwin's theory, explain how natural selection occurs.

(4 marks)

(b) Give **three** reasons why Darwin originally had trouble getting his ideas accepted.

(3 marks)

(c) Jean-Baptiste Lamarck had different ideas to Darwin about how evolution occurred.

(i) Describe Lamarck's hypothesis about evolution.

(2 marks)

(ii) Explain why Darwin's ideas were accepted over Lamarck's.

(2 marks)

Revision Summary for Biology 1b

There's a lot to remember from this section and some of the topics are controversial, like cloning and genetic engineering. You need to know all sides of the story, as well as all the facts... so, here are some questions to help you figure out what you know. If you get any wrong, go back and learn the stuff.

1) Name four ways in which a desert animal may be adapted to its environment.
2) State three ways that plants might be adapted to deter predators.
3) Name three things that: a) plants compete for, b) animals compete for.
4) Give two examples of non-living factors that can cause environmental changes.
5) Explain how lichen can be used as an indicator of air pollution.
6) Name an organism that can be used as an indicator of water pollution.
7) What does each bar on a pyramid of biomass represent?
8) Give one way that energy is lost from a food chain.
9) Give three ways that carbon compounds in a food chain become carbon dioxide in the air again.
10) Name three animal characteristics that are determined only by genes.
11) Name three animal characteristics that are determined by a mixture of genes and the environment.
12) Give an example of an organism that can produce offspring using asexual reproduction.
13) The table below compares sexual and asexual reproduction. Copy and complete the table by ticking whether each statement is true for sexual or asexual reproduction.

	Sexual reproduction	Asexual reproduction
Reproduction involves two parents.		
Offspring are clones of the parent.		
There is variation in the offspring.		
There is no fusion of gametes.		

14) Describe how you could clone a prize cow using embryo transplantation.
15) State two examples of useful applications of genetic engineering.
16) Why are some people concerned about genetic engineering?
17) Describe a mutation seen in some strains of bacteria that is beneficial to the bacteria.
18) Explain how Lamarck's hypothesis was different from Darwin's.
19) Why might two scientists come up with different hypotheses to explain similar observations?

Cells

All living things are made of cells. When someone first peered down a microscope at a slice of cork and drew the boxes they saw, little did they know that they'd seen the building blocks of every organism on the planet.

Most Animal Cells Have Certain Features in Common

Most human cells, like most animal cells, have the following parts — make sure you know them all:

1) Nucleus — contains genetic material that controls the activities of the cell.

2) Cytoplasm — gel-like substance where most of the chemical reactions happen. It contains enzymes (see page 100) that control these chemical reactions.

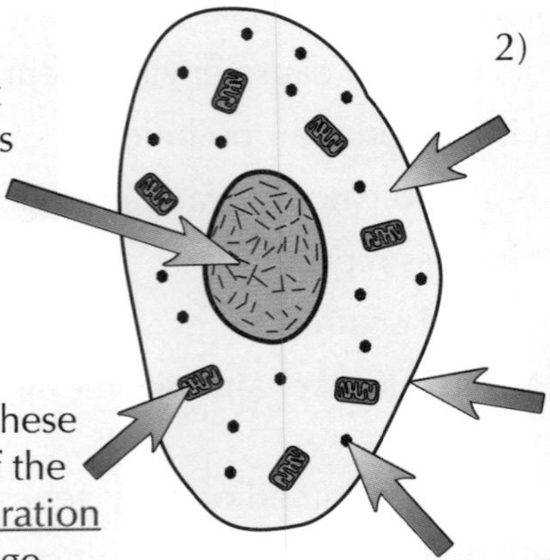

3) Cell membrane — holds the cell together and controls what goes in and out.

4) Mitochondria — these are where most of the reactions for respiration take place (see page 105). Respiration releases energy that the cell needs to work.

5) Ribosomes — these are where proteins are made in the cell.

Plant Cells have Some Extra Features

Plant cells usually have all the bits that animal cells have, plus a few extra things that animal cells don't have:

1) Rigid cell wall — made of cellulose. It supports the cell and strengthens it.

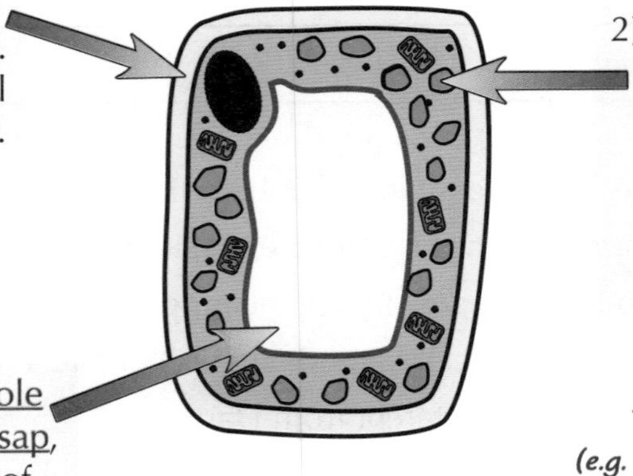

2) Chloroplasts — these are where photosynthesis occurs, which makes food for the plant (see page 88). They contain a green substance called chlorophyll.

3) Permanent vacuole — contains cell sap, a weak solution of sugar and salts.

The cells of algae (e.g. seaweed) also have a rigid cell wall and chloroplasts.

There's quite a bit to learn in biology — but that's life, I guess...

On this page are a typical animal cell and a typical plant cell with all the typical bits you need to know. But not all plant or animal cells are the same — they have different structures and produce different substances depending on the job they do.

Cells

You also need to know about yeast and bacterial cells...

Yeast is a Single-Celled Organism

1) Yeast is a microorganism.
2) A yeast cell has a nucleus, cytoplasm, and a cell membrane surrounded by a cell wall.

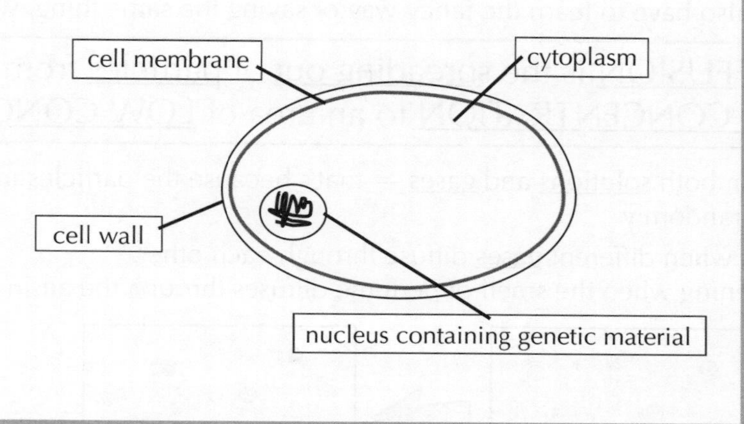

Bacterial Cells Have No Nucleus

1) Bacteria are also single-celled microorganisms.
2) A bacterial cell has cytoplasm and a cell membrane surrounded by a cell wall.
3) The genetic material floats in the cytoplasm because bacterial cells don't have a nucleus.

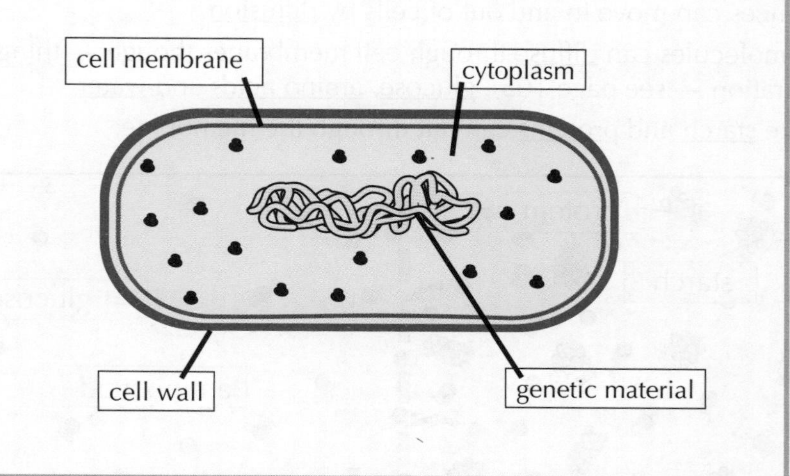

Both yeast and bacteria are single-celled microorganisms

On this page are a typical yeast cell and a typical bacterial cell. Make sure you know their structures. Copy out the diagrams, without looking at the book, and see if you can remember all the labels.

Diffusion

Particles move about randomly, and after a bit they end up evenly spaced.

Don't Be Put Off by the Fancy Word

1) "Diffusion" is simple. It's just the gradual movement of particles from places where there are lots of them to places where there are fewer of them.
2) That's all it is — just the natural tendency for stuff to spread out.
3) Unfortunately you also have to learn the fancy way of saying the same thing, which is this:

> DIFFUSION is the spreading out of particles from an area of HIGH CONCENTRATION to an area of LOW CONCENTRATION

4) Diffusion happens in both solutions and gases — that's because the particles in these substances are free to move about randomly.
5) The simplest type is when different gases diffuse through each other. This is what's happening when the smell of perfume diffuses through the air in a room:

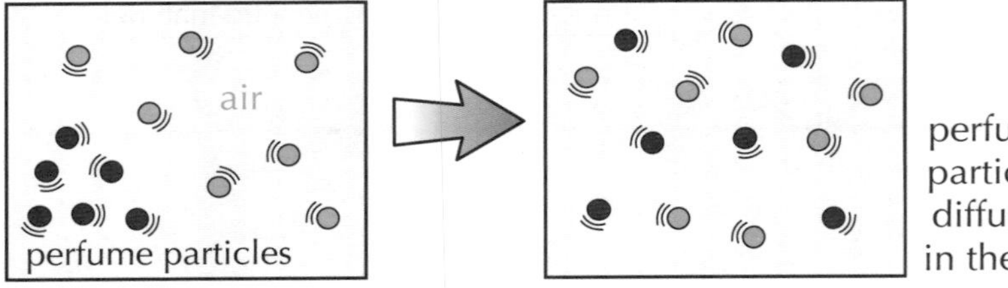

6) The bigger the difference in concentration, the faster the diffusion rate.

Cell Membranes Are Kind of Clever...

1) They're clever because they hold the cell together but they let stuff in and out as well.
2) Dissolved substances can move in and out of cells by diffusion.
3) Only very small molecules can diffuse through cell membranes though — things like oxygen (needed for respiration — see page 105), glucose, amino acids and water.
4) Big molecules like starch and proteins can't fit through the membrane:

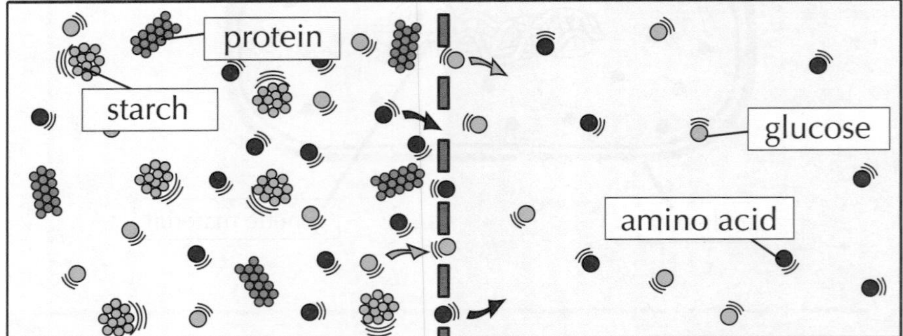

5) Just like with diffusion in air, particles flow through the cell membrane from where there's a high concentration (a lot of them) to where there's a low concentration (not such a lot of them).
6) They're only moving about randomly of course, so they go both ways — but if there are a lot more particles on one side of the membrane, there's a net (overall) movement from that side.

Specialised Cells

Page 80 shows the structure of some typical cells. However, most cells are specialised for their specific function, so their structure can vary...

1) Palisade Leaf Cells Are Adapted for Photosynthesis

1) Packed with chloroplasts for photosynthesis. More of them are crammed at the top of the cell — so they're nearer the light.
2) Tall shape means a lot of surface area exposed down the side for absorbing CO_2 from the air in the leaf.
3) Thin shape means that you can pack loads of them in at the top of a leaf.

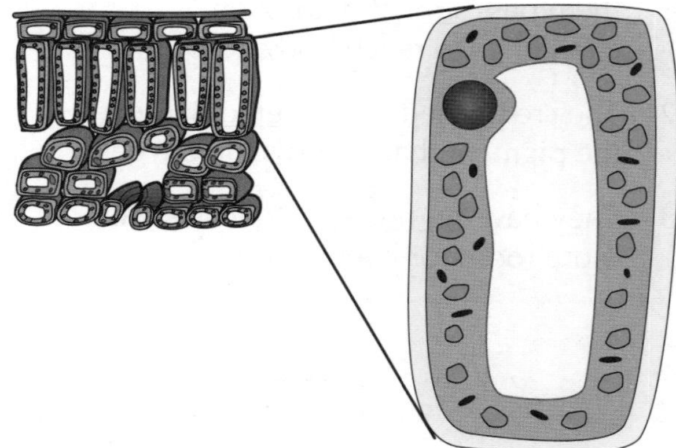

Palisade leaf cells are grouped together at the top of the leaf where most of the photosynthesis happens.

2) Guard Cells Are Adapted to Open and Close Pores

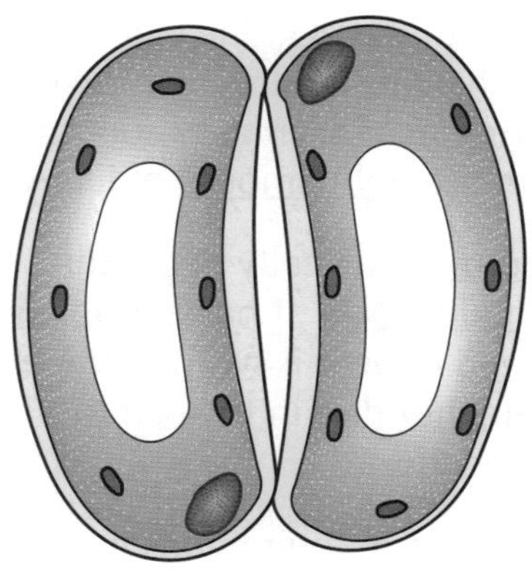

1) Special kidney shape which opens and closes the stomata (pores) in a leaf.
2) When the plant has lots of water the guard cells fill with it and go plump and turgid. This makes the stomata open so gases can be exchanged for photosynthesis.
3) When the plant is short of water, the guard cells lose water and become flaccid, making the stomata close. This helps stop too much water vapour escaping.
4) Thin outer walls and thickened inner walls make the opening and closing work.
5) They're also sensitive to light and close at night to save water without losing out on photosynthesis.

Guard cells are therefore adapted to their function of allowing gas exchange and controlling water loss within a leaf.

Specialised Cells

3) Red Blood Cells Are Adapted to Carry Oxygen

1) Concave shape gives a big surface area for absorbing oxygen. It also helps them pass smoothly through capillaries to reach body cells.
2) They're packed with haemoglobin — the pigment that absorbs the oxygen.
3) They have no nucleus, to leave even more room for haemoglobin.

Red blood cells are an important part of the blood.

4) Sperm and Egg Cells Are Specialised for Reproduction

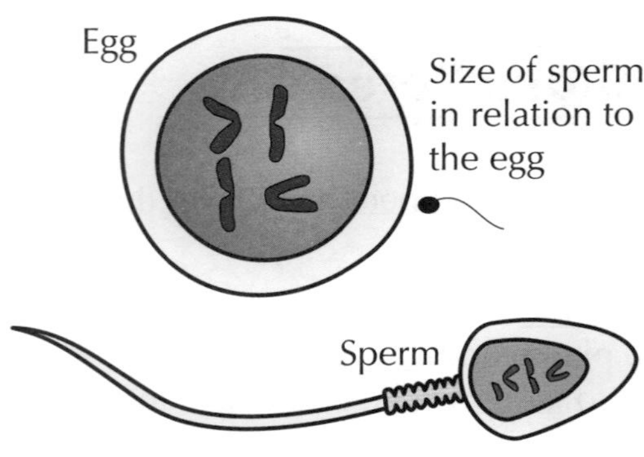

1) The main functions of an egg cell are to carry the female DNA and to nourish the developing embryo in the early stages. The egg cell contains huge food reserves to feed the embryo.
2) When a sperm fuses with the egg, the egg's membrane instantly changes its structure to stop any more sperm getting in. This makes sure the offspring end up with the right amount of DNA.
3) The function of a sperm is basically to get the male DNA to the female DNA. It has a long tail and a streamlined head to help it swim to the egg. There are a lot of mitochondria in the cell to provide the energy needed.
4) Sperm also carry enzymes in their heads to digest through the egg cell membrane.

Sperm and eggs are very important cells in reproduction.

Cells have the same basic bits but are specialised for their function

These cells all have all the bits shown on page 80, even though they look completely different and do totally different jobs. Apart from red blood cells — which, for example, don't have a nucleus.

Cell Organisation

How, you might wonder, does having all these specialised cells mean you end up with a working human... the answer's organisation.

Large Multicellular Organisms are Made Up of Organ Systems

1) As you know from the previous pages, specialised cells carry out a particular function.
2) The process by which cells become specialised for a particular job is called differentiation.

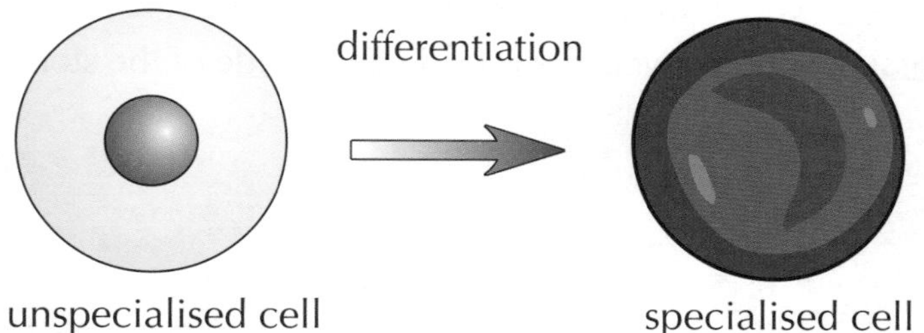

3) Differentiation occurs during the development of a multicellular organism.
4) These specialised cells form tissues, which form organs, which form organ systems (see page 86).
5) Large multicellular organisms (e.g. humans) have different systems inside them for exchanging and transporting materials.

Similar Cells are Organised into Tissues

1) A tissue is a group of similar cells that work together to carry out a particular function.
2) It can include more than one type of cell.
3) In mammals (like humans), examples of tissues include:

- Muscular tissue, which contracts (shortens) to move whatever it's attached to.
- Glandular tissue, which makes and secretes chemicals like enzymes and hormones.
- Epithelial tissue, which covers some parts of the body, e.g. the inside of the gut.

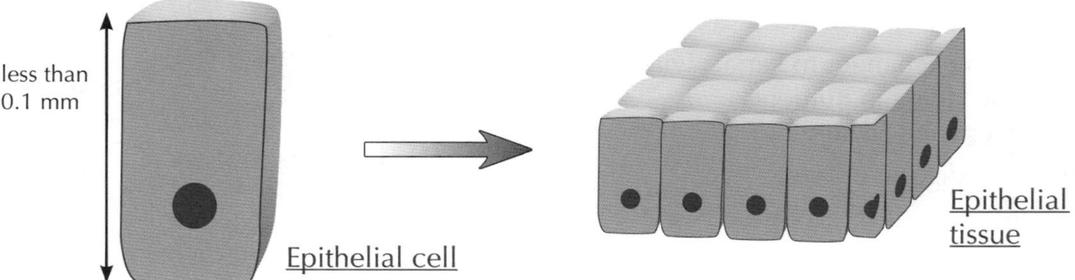

Cell Organisation

We left off at tissues on the previous page — now you need to know how they're organised...

Tissues *are Organised into* ***Organs***

1) An organ is a group of different tissues that work together to perform a certain function.
2) For example, the stomach is an organ made of these tissues:

- Muscular tissue, which moves the stomach wall to churn up the food.
- Glandular tissue, which makes digestive juices to digest food.
- Epithelial tissue, which covers the outside and inside of the stomach.

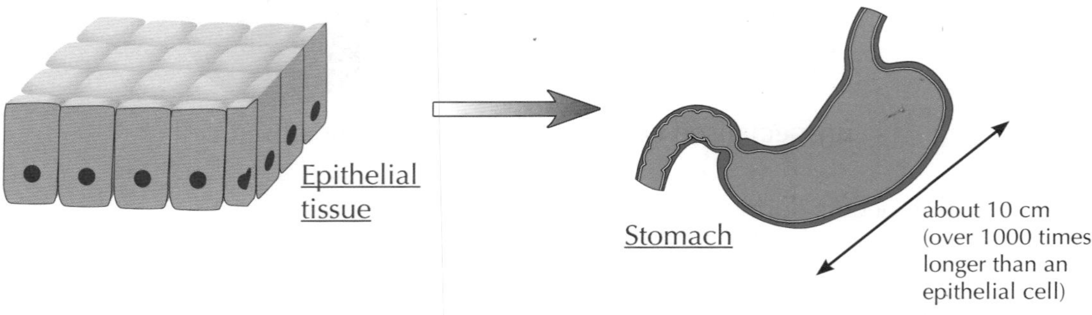

Organs *are Organised into* ***Organ Systems***

An organ system is a group of organs working together to perform a particular function. For example, the digestive system (found in humans and mammals) breaks down food and is made up of these organs:

1) Glands (e.g. the pancreas and salivary glands), which produce digestive juices.
2) The stomach and small intestine, which digest food.
3) The liver, which produces bile.
4) The small intestine, which absorbs soluble food molecules.
5) The large intestine, which absorbs water from undigested food, leaving faeces.

The digestive system exchanges materials with the environment by taking in nutrients and releasing substances such as bile.

There's more on the digestive system on pages 102-103.

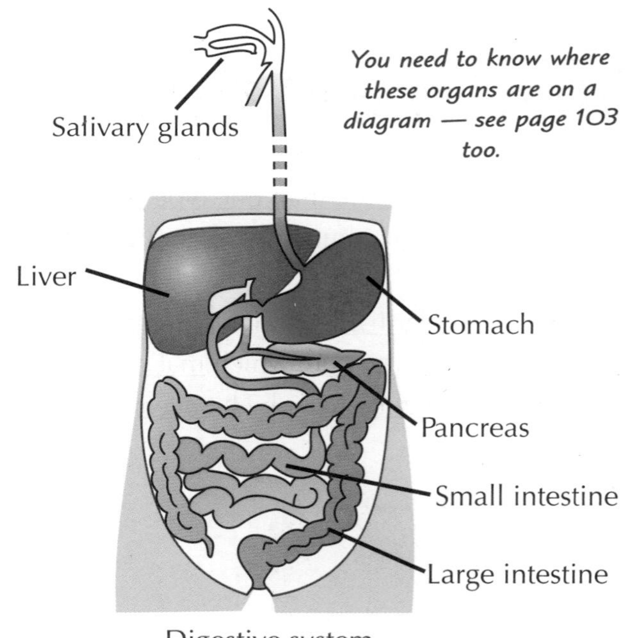

Digestive system

You need to know where these organs are on a diagram — see page 103 too.

Remember — cells, tissues, organs, organ systems...

OK, so from the last couple of pages you know that cells are organised into tissues, the tissues into organs, the organs into organ systems and the organ systems into a whole organism.

Warm-Up and Exam Questions

So, hopefully you've read the last seven pages. But could you cope if a question on cells or diffusion came up in the exam? With amazing new technology we can simulate that very situation....

Warm-Up Questions

1) Give three ways in which animal cells are different from plant cells.
2) Define diffusion.
3) a) What is the function of a red blood cell?
   b) Describe two ways in which a red blood cell is adapted to its function.
4) Name the process by which cells become specialised for a particular job.
5) What is an organ system?
6) Name five organs that are part of the human digestive system.

Exam Questions

1 The diagram shows a palisade cell from a leaf.

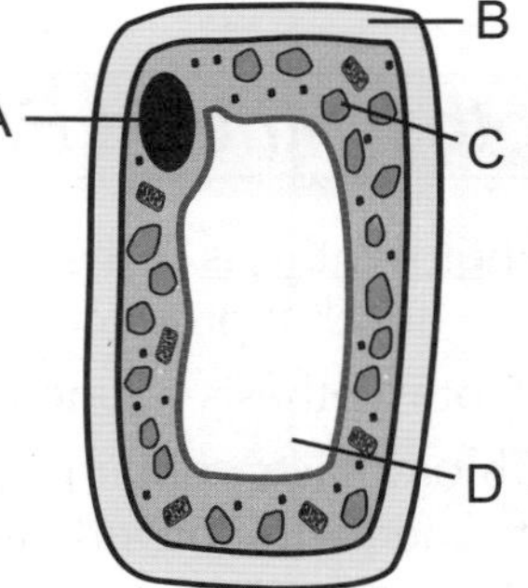

(a) Which label points to a chloroplast?

(1 mark)

(b) Name the green substance present in chloroplasts.

(1 mark)

(c) Apart from having chloroplasts, suggest **one** other way in which a palisade cell is adapted for photosynthesis.

(1 mark)

2 Below are three diagrams showing cells surrounded by glucose.

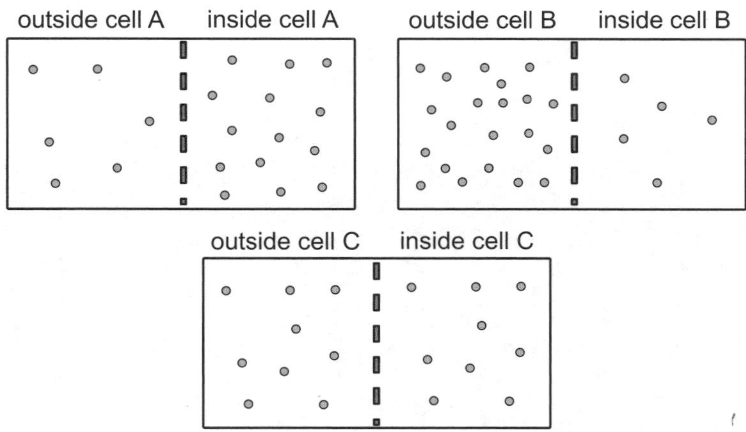

(a) Into which cell, **A**, **B** or **C**, will there be a net movement of glucose? Explain your answer.

(2 marks)

(b) Other than glucose, name **one** molecule that can diffuse through cell membranes into cells.

(1 mark)

Plant Structure and Photosynthesis

Take a good look at the photosynthesis equation below — you must learn it.

Plant Cells Are Organised Into *Tissues* And *Organs* Too

Plants are made of organs like stems, roots and leaves. These organs are made of tissues.
For example, leaves are made of:

- Mesophyll tissue — this is where most of the photosynthesis in a plant occurs.
- Xylem and phloem — they transport things like water, mineral ions and sucrose around the plant.
- Epidermal tissue — this covers the whole plant.

The leaf diagram at the bottom of the page shows where these tissues are in a plant.

Learn the *Equation* for *Photosynthesis*:

Carbon dioxide + water 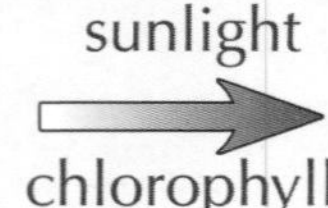 glucose + oxygen

Photosynthesis Produces *Glucose* Using *Sunlight*

1) Photosynthesis is the process that produces 'food' in plants and algae. The 'food' it produces is glucose.
2) Photosynthesis happens inside the chloroplasts.
3) Chloroplasts contain a green substance called chlorophyll, which absorbs sunlight and uses its energy to convert carbon dioxide (from the air) and water (from the soil) into glucose. Oxygen is also produced as a by-product.
4) Photosynthesis happens in the leaves of all green plants — this is largely what the leaves are for. Below is a cross-section of a leaf showing the four raw materials needed for photosynthesis.

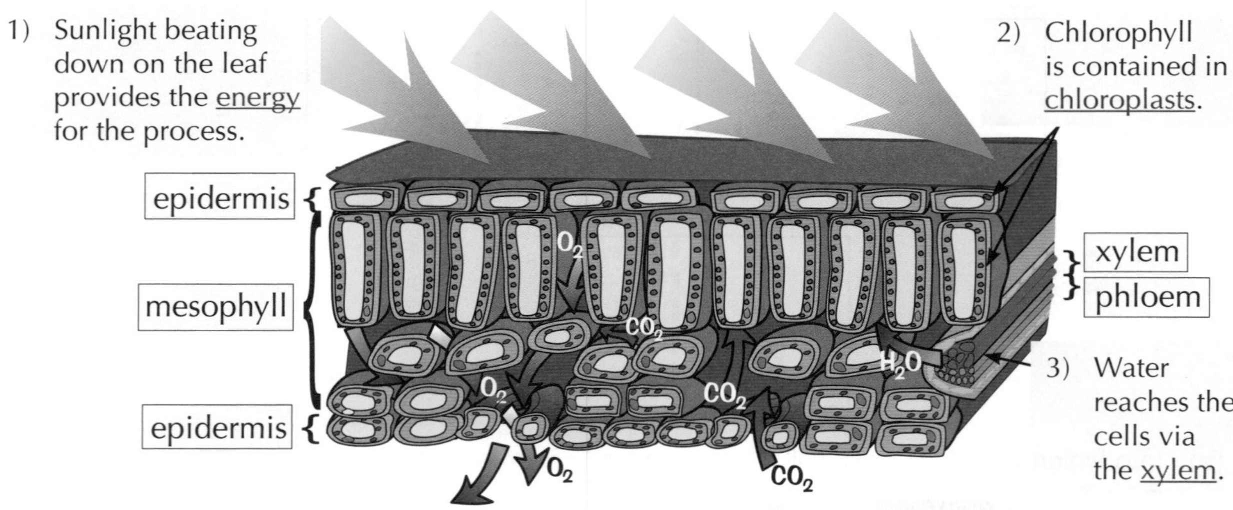

'Photo' means light and 'synthesis' means putting together...

...so photosynthesis is 'putting together glucose'. See, it's not too bad. But you must learn the equation.

The Rate of Photosynthesis

The rate of photosynthesis is affected by the intensity of light, the volume of CO_2, and the temperature. Plants also need water for photosynthesis, but when a plant is so short of water that it becomes the limiting factor in photosynthesis, it's already in such trouble that this is the least of its worries.

The **Limiting Factor** Depends on the Conditions

Any of these three factors can become the limiting factor. This just means that it's stopping photosynthesis from happening any faster.

Which factor is limiting at a particular time depends on the environmental conditions:

- at night it's pretty obvious that light is the limiting factor,
- in winter it's often the temperature,
- if it's warm enough and bright enough, the amount of CO_2 is usually limiting.

You can do experiments to work out the ideal conditions for photosynthesis in a particular plant. The easiest type to use is a water plant like Canadian pondweed — you can easily measure the amount of oxygen produced in a given time to show how fast photosynthesis is happening (remember, oxygen is made during photosynthesis).

You could either count the bubbles given off, or if you want to be a bit more accurate you could collect the oxygen in a gas syringe.

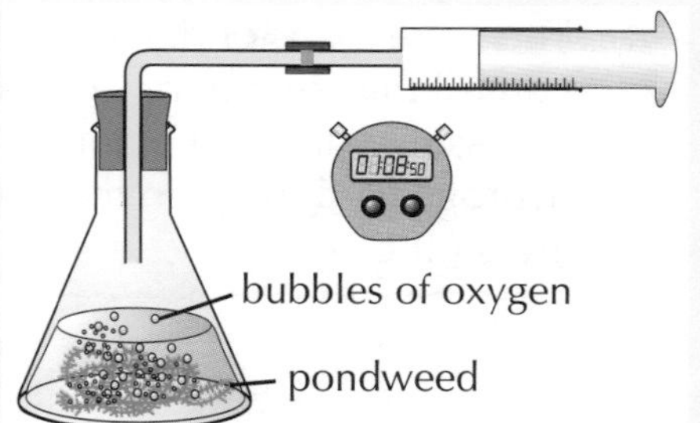

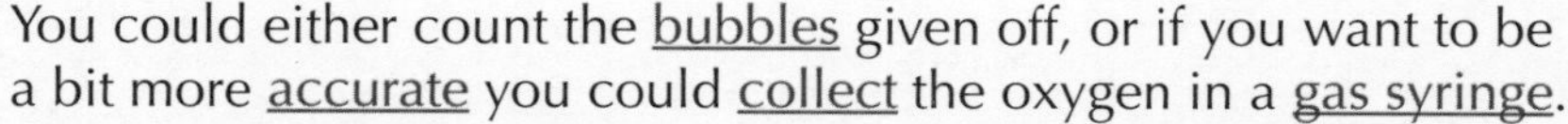

Not Enough **Light** Slows Down the Rate of Photosynthesis

1) Light provides the energy needed for photosynthesis.
2) As the light level is raised, the rate of photosynthesis increases steadily — but only up to a certain point.
3) Beyond that, it won't make any difference because then it'll be either the temperature or the CO_2 level which is the limiting factor.
4) In the lab you can change the light intensity by moving a lamp closer to or further away from your plant.

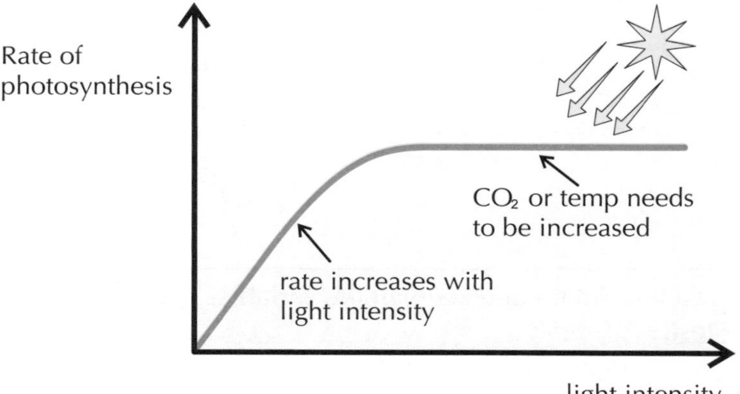

5) But if you just plot the rate of photosynthesis against "distance of lamp from the beaker", you get a weird-shaped graph. To get a graph like the one above you either need to measure the light intensity at the beaker using a light meter or do a bit of nifty maths with your results.

The Rate of Photosynthesis

Too Little **Carbon Dioxide** Also Slows it Down

1) CO_2 is one of the raw materials needed for photosynthesis.
2) As with light intensity the amount of CO_2 will only increase the rate of photosynthesis up to a point. After this the graph flattens out showing that CO_2 is no longer the limiting factor.
3) As long as light and CO_2 are in plentiful supply then the factor limiting photosynthesis must be temperature.
4) There are loads of different ways to control the amount of CO_2. One way is to dissolve different amounts of sodium hydrogencarbonate in the water, which gives off CO_2.

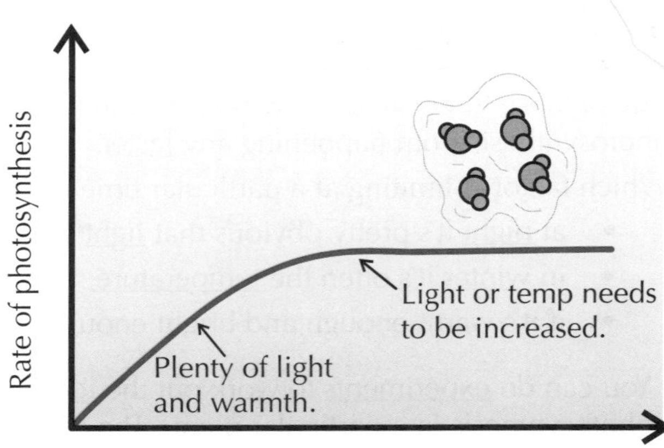

The **Temperature** has to be Just Right

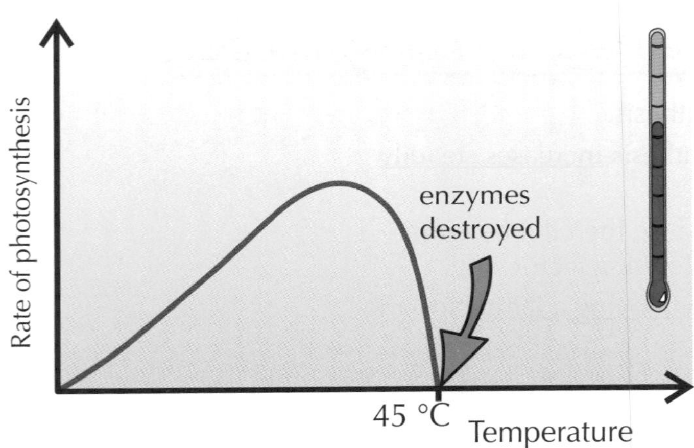

1) Usually, if the temperature is the limiting factor it's because it's too low — the enzymes needed for photosynthesis work more slowly at low temperatures.
2) But if the plant gets too hot, the enzymes it needs for photosynthesis and its other reactions will be damaged.
3) This happens at about 45 °C (which is pretty hot for outdoors, although greenhouses can get that hot if you're not careful).
4) Experimentally, the best way to control the temperature of the flask is to put it in a water bath.

In all these experiments, you have to try and keep all the variables constant apart from the one you're investigating, so it's a fair test:

- use a bench lamp to control the intensity of the light (careful not to block the light with anything)
- keep the flask in a water bath to help keep the temperature constant
- you can't really do anything about the CO_2 levels — you just have to use a large flask, and do the experiments as quickly as you can, so that the plant doesn't use up too much of the CO_2 in the flask. If you're using sodium hydrogencarbonate make sure it's changed each time.

The Rate of Photosynthesis

Growing plants outdoors can be very difficult, especially on a large scale — it's almost impossible to control the weather and other conditions. But there's a way around that...

You can *Artificially Create* the *Ideal Conditions* for *Farming*

1) The most common way to artificially create the ideal environment for plants is to grow them in a greenhouse.
2) Greenhouses help to trap the Sun's heat, and make sure that the temperature doesn't become limiting. In winter a farmer or gardener might use a heater as well to keep the temperature at the ideal level. In summer it could get too hot, so they might use shades and ventilation to cool things down.
3) Light is always needed for photosynthesis, so commercial farmers often supply artificial light after the Sun goes down to give their plants more quality photosynthesis time.

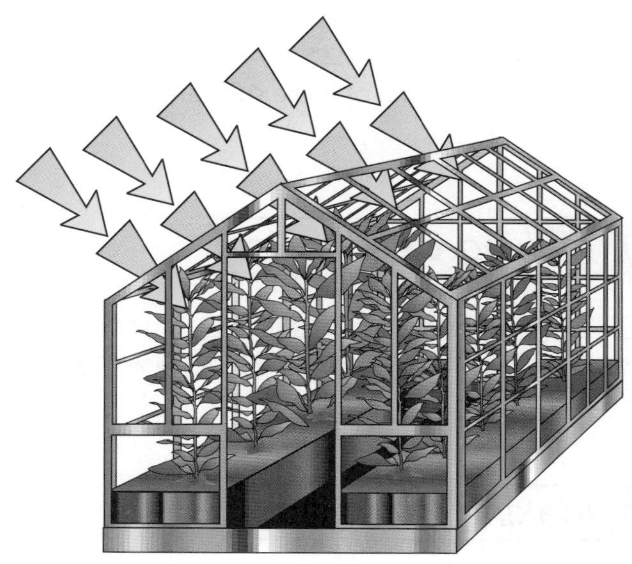

Greenhouses are used to grow plants, including food crops, flowers and tobacco plants.

4) Farmers and gardeners can also increase the level of carbon dioxide in the greenhouse. A fairly common way is to use a paraffin heater to heat the greenhouse. As the paraffin burns, it makes carbon dioxide as a by-product.
5) Keeping plants enclosed in a greenhouse also makes it easier to keep them free from pests and diseases. The farmer can add fertilisers to the soil as well, to provide all the minerals needed for healthy growth.
6) Sorting all this out costs money — but if the farmer can keep the conditions just right for photosynthesis, the plants will grow much faster and a decent crop can be harvested much more often, which can then be sold. It's important that a farmer supplies just the right amount of heat, light, etc. — enough to make the plants grow well, but not more than the plants need, as this would just be wasting money.

Greenhouses control the growing environment

Farmers use greenhouses to make sure crops get the right amount of carbon dioxide, light and heat. They can alter the conditions using paraffin heaters, artificial light and ventilation. This ensures nothing becomes a limiting factor for photosynthesis, which means a good crop is produced.

How Plants Use Glucose

Once plants have made the glucose, there are various ways they can use it.

1) For **Respiration**

1) Plants manufacture glucose in their leaves.
2) They then use some of the glucose for respiration (see page 105).
3) This releases energy which enables them to convert the rest of the glucose into various other useful substances, which they can use to build new cells and grow.
4) To produce some of these substances they also need to gather a few minerals from the soil.

2) Making **Cell Walls**

Glucose is converted into cellulose for making strong cell walls (see page 80), especially in a rapidly growing plant.

Algae also use glucose to make cellulose for cell walls, fats and oils for storage, and amino acids for proteins.

3) Making **Proteins**

Glucose is combined with nitrate ions (absorbed from the soil) to make amino acids, which are then made into proteins.

4) Stored in **Seeds**

Glucose is turned into lipids (fats and oils) for storing in seeds. Sunflower seeds, for example, contain a lot of oil — we get cooking oil and margarine from them. Seeds also store starch (see below).

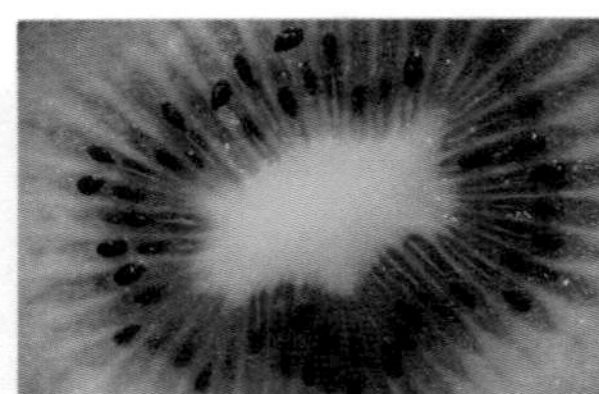

5) Stored as **Starch**

1) Glucose is turned into starch and stored in roots, stems and leaves, ready for use when photosynthesis isn't happening, like in the winter.
2) Starch is insoluble which makes it much better for storing than glucose — a cell with lots of glucose in would draw in loads of water and swell up.
3) Potato and parsnip plants store a lot of starch underground over the winter so a new plant can grow from it the following spring. We eat the swollen storage organs.

All life depends on photosynthesis

Plants are pretty crucial in ensuring the flow of energy through nature. They are able to use the Sun's energy to make glucose, the energy source that humans and other animals need for respiration. Make sure you know the photosynthesis equation inside out — look back at p.88 if you don't.

Warm-Up and Exam Questions

So, here we go again — another set of questions to test your knowledge. But don't roll your eyes, I promise they'll be really, really enjoyable. OK, don't hold me to that, but make sure you do them...

Warm-Up Questions

1) Name four factors that are needed for photosynthesis.
2) What is meant by a limiting factor for the rate of photosynthesis?
3) Sketch a graph to show how the rate of photosynthesis varies with increasing CO_2.
4) Give one way in which a farmer could increase the level of CO_2 in his greenhouse.
5) Name the process that converts glucose into energy in plants.

Exam Questions

1 Photosynthesis makes glucose. The glucose may then be converted to other substances. Some of these substances are listed below:

starch **cellulose** **amino acids**

Match each of these substances to its correct function from the list below.

- Making cell walls.
- Making proteins.
- Storing energy.

(3 marks)

2 The diagram shows part of the structure of a leaf as it looks under a microscope.

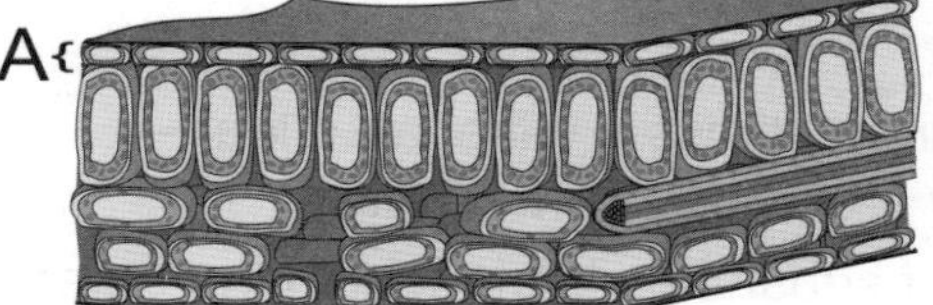

(a) Name the tissue labelled **A**.

(1 mark)

(b) Name **two** other tissues that can be found in a leaf.

(2 marks)

3 The table shows the rate of photosynthesis of a plant at different temperatures.

Temperature (°C)	Rate of photosynthesis (arbitrary units)
0	0
10	17
20	35
30	67
40	82
50	0

(a) Explain the difference between:

(i) the rates of photosynthesis at 10 °C and at 20 °C.

(1 mark)

(ii) the rates of photosynthesis at 40 °C and at 50 °C.

(1 mark)

(b) A student said that the optimum temperature for photosynthesis in this plant was 40 °C. Comment on this statement.

(2 marks)

Exam Questions

4 Jane did an experiment to see how the rate of photosynthesis depends on light intensity. The diagram shows her apparatus.

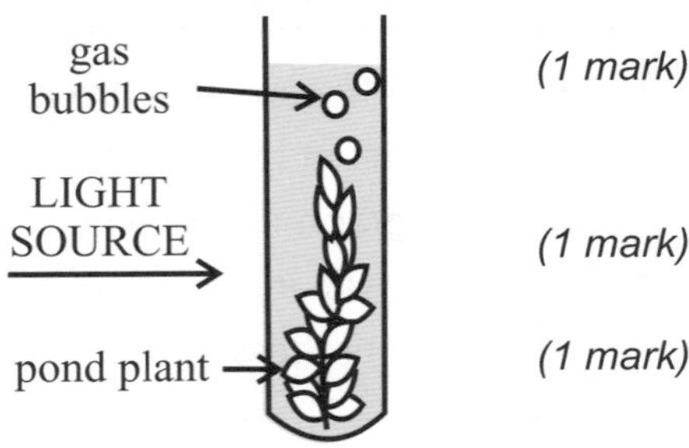

(a) How can Jane measure the rate of photosynthesis? *(1 mark)*

(b) In this experiment:

(i) what is the dependent variable? *(1 mark)*

(ii) what is the independent variable? *(1 mark)*

(c) State **one** factor that should be kept constant during this experiment. *(1 mark)*

5 The graph shows how a plant's rate of photosynthesis varies with the light intensity.

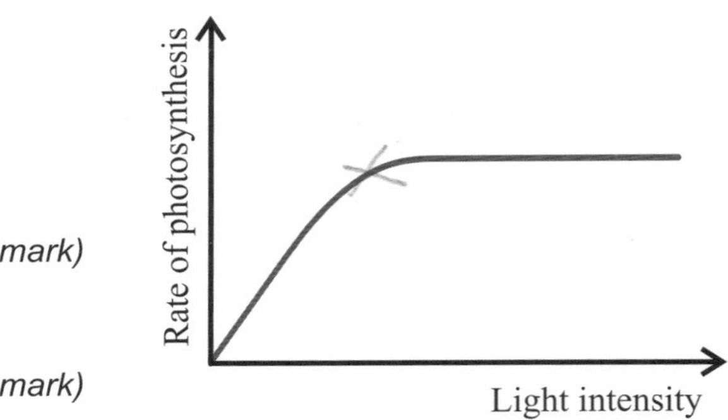

(a) Label a point at which light intensity is the limiting factor for photosynthesis. *(1 mark)*

(b) What else can limit a plant's rate of photosynthesis? *(1 mark)*

6 The diagram shows a variegated leaf — it's partly green and partly white.

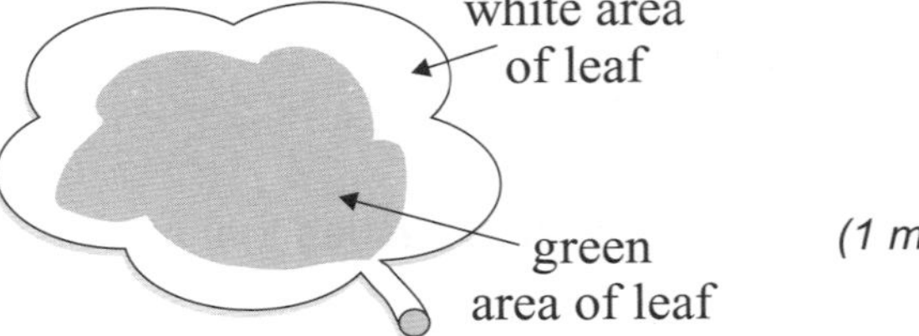

(a) What substance is present in the green parts of the leaf but not the white parts? *(1 mark)*

Abisola did an experiment in which part of the leaf was covered with black paper, as shown:
The leaf was then exposed to light for four hours and was then tested for starch.

(b) (i) Copy and complete the diagram below by shading in the part(s) of the leaf that you would expect to contain **starch**.

(1 mark)

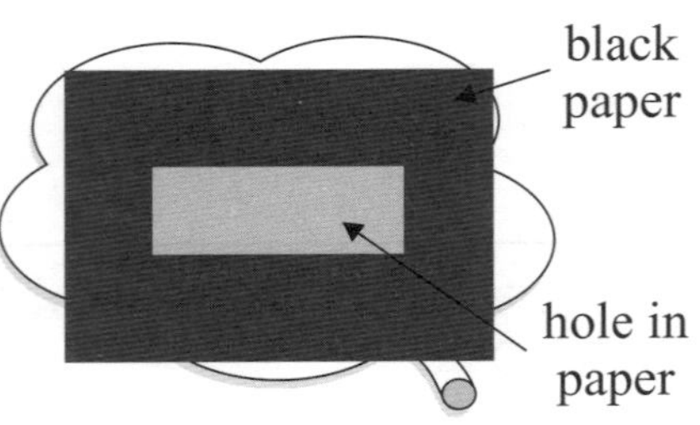

(ii) Explain your answer to part (b)(i). *(2 marks)*

Distribution of Organisms

Don't worry — you're nearly at the end of this section. But first you need to get your head around some ecology. These next few pages are all about investigating the distribution of organisms...

The *Environment Varies*, So *Organisms Live* in *Different Places*

1) A habitat is the place where an organism lives, e.g. a playing field.
2) The distribution of an organism is where an organism is found, e.g. in a part of the playing field.
3) Where an organism is found is affected by environmental factors such as:
   - Temperature.
   - Availability of water.
   - Availability of oxygen and carbon dioxide.
   - Availability of nutrients.
   - Amount of light.
4) An organism might be more common in one area than another due to differences in environmental factors between the two areas. For example, in a field, you might find that daisies are more common in the open, than under trees, because there's more light available in the open.
5) There are a couple of ways to study the distribution of an organism. You can:
   - measure how common an organism is in two sample areas (e.g. using quadrats) and compare them.
   - study how the distribution changes across an area, e.g. by placing quadrats along a transect (p. 96).

Use *Quadrats* to *Study* The *Distribution* of *Small* Organisms

A quadrat is a square frame enclosing a known area, e.g. 1 m^2. To compare how common an organism is in two sample areas, just follow these simple steps:

A quadrat

1 m

1 m

1) Place a 1 m^2 quadrat on the ground at a random point within the first sample area. E.g. divide the area into a grid and use a random number generator to pick coordinates.
2) Count all the organisms within the quadrat.
3) Repeat steps 1 and 2 as many times as you can.
4) Work out the mean number of organisms per quadrat within the first sample area.

- For example, Anna counted the number of daisies in 7 quadrats within her first sample area and recorded the following results: 18, 20, 22, 23, 23, 23, 25
- Here the MEAN is: $\frac{\text{TOTAL number of organisms}}{\text{NUMBER of quadrats}} = \frac{154}{7} = 22$ daisies per quadrat.
- You also need to know about the MODE, which is the MOST COMMON value. In this example it's 23.
- And the MEDIAN is the MIDDLE value, when they're in order of size. In this example it's 23 also.

5) Repeat steps 1 to 4 in the second sample area.
6) Finally compare the two means. E.g. you might find 2 daisies per m^2 in the shade, and 22 daisies per m^2 (lots more) in the open field.

Count all the organisms in a quadrat, but first remember to...

...put down your quadrat in a random place before you start counting. Even chucking the quadrat over your shoulder is better than putting it down on the first big patch of organisms that you see.

Distribution of Organisms

I'm afraid you need to know a bit more about the distribution of organisms...

In the Exam You Might Have to Work Out **Population Size**

To work out the population size of an organism in one sample area:

1) Work out the mean number of organisms per m^2.
   (If your quadrat has an area of 1 m^2, this is the same as the mean number of organisms per quadrat, worked out on the previous page.)
2) Then multiply the mean by the total area (in m^2) of the habitat.

> E.g. if the area of an open field is 800 m^2, and there are 22 daisies per m^2, then the size of the daisy population is 22 x 800 = 17 600.

Transects *Show How Organisms are* ***Distributed Along a Line***

You can use lines called transects to help find out how organisms (like plants) are distributed across an area — e.g. if an organism becomes more or less common as you move from a hedge towards the middle of a field. Here's what to do:

1) Mark out a line in the area you want to study using a tape measure.

2) Then collect data along the line.

3) You can do this by just counting all the organisms you're interested in that touch the line.

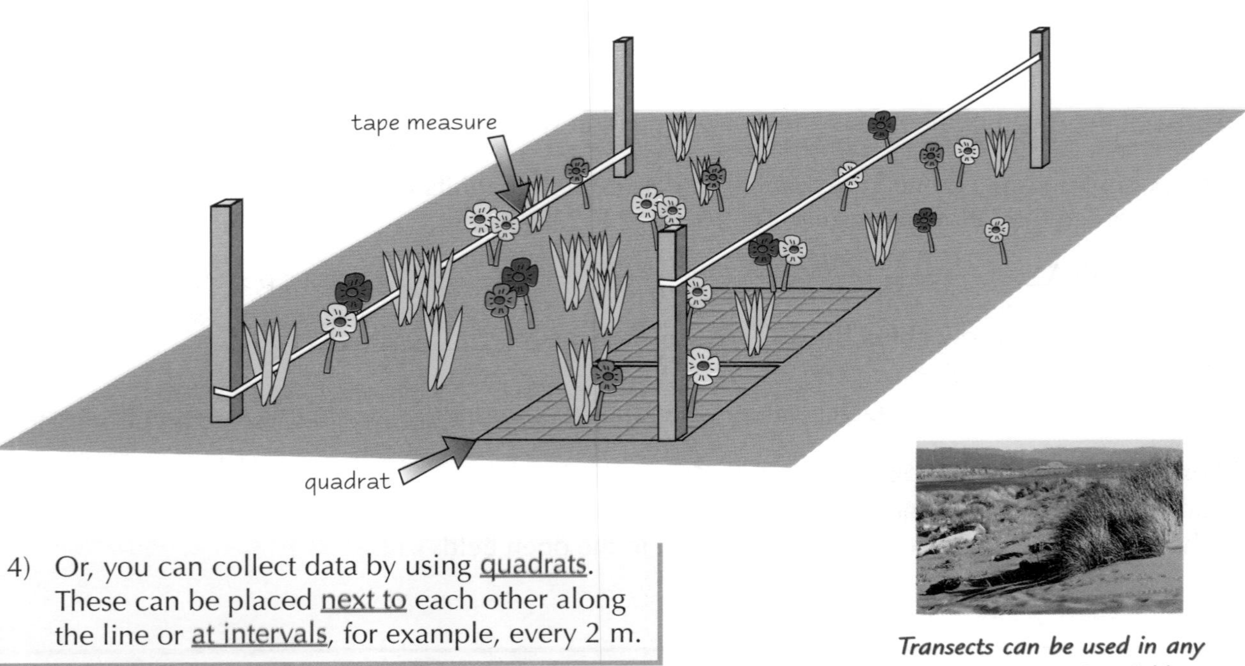

4) Or, you can collect data by using quadrats. These can be placed next to each other along the line or at intervals, for example, every 2 m.

Transects can be used in any ecosystem, not just fields. For example, along a beach.

Distribution of Organisms

When **Collecting Environmental Data** You Need to Think About...

1) Reliability

1) Quadrats and transects are pretty good tools for finding out how an organism is distributed.
2) But, you have to work hard to make sure your results are reliable — which means making sure they are repeatable and reproducible.
3) To make your results more reliable you need to:

- Take a large sample size, e.g. use as many quadrats and transects as possible in your sample area. Bigger samples are more representative of the whole population.
- Use random samples, e.g. randomly put down or mark out your quadrat or transect. If all your samples are in one spot, and everywhere else is different, the results you get won't be reproducible.

2) Validity

1) For your results to be valid they must be reliable (see above) and answer the original question.

2) To answer the original question, you need to control all the variables.

3) The question you want to answer is whether a difference in distribution between two sample areas is due to a difference in one environmental factor.

4) If you've controlled all the other variables that could be affecting the distribution, you'll know whether a difference in distribution is caused by the environmental factor or not.

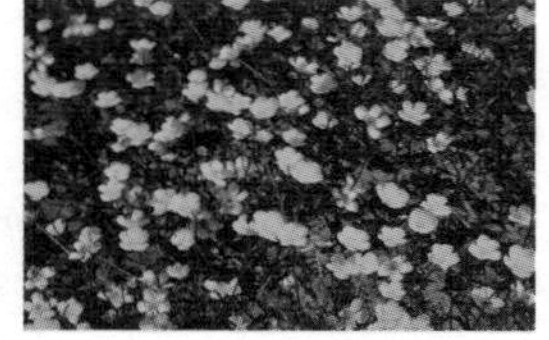

Look back at page 95 for the different environmental factors that can affect distribution. E.g. some types of buttercups are more common in moist areas.

5) If you don't control the other variables you won't know whether any correlation you've found is because of chance, because of the environmental factor you're looking at or because of a different variable — the study won't give you valid data.

Your investigation needs to be reliable and valid

Take a look back at How Science Works (page 3) to remind yourself all about reliability and validity. If you get a question in the exam about how to make an investigation using quadrats or transects more reliable, think about the sample size and whether samples have been taken randomly.

Warm-Up and Exam Questions

It's finally the end of the section, but before you go on to the next one a few questions need answering.

Warm-Up Questions

1) What do we mean by the 'distribution of an organism'?
2) What is a quadrat?
3) Claire used a 1 m^2 quadrat to count the number of buttercups in a sample area. She placed the quadrat nine times. Here are her results: 2, 15, 4, 6, 8, 3, 11, 10, 9. Work out the median number of buttercups per quadrat in her sample area.
4) What is the name of a line used to measure the distribution of organisms across an area?

Exam Questions

1 Paul investigated the distribution of dandelions.
He counted the number of dandelions in 10 quadrats in five different fields.
His quadrat measured 1 m^2. Paul's results are shown in the table below.

Field	Mean number of dandelions per quadrat
A	10
B	35
C	21
D	37
E	21

(a) What is the mode of Paul's data?

(1 mark)

(b) (i) A week later Paul repeated his experiment in a sixth field, Field F.
His results for each quadrat are shown below:

6 15 9 14 20 5 3 11 10 7

Using this data, estimate the mean number of dandelions per m^2 in Field F.

(2 marks)

(ii) Field F measures 90 m by 120 m.
Estimate the number of dandelions in the whole of Field F.

(2 marks)

(c) Paul's friend Anna also investigated the number of dandelions in the same six fields. Anna also used a 1 m^2 quadrat.
She counted the number of dandelions in 20 quadrats per field.
Which investigation, Paul's or Anna's, is likely to produce more reliable data?
Give a reason for your answer.

(1 mark)

Revision Summary for Biology 2a

And where do you think you're going? It's no use just reading through and thinking you've got it all — this stuff will only stick in your head if you've learnt it properly. And that's what these questions are for. I won't pretend they'll be easy — they're not meant to be, but all the information's in the section somewhere. Have a go at all the questions, then if there are any you can't answer, go back, look stuff up and try again. Enjoy...

1) Name five parts of a cell that both plant and animal cells have.
2) Name three features of a yeast cell.
3) Where is the genetic material found in:
   a) bacterial cells
   b) animal cells?
4) Name three substances that can diffuse through cell membranes, and two that can't.
5) Give one way that a guard cell is adapted for controlling water loss.
6) Give three ways that a sperm cell is adapted for swimming to an egg cell.
7) What is a tissue? What is an organ?
8) Give three examples of tissues in the human stomach, and say what job they do.
9) Name one organ system found in the human body.
10) Give an example of a plant tissue and a plant organ.
11) Write down the equation for photosynthesis.
12) What is the green substance in leaves that absorbs sunlight?
13) Name the three factors that can limit the rate of photosynthesis.
14) You carry out an experiment where you change the light intensity experienced by a piece of Canadian pondweed by changing the distance between the pondweed and a lamp supplying it with light. Write down three important things which must be kept constant for this experiment to be a fair test.
15) Explain why it's important that a plant doesn't get too hot.
16) Describe three things that a gardener could do to make sure she grows a good crop of tomatoes in her greenhouse.
17) Why is glucose turned into starch when plants need to store it for later?
18) Write down four other ways that plants can use the glucose produced by photosynthesis.
19) What is a habitat?
20) Give five environmental factors that can affect the distribution of organisms.
21) Briefly describe how you could find out how common an organism is in two sample areas using quadrats.
22) Describe one way of using a transect to find out how an organism is distributed across an area.

Enzymes

Chemical reactions are what make you work. And enzymes are what make them work.

Enzymes Are Catalysts Produced by Living Things

1) Living things have thousands of different chemical reactions going on inside them all the time.
2) These reactions need to be carefully controlled — to get the right amounts of substances.
3) You can usually make a reaction happen more quickly by raising the temperature. This would speed up the useful reactions but also the unwanted ones too... not good. There's also a limit to how far you can raise the temperature inside a living creature before its cells start getting damaged.
4) So... living things produce enzymes that act as biological catalysts. Enzymes reduce the need for high temperatures and we only have enzymes to speed up the useful chemical reactions in the body.

A CATALYST is a substance which INCREASES the speed of a reaction, without being CHANGED or USED UP in the reaction.

5) Enzymes are all proteins and all proteins are made up of chains of amino acids. These chains are folded into unique shapes, which enzymes need to do their jobs (see below).
6) As well as catalysts, proteins act as structural components of tissues (e.g. muscles), hormones and antibodies.

Enzymes Have Special Shapes So They Can Catalyse Reactions

1) Chemical reactions usually involve things either being split apart or joined together.
2) Every enzyme has a unique shape that fits onto the substance involved in a reaction.
3) Enzymes are really picky — they usually only catalyse one reaction.
4) This is because, for the enzyme to work, the substance has to fit its special shape. If the substance doesn't match the enzyme's shape, then the reaction won't be catalysed.

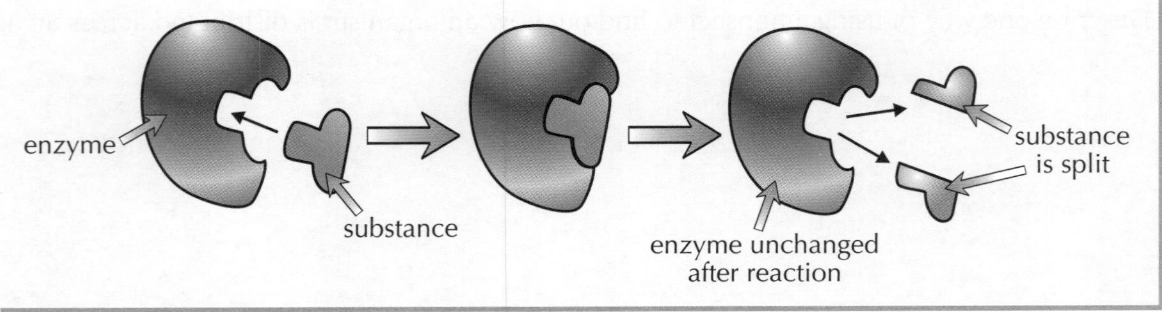

Enzymes speed up chemical reactions

Just like you've got to have the correct key for a lock, you've got to have the right substance for an enzyme. If the substance doesn't fit, the enzyme won't catalyse the reaction...

Enzymes

Enzymes are clearly very clever, but they're not very versatile. They need just the right conditions if they're going to work properly.

Enzymes Need the Right Temperature...

1) Changing the temperature changes the rate of an enzyme-catalysed reaction.
2) Like with any reaction, a higher temperature increases the rate at first.
3) But if it gets too hot, some of the bonds holding the enzyme together break. This destroys the enzyme's special shape and so it won't work any more. It's said to be denatured.
4) Enzymes in the human body normally work best at around 37 °C.

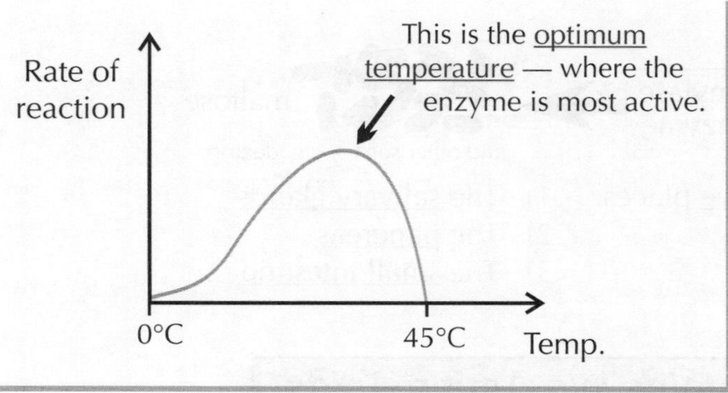

...and the Right pH

1) The pH also affects enzymes. If it's too high or too low, the pH interferes with the bonds holding the enzyme together.
2) This changes the shape and denatures the enzyme.
3) All enzymes have an optimum pH that they work best at. It's often neutral pH 7, but not always — e.g. pepsin is an enzyme used to break down proteins in the stomach. It works best at pH 2, which means it's well-suited to the acidic conditions there.

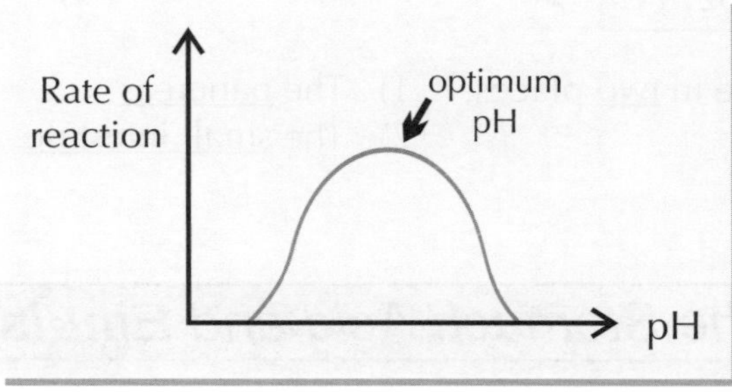

Most enzymes catalyse just one reaction

The optimum temperature for most human enzymes is around normal body temperature.
And stomach enzymes work best at low pH, but the enzymes in your small intestine like high pH.

Enzymes and Digestion

Not all enzymes work inside body cells — some work outside cells. For example, the enzymes used in digestion are produced by cells and then released into the gut to mix with food.

Digestive Enzymes** Break Down **Big Molecules** into **Smaller Ones

1) Starch, proteins and fats are big molecules. They're too big to pass through the walls of the digestive system.
2) Sugars, amino acids, glycerol and fatty acids are much smaller molecules. They can pass easily through the walls of the digestive system.
3) The digestive enzymes break down the big molecules into the smaller ones.

Amylase** Converts **Starch** into **Sugars

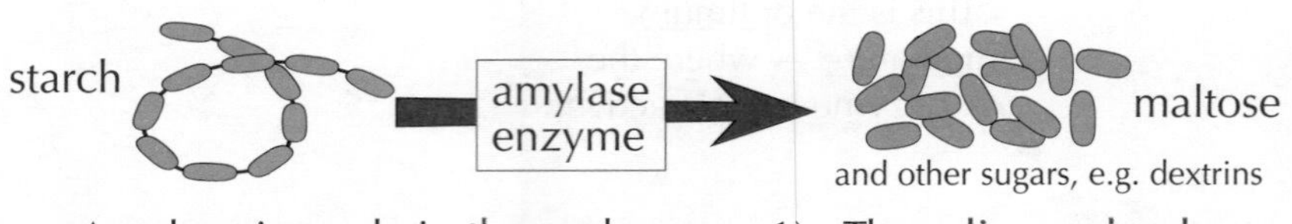

Amylase is made in three places:
1) The salivary glands
2) The pancreas
3) The small intestine

Protease** Converts **Proteins** into **Amino Acids

Protease is made in three places:
1) The stomach (it's called pepsin there)
2) The pancreas
3) The small intestine

Lipase** Converts **Lipids** into **Glycerol** and **Fatty Acids

Remember, lipids are fats and oils.

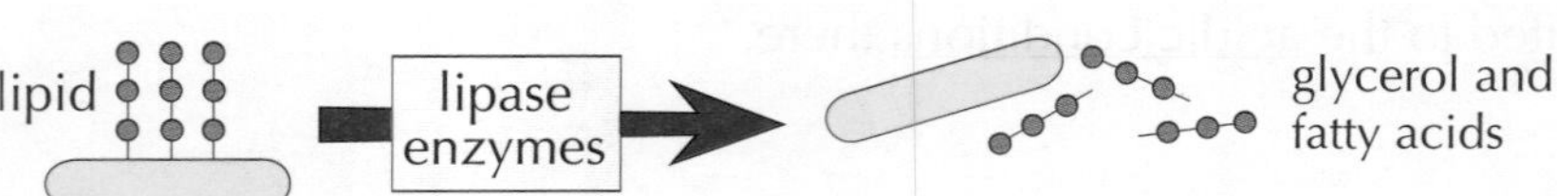

Lipase is made in two places:
1) The pancreas
2) The small intestine

***Bile Neutralises** the Stomach Acid and **Emulsifies** Fats*

1) Bile is produced in the liver. It's stored in the gall bladder before it's released into the small intestine.
2) The hydrochloric acid in the stomach makes the pH too acidic for enzymes in the small intestine to work properly. Bile is alkaline — it neutralises the acid and makes conditions alkaline. The enzymes in the small intestine work best in these alkaline conditions.
3) It emulsifies fats. In other words it breaks the fat into tiny droplets. This gives a much bigger surface area of fat for the enzyme lipase to work on — which makes its digestion faster.

Enzymes and Digestion

So now you know what the enzymes do, here's a nice big picture of the whole of the digestive system.

The Breakdown of Food is Catalysed by Enzymes

1) Enzymes used in the digestive system are produced by specialised cells in glands and in the gut lining.

2) Different enzymes catalyse the breakdown of different food molecules.

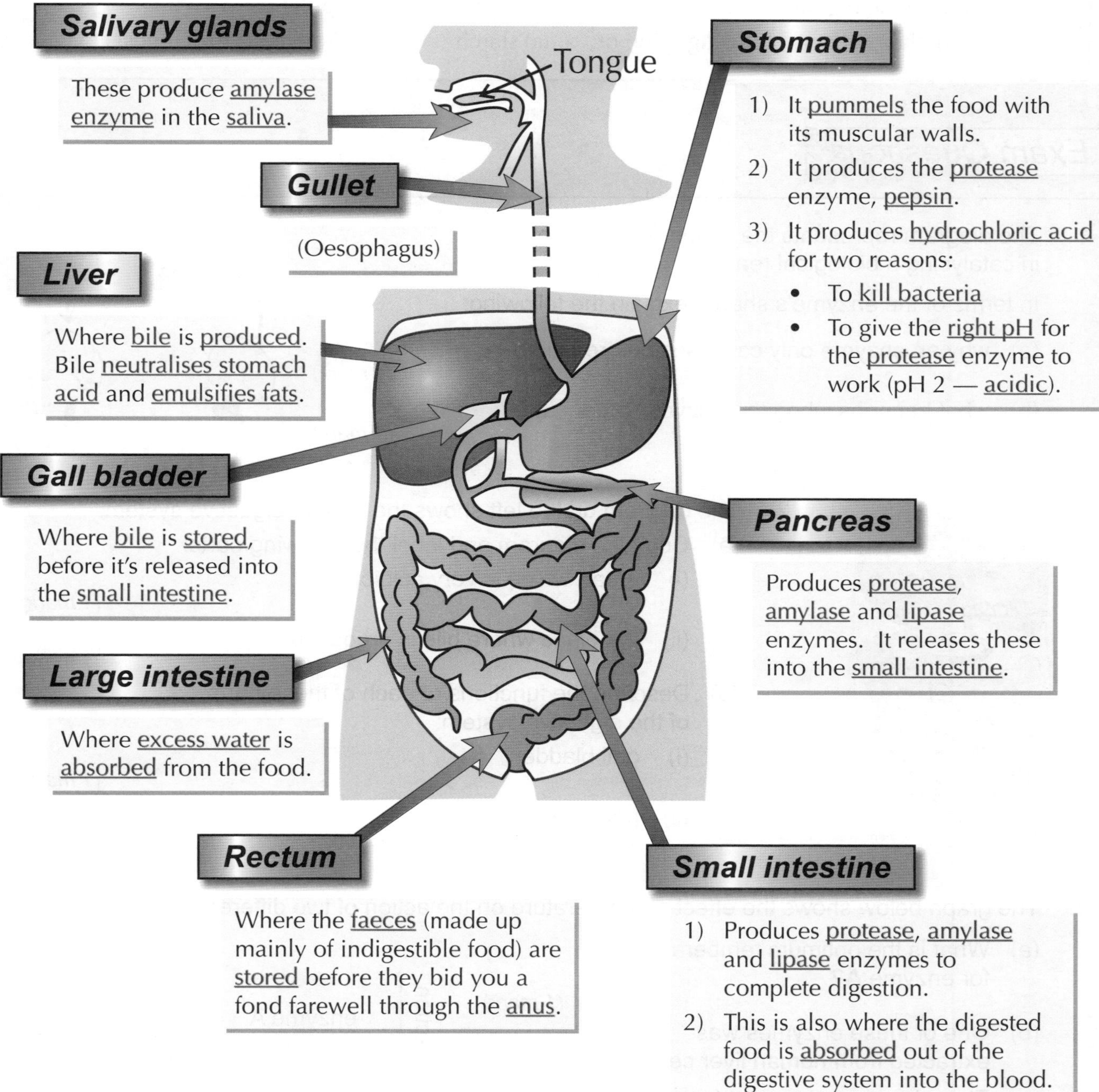
Salivary glands
These produce amylase enzyme in the saliva.
Tongue
Gullet
(Oesophagus)
Liver
Where bile is produced. Bile neutralises stomach acid and emulsifies fats.
Gall bladder
Where bile is stored, before it's released into the small intestine.
Large intestine
Where excess water is absorbed from the food.
Rectum
Where the faeces (made up mainly of indigestible food) are stored before they bid you a fond farewell through the anus.
Stomach
1) It pummels the food with its muscular walls.
2) It produces the protease enzyme, pepsin.
3) It produces hydrochloric acid for two reasons:
• To kill bacteria
• To give the right pH for the protease enzyme to work (pH 2 — acidic).
Pancreas
Produces protease, amylase and lipase enzymes. It releases these into the small intestine.
Small intestine
1) Produces protease, amylase and lipase enzymes to complete digestion.
2) This is also where the digested food is absorbed out of the digestive system into the blood.

That's nine different bits of the digestive system you need to know

Did you know that the whole of your digestive system is actually a big hole that goes right through your body? It just gets loads of food, digestive juices and enzymes piled into it...

Warm-Up and Exam Questions

Doing well in exams isn't just about remembering all the facts, although that's important. You have to get used to the way the exams are phrased and make sure you always read the question carefully.

Warm-Up Questions

1) Enzymes are sometimes referred to as 'biological catalysts'. What is a catalyst?
2) What is meant by the optimum pH of an enzyme?
3) What is the function of digestive enzymes?
4) Which enzyme digests: (a) starch (b) protein (c) lipids?
5) What are the products of the digestion of: (a) starch (b) protein (c) lipids?

Exam Questions

1 The diagram represents the action of an enzyme in catalysing a biological reaction.

In terms of the enzyme's shape, explain the following:

(a) why an enzyme only catalyses one reaction.

(1 mark)

(b) what happens when the enzyme is denatured.

(1 mark)

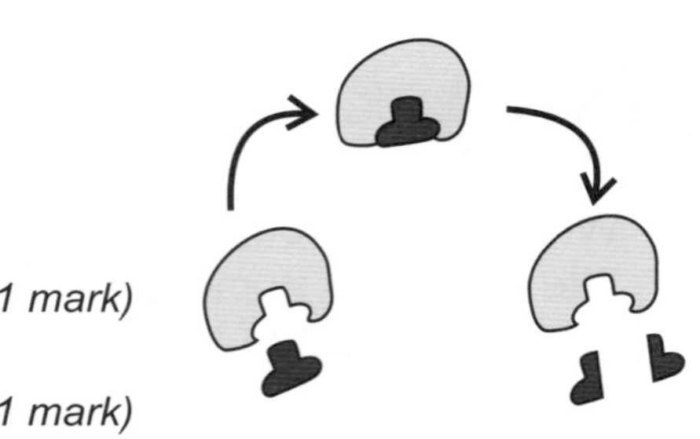

2 The diagram on the left shows the human digestive system.

(a) Copy the diagram and label the following parts:

(i) a part which is very acidic

(1 mark)

(ii) the place where bile is produced

(1 mark)

(b) Describe the functions of each of these parts of the digestive system:

(i) gall bladder

(1 mark)

(ii) pancreas

(2 marks)

3 The graph below shows the effect of temperature on the action of two different enzymes.

(a) What is the optimum temperature for enzyme **A**?

(1 mark)

(b) One of these enzymes was extracted from human liver cells.

The other was extracted from bacteria living in hot underwater vents.

Suggest which enzyme came from the bacteria. Give a reason for your answer.

(1 mark)

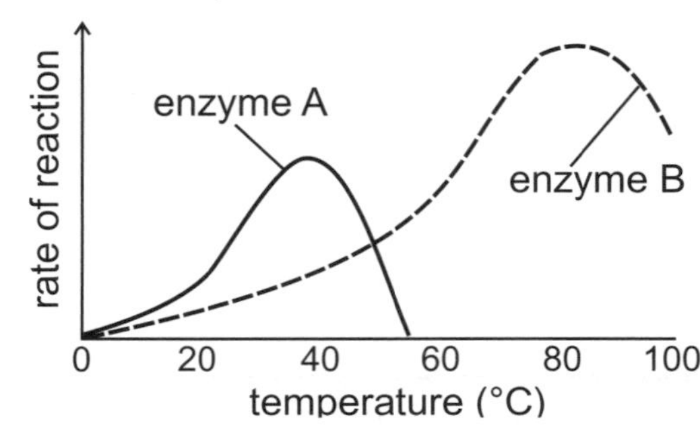

Enzymes and Respiration

Many chemical reactions inside cells are controlled by enzymes — including the ones in respiration.

Respiration is NOT "Breathing In and Out"

Respiration involves many reactions, all of which are catalysed by enzymes. These are really important reactions, as respiration releases the energy that the cell needs to do just about everything.

1) Respiration is not breathing in and breathing out, as you might think.
2) Respiration is the process of releasing energy from the breakdown of glucose — and it goes on in every cell in your body.
3) It happens in plants too. All living things respire. It's how they release energy from their food.

RESPIRATION is the process of RELEASING ENERGY FROM GLUCOSE, which goes on IN EVERY CELL.

Aerobic Respiration Needs Plenty of Oxygen

1) Aerobic respiration is respiration using oxygen. It's the most efficient way to release energy from glucose. (You can also have anaerobic respiration, which happens without oxygen, but that doesn't release nearly as much energy — see page 107.)
2) Aerobic respiration goes on all the time in plants and animals.
3) Most of the reactions in aerobic respiration happen inside mitochondria (see page 80).
4) You need to learn the overall word equation:

Glucose + oxygen → carbon dioxide + water + ENERGY

Respiration Releases Energy for All Kinds of Things

You need to learn these four examples of what the energy released by aerobic respiration is used for:

1) To build up larger molecules from smaller ones (like proteins from amino acids).
2) In animals, to allow the muscles to contract (which in turn allows them to move about).
3) In mammals and birds the energy is used to keep their body temperature steady (unlike other animals, mammals and birds keep their bodies constantly warm).
4) In plants, to build sugars, nitrates and other nutrients into amino acids, which are then built up into proteins.

Respiration releases energy from glucose

So... respiration — that's a pretty important thing. Cyanide is a really nasty toxin that stops respiration by stopping enzymes involved in the process from working — so it's pretty poisonous (it can kill you). Your brain, heart and liver are affected first because they have the highest energy demands... nice.

Exercise

When you exercise, your body quickly adapts so that your muscles get more oxygen and more glucose. This provides your muscles with more energy.

Exercise Increases the Heart Rate

1) Muscles are made of muscle cells. These use oxygen to release energy from glucose (aerobic respiration — see page 105), which is used to contract the muscles.
2) An increase in muscle activity requires more glucose and oxygen to be supplied to the muscle cells. Extra carbon dioxide needs to be removed from the muscle cells. For this to happen the blood has to flow at a faster rate.
3) This is why physical activity:

- increases your breathing rate and makes you breathe more deeply to meet the demand for extra oxygen.
- increases the speed at which the heart pumps.

An unfit person's heart rate goes up a lot more during exercise than a fit person, and they take longer to recover.

Glycogen is Used During Exercise

1) Some glucose from food is stored as glycogen.
2) Glycogen's mainly stored in the liver, but each muscle also has its own store.
3) During vigorous exercise muscles use glucose rapidly, so some of the stored glycogen is converted back to glucose to provide more energy.

Glucose is stored as glycogen in the liver and muscles

I bet you're exhausted after reading this page. But nonetheless, you need to know about the changes that happen in your body when you exercise — your breathing rate increases, your breathing depth increases and your heart rate increases too. All this helps plenty of glucose and oxygen to get to your muscles, and carbon dioxide to be taken away, which is just what you need to keep them working.

Exercise and Anaerobic Respiration

If your body can't get enough oxygen or glucose to your muscles, it has a back-up plan ready...

Anaerobic Respiration is Used if There's **Not Enough Oxygen**

1) When you do vigorous exercise and your body can't supply enough oxygen to your muscles, they start doing anaerobic respiration instead of aerobic respiration.
2) "Anaerobic" just means "without oxygen". It's the incomplete breakdown of glucose, which produces lactic acid.

glucose → energy + lactic acid

3) This is NOT the best way to convert glucose into energy because lactic acid builds up in the muscles, which gets painful. It also causes muscle fatigue — the muscles get tired and the stop contracting efficiently.
4) Another downside is that anaerobic respiration does not release nearly as much energy as aerobic respiration — but it's useful in emergencies.
5) The advantage is that at least you can keep on using your muscles for a while longer.

Anaerobic Respiration Leads to an **Oxygen Debt**

1) After resorting to anaerobic respiration, when you stop exercising you'll have an "oxygen debt".

2) In other words you have to "repay" the oxygen that you didn't get to your muscles in time, because your lungs, heart and blood couldn't keep up with the demand earlier on.

3) This means you have to keep breathing hard for a while after you stop, to get more oxygen into your blood. Blood flows through your muscles to remove the lactic acid by oxidising it to harmless CO_2 and water.

4) While high levels of CO_2 and lactic acid are detected in the blood (by the brain), the pulse and breathing rate stay high to try and rectify the situation.

These rowers have finished rowing, but they're still breathing hard to replace their oxygen debt.

Oxygen debt needs to be repaid

Yeast also respire anaerobically, but they produce ethanol (and carbon dioxide). So perhaps it's just as well humans produce lactic acid instead — or after a bit of vigorous exercise we'd all be drunk.

Uses of Enzymes

Some microorganisms produce enzymes which pass out of their cells and catalyse reactions outside them (e.g. to digest the microorganism's food). These enzymes have many uses in the home and in industry.

Enzymes Are Used in **Biological Detergents**

1) Enzymes are the 'biological' ingredients in biological detergents and washing powders.
2) They're mainly protein-digesting enzymes (proteases) and fat-digesting enzymes (lipases).
3) Because the enzymes break down animal and plant matter, they're ideal for removing stains like food or blood.
4) Biological detergents are also more effective at working at low temperatures (e.g. 30 °C) than other types of detergents.

Enzymes Are Used to **Change Foods**

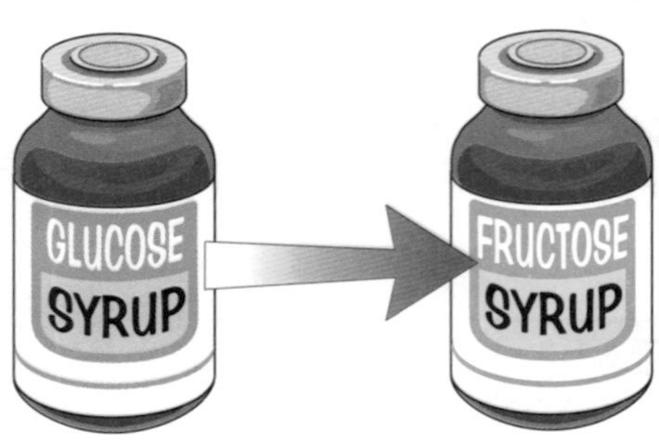

1) The proteins in some baby foods are 'pre-digested' using protein-digesting enzymes (proteases), so they're easier for the baby to digest.
2) Carbohydrate-digesting enzymes (carbohydrases) can be used to turn starch syrup into sugar syrup.
3) Glucose syrup can be turned into fructose syrup using an isomerase enzyme. Fructose is sweeter, so you can use less of it — good for slimming foods and drinks.

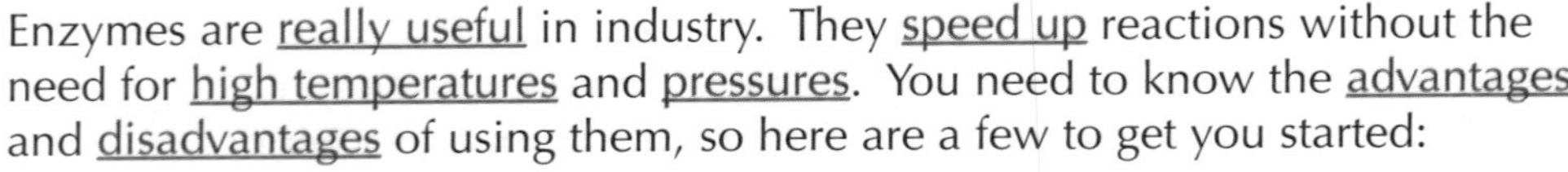

Using Enzymes in **Industry** Takes a Lot of **Control**

Enzymes are really useful in industry. They speed up reactions without the need for high temperatures and pressures. You need to know the advantages and disadvantages of using them, so here are a few to get you started:

ADVANTAGES:
1) They're specific, so they only catalyse the reaction you want them to.
2) Using lower temperatures and pressures means a lower cost as it saves energy.
3) Enzymes work for a long time, so after the initial cost of buying them, you can continually use them.
4) They are biodegradable and therefore cause less environmental pollution.

DISADVANTAGES:
1) Some people can develop allergies to the enzymes (e.g. in biological washing powders).
2) Enzymes can be denatured by even a small increase in temperature. They're also susceptible to poisons and changes in pH. This means the conditions in which they work must be tightly controlled.
3) Enzymes can be expensive to produce.
4) Contamination of the enzyme with other substances can affect the reaction.

From baby food to washing powder — enzymes make life easier

There's no denying that enzymes are useful, but they're also quite picky — e.g. tiny changes in pH can stop them working. Make sure you know both the advantages and disadvantages of using enzymes.

Warm-Up and Exam Questions

You know the drill by now — work your way through the warm-up questions, then the exam questions. After all, plenty of practice is the only way to make sure that you're well-prepared for the exams.

Warm-Up Questions

1) Define respiration.
2) State three changes that take place in the body during vigorous exercise.
3) What substance, stored in the liver and muscles, is broken down during exercise to release glucose?
4) Explain why proteases are used in some baby food.
5) What type of enzymes are used to turn starch syrup into sugar syrup?

Exam Questions

1 In the human body, respiration may be aerobic or anaerobic at different times.

(a) Explain why the body uses anaerobic respiration during vigorous exercise.

(2 marks)

(b) Write down the word equation for anaerobic respiration.

(1 mark)

(c) Give **two** disadvantages of anaerobic respiration.

(2 marks)

2 Enzymes are used in the food industry to turn glucose syrup into fructose syrup.

(a) Name the enzyme used to turn glucose syrup into fructose syrup.

(1 mark)

(b) Explain why this process is carried out.

(2 marks)

3 The graph below shows the rate of oxygen use by a person before, during and after a period of exercise.

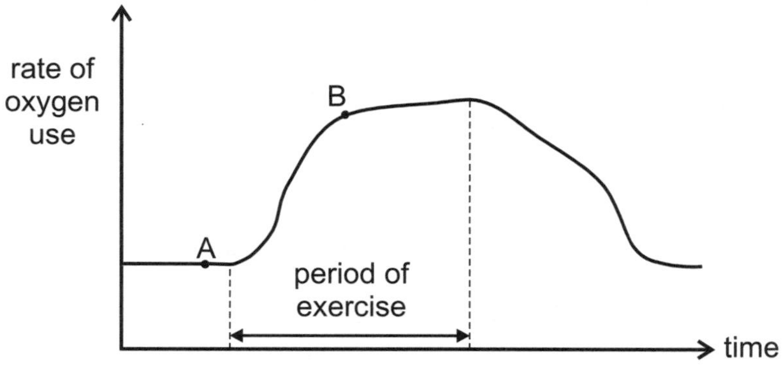

(a) Why is the rate of oxygen consumption higher at **B** than at **A**?

(1 mark)

(b) Suggest why oxygen use remains high, even after the period of exercise ends.

(1 mark)

DNA

The first step in understanding genetics is getting to grips with DNA.

Chromosomes *Are Really Long Molecules of* ***DNA***

1) DNA stands for deoxyribonucleic acid.
2) It contains all the instructions to put an organism together and make it work.
3) It's found in the nucleus of animal and plant cells, in really long molecules called chromosomes.

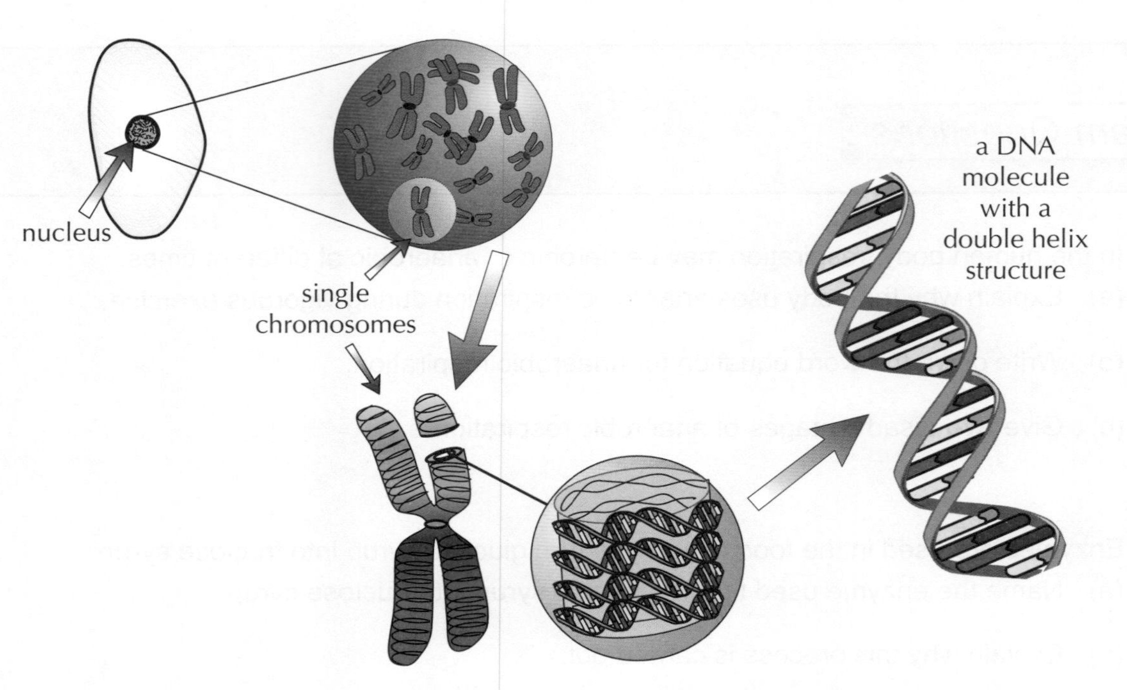

A ***Gene*** *Codes for a* ***Specific Protein***

1) A gene is a section of DNA. It contains the instructions to make a specific protein.
2) Cells make proteins by stringing amino acids together in a particular order.
3) Only 20 amino acids are used, but they make up thousands of different proteins.
4) Genes simply tell cells in what order to put the amino acids together.
5) DNA also determines what proteins the cell produces, e.g. haemoglobin, keratin.
6) That in turn determines what type of cell it is, e.g. red blood cell, skin cell.

Your genes make you different from everyone else

You've got to make sure you know exactly what chromosomes and genes are. If you don't get that sorted out first, then anything else you read about them later on won't make a lot of sense.

DNA Fingerprinting

Now this is interesting — you can use DNA to catch criminals or to identify the father of a child.

Everyone has Unique DNA...

...except identical twins and clones

1) Almost everyone's DNA is unique. The only exceptions are identical twins, where the two people have identical DNA, and clones.
2) DNA fingerprinting (or genetic fingerprinting) is a way of cutting up a person's DNA into small sections and then separating them.
3) Every person's genetic fingerprint has a unique pattern (unless they're identical twins or clones of course). This means you can tell people apart by comparing samples of their DNA.

DNA fingerprinting is used in...

1) Forensic Science

DNA (from hair, skin flakes, blood, semen etc.) taken from a crime scene is compared with a DNA sample taken from a suspect.

In the diagram, suspect 1's DNA has the same pattern as the DNA from the crime scene — so suspect 1 was probably at the crime scene.

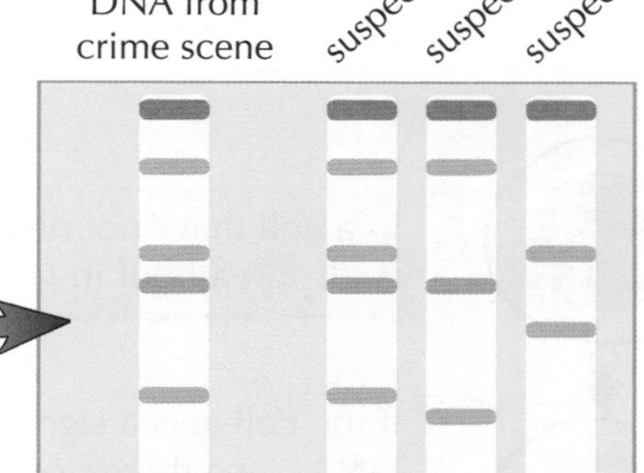

2) Paternity Testing

To see if a man is the father of a particular child.

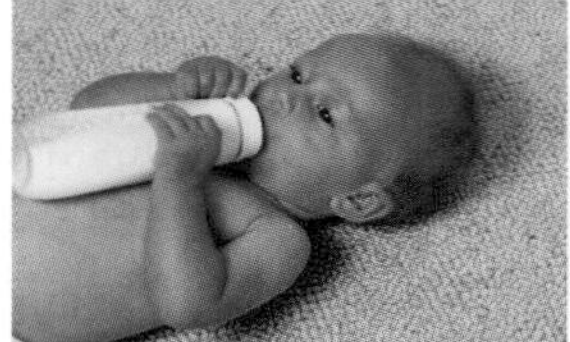

- Some people would like there to be a national genetic database of everyone in the country. That way, DNA from a crime scene could be checked against everyone in the country to see whose it was.
- But others think this is a big invasion of privacy, and they worry about how safe the data would be and what else it might be used for.
- There are also scientific problems — false positives can occur if errors are made in the procedure or if the data is misinterpreted.

Forensic science is useful, but some people have concerns

In the exam you might have to interpret data on DNA fingerprinting for identification. They could give you the results of a paternity test — the DNA fingerprint of a child, its mother and some possible fathers. Remember, half of the child's DNA will match the mother's DNA and half will match the father's DNA.

Cell Division — Mitosis

In order to survive and grow, our cells have got to be able to divide. And that means our DNA as well...

Mitosis Makes New Cells for *Growth* and *Repair*

1) Body cells normally have two copies of each chromosome — one from the organism's 'mother', and one from its 'father'. So, humans have two copies of chromosome 1, two copies of chromosome 2, etc.
2) The diagram shows the 23 pairs of chromosomes from a human cell. The 23rd pair are a bit different — see page 117.
3) When a body cell divides it needs to make new cells identical to the original cell — with the same number of chromosomes.
4) This type of cell division is called mitosis. It's used when plants and animals want to grow or to replace cells that have been damaged.

"MITOSIS is when a cell reproduces itself by splitting to form two identical offspring."

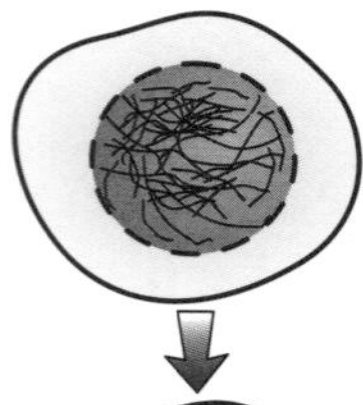

In a cell that's not dividing, the DNA is all spread out in long strings.

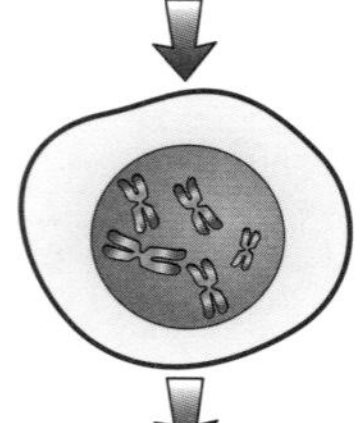

If the cell gets a signal to divide, it needs to duplicate its DNA — so there's one copy for each new cell. The DNA is copied and forms X-shaped chromosomes. Each 'arm' of the chromosome is an exact duplicate of the other.

The left arm of the chromosome has the same DNA as the right arm.

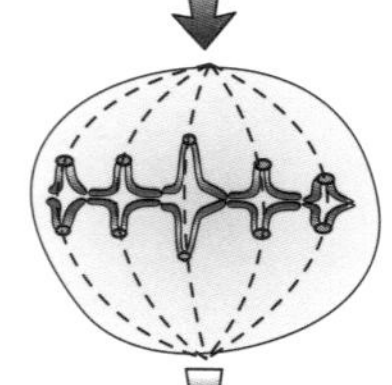

The chromosomes then line up at the centre of the cell and cell fibres pull them apart. The two arms of each chromosome go to opposite ends of the cell.

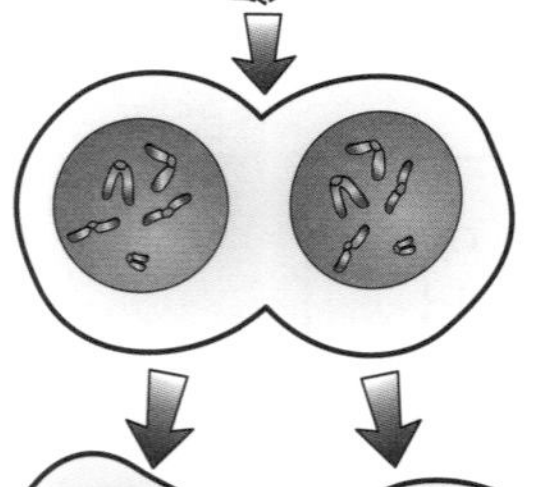

Membranes form around each of the sets of chromosomes. These become the nuclei of the two new cells.

Lastly, the cytoplasm divides.

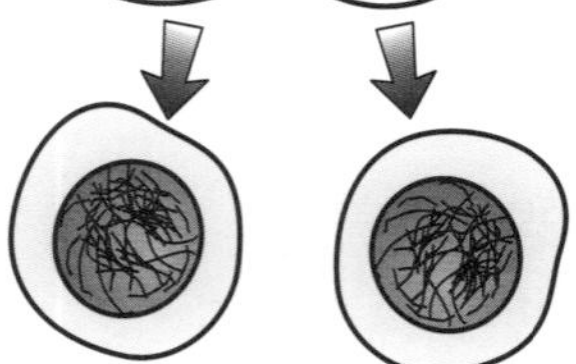

You now have two new cells containing exactly the same DNA — they're identical.

Asexual Reproduction Also Uses *Mitosis*

1) Some organisms also reproduce by mitosis, e.g. strawberry plants form runners in this way, which become new plants.
2) This is an example of asexual reproduction.
3) The offspring have exactly the same genes as the parent — so there's no variation.

Cell Division — Meiosis

Mitosis makes identical cells, but there's another type of cell division which doesn't — it's meiosis...

Gametes Have Half the Usual Number of Chromosomes

1) During sexual reproduction, two cells called gametes (sex cells) combine to form a new individual.
2) Gametes only have one copy of each chromosome. This is so that you can combine one sex cell from the 'mother' and one sex cell from the 'father' and still end up with the right number of chromosomes in body cells. For example, human body cells have 46 chromosomes. The gametes have 23 chromosomes each, so that when an egg and sperm combine, you get 46 chromosomes again.

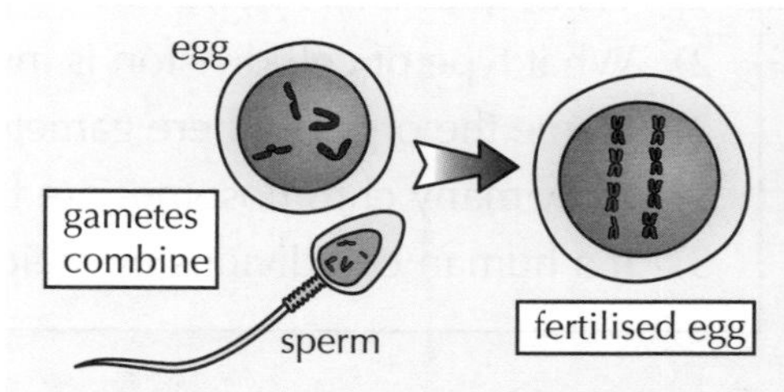

3) The new individual will have a mixture of two sets of chromosomes, so it will inherit features from both parents. This is how sexual reproduction produces variation.

Meiosis Involves Two Divisions

To make new cells which only have half the original number of chromosomes, cells divide by meiosis. In humans, it only happens in the reproductive organs (e.g. ovaries and testes).

"MEIOSIS produces cells which have half the normal number of chromosomes."

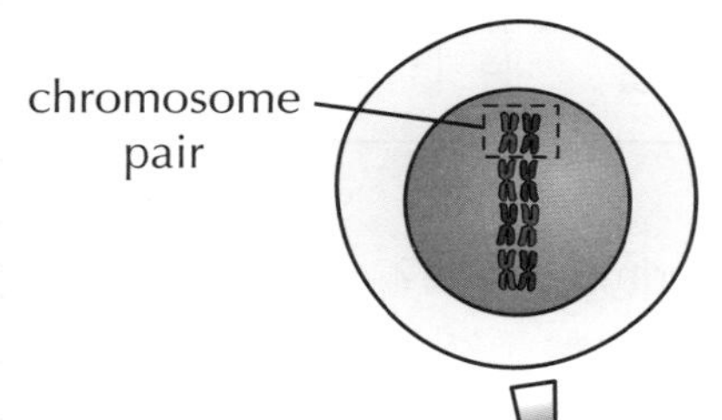

As with mitosis, before the cell starts to divide, it duplicates its DNA — one arm of each chromosome is an exact copy of the other arm.

In the first division in meiosis (there are two divisions) the chromosome pairs line up in the centre of the cell.

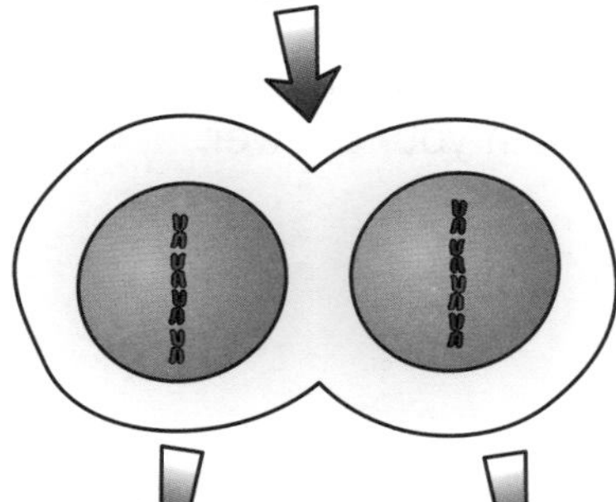

The pairs are then pulled apart, so each new cell only has one copy of each chromosome. Some of the father's chromosomes (shown in blue) and some of the mother's chromosomes (shown in red) go into each new cell.

In the second division the chromosomes line up again in the centre of the cell. It's a lot like mitosis. The arms of the chromosomes are pulled apart.

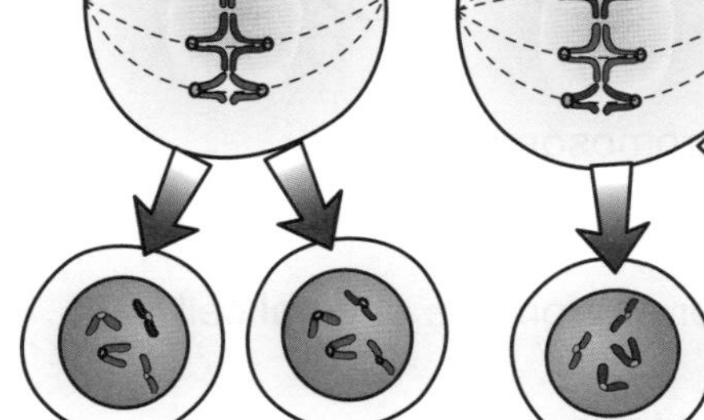

You get four gametes each with only a single set of chromosomes in it.

After two gametes join at fertilisation, the cell grows by repeatedly dividing by mitosis.

Warm-Up and Exam Questions

It's time to see how much you picked up about DNA and cell division, with the help of a few questions...

Warm-Up Questions

1) What does DNA stand for?
2) What type of cell division is involved in the regeneration of body parts?
3) Name the organs where gametes are formed.
4) How many chromosomes are there in a human liver cell?
5) If a human cell divides by meiosis, how many chromosomes do the new cells each have?

Exam Questions

1 Describe how a cell divides to form gametes.

(3 marks)

2 Mr X and Mr Y are both suspects in a burglary. A blood stain has been found on a crowbar at the crime scene. The police carry out a DNA fingerprint on Mr X, Mr Y and the blood from the crime scene.

The diagram shows part of the test results.

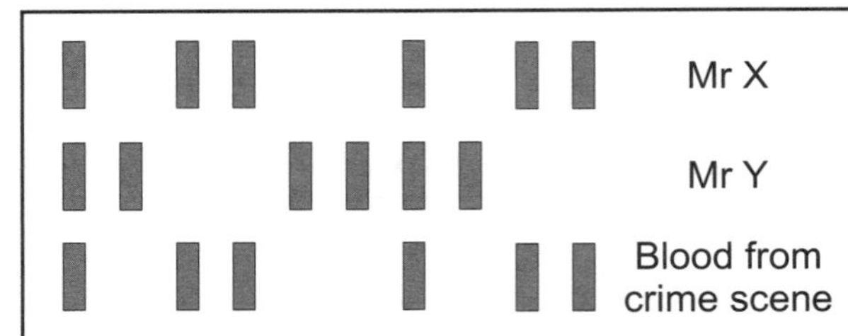

(a) Do the results suggest that either of the suspects were at the crime scene? Explain your answer.

(1 mark)

(b) A police officer investigating the burglary says that no two people have exactly the same genetic fingerprint. Is he correct? Explain your answer.

(2 marks)

3 (a) The diagram below shows the chromosomes of a cell that is about to divide by meiosis.

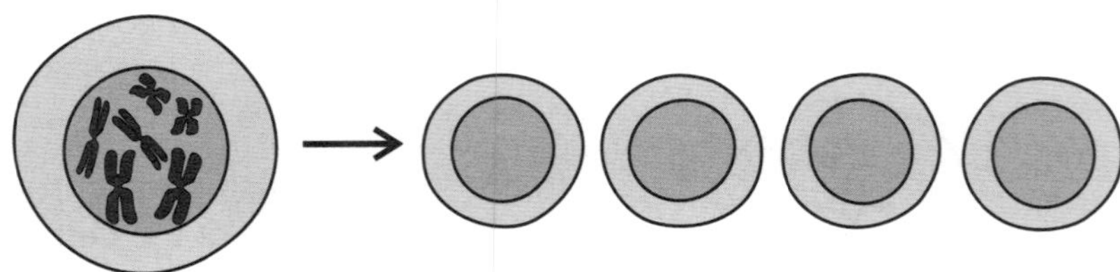

(i) Copy and complete the diagram to show the chromosomes in the daughter cells.

(2 marks)

(ii) How is the genetic content of the new cells different from the original cell?

(1 mark)

(b) State **three** ways in which meiosis is different from mitosis.

(3 marks)

Stem Cells

Most cells have specific features that make them particularly suited to the job that they do. But stem cells are a bit like a blank canvas — they have the potential to turn into other types of cells. And because of that, they're very important little cells...

Embryonic Stem Cells Can Turn into **ANY** Type of Cell

1) You know that differentiation is the process by which a cell changes to become specialised for its job (see page 85).

2) In most animal cells, the ability to differentiate is lost at an early stage, but lots of plant cells don't ever lose this ability.

3) Some cells are undifferentiated. They can develop into different types of cell depending on what instructions they're given. These cells are called STEM CELLS.

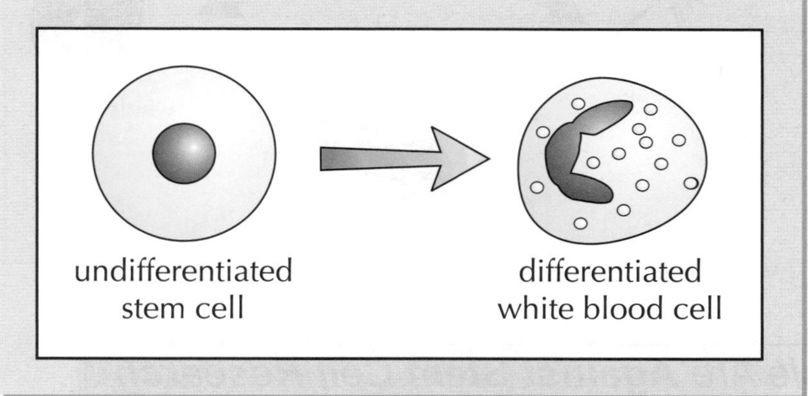

4) Stem cells are found in early human embryos. They're exciting to doctors and medical researchers because they have the potential to turn into any kind of cell at all. This makes sense if you think about it — all the different types of cell found in a human being have to come from those few cells in the early embryo.

5) Adults also have stem cells, but they're only found in certain places, like bone marrow. These aren't as versatile as embryonic stem cells — they can't turn into any cell type at all, only certain ones.

Stem cells are pretty versatile little cells...

Your cells are pretty highly specialised for the jobs that they do — think how different a red blood cell is from any other cell. But you can trace all cells back to undifferentiated stem cells in the embryo.

Stem Cells

Stem cell research has exciting possibilities, but it's also pretty controversial.

Stem Cells May Be Able to Cure Many Diseases

1) Medicine already uses adult stem cells to cure disease. For example, people with some blood diseases (e.g. sickle cell anaemia) can be treated by bone marrow transplants. Bone marrow contains stem cells that can turn into new blood cells to replace the faulty old ones.
2) Scientists can also extract stem cells from very early human embryos and grow them.
3) These embryonic stem cells could be used to replace faulty cells in sick people — you could make beating heart muscle cells for people with heart disease, insulin-producing cells for people with diabetes, nerve cells for people paralysed by spinal injuries, and so on.
4) To get cultures of one specific type of cell, researchers try to control the differentiation of the stem cells by changing the environment they're growing in. So far, it's still a bit hit and miss — lots more research is needed.

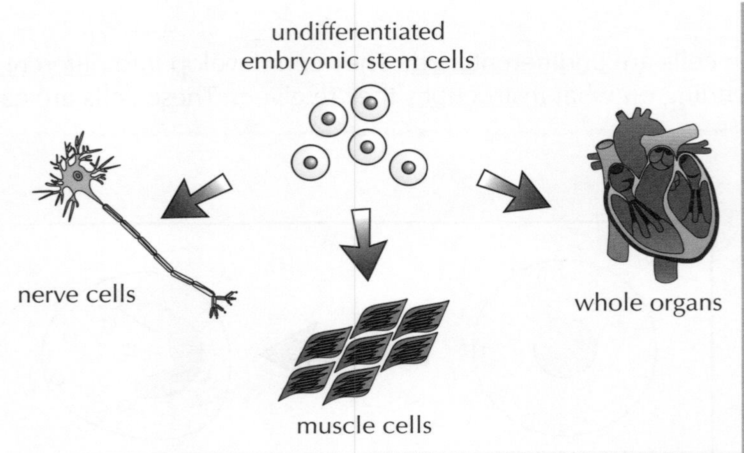

Some People Are Against Stem Cell Research

1) Some people are against stem cell research because they feel that human embryos shouldn't be used for experiments since each one is a potential human life.
2) Others think that curing patients who already exist and who are suffering is more important than the rights of embryos.
3) One fairly convincing argument in favour of this point of view is that the embryos used in the research are usually unwanted ones from fertility clinics that would probably just be destroyed if they weren't used for research. But of course, campaigners for the rights of embryos usually want this banned too.
4) These campaigners feel that scientists should concentrate more on finding and developing other sources of stem cells, so people could be helped without having to use embryos.
5) In some countries stem cell research is banned, but it's allowed in the UK as long as it follows strict guidelines.

Alternative sources of stem cells would avoid the controversy

Research has been done into getting stem cells from other sources — for example, some scientists think it might be possible to get cells from umbilical cords to behave like embryonic stem cells.

X and Y Chromosomes

Now for a couple of very important little chromosomes...

*Your **Chromosomes** Control Whether You're **Male** or **Female***

1) There are 22 matched pairs of chromosomes in every human body cell.
2) The 23rd pair are labelled XX or XY.
3) They're the two chromosomes that decide whether you turn out male or female.

All men have an X and a Y chromosome: XY
The Y chromosome causes male characteristics.

All women have two X chromosomes: XX
The XX combination allows female characteristics to develop.

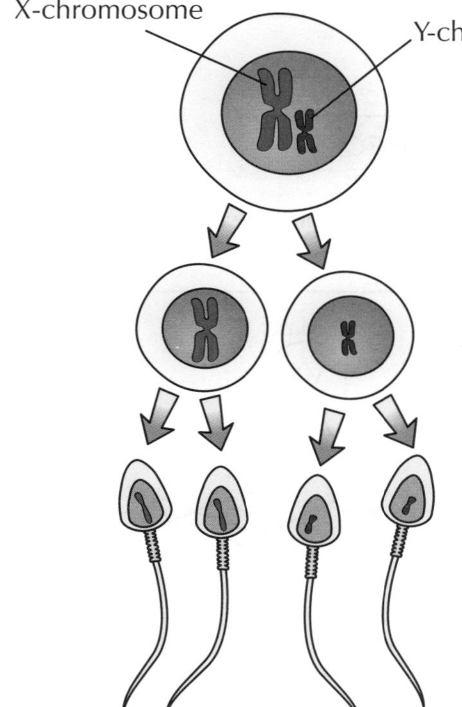

When making sperm, the X and Y chromosomes are drawn apart in the first division in meiosis. There's a 50% chance each sperm cell gets an X chromosome and a 50% chance it gets a Y chromosome.

A similar thing happens when making eggs. But the original cell has two X chromosomes, so all the eggs have one X chromosome.

The Y chromosome is physically smaller than the X chromosome

It's possible for people to have one X and two Y chromosomes, or even three X chromosomes, in their cells. But you don't really need to know this — just remember that it's XX for girls and XY for boys.

X and Y Chromosomes

You can work out the probability of offspring being male or female by using a genetic diagram.

Genetic Diagrams Show the Possible Combinations of Gametes

1) To find the probability of getting a boy or a girl, you can draw a genetic diagram.
2) Put the possible gametes from one parent down the side, and those from the other parent along the top.
3) Then in each middle square you fill in the letters from the top and side that line up with that square. The pairs of letters in the middle show the possible combinations of the gametes.
4) There are two XX results and two XY results, so there's the same probability of getting a boy or a girl.
5) Don't forget that this 50:50 ratio is only a probability at each pregnancy. If you had four kids they could all be boys.

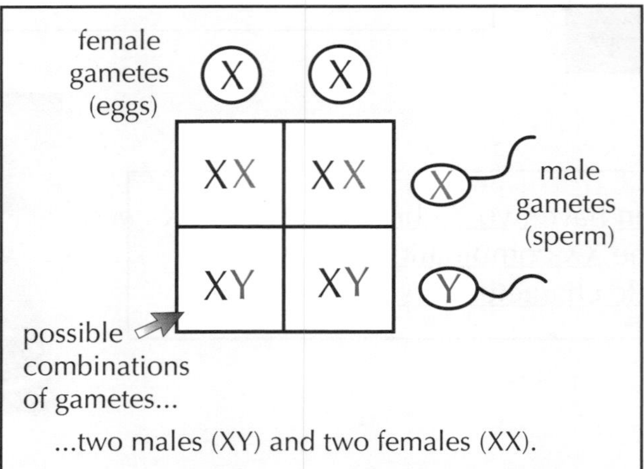

There's More Than One Type of Genetic Diagram

The other type of genetic diagram looks a bit more complicated, but it shows exactly the same thing.

1) At the top are the parents.
2) The middle circles show the possible gametes that are formed. One gamete from the female combines with one gamete from the male (during fertilisation).
3) The criss-cross lines show all the possible ways the X and Y chromosomes could combine.
4) The possible combinations of the offspring are shown in the bottom circles.
5) Remember, only one of these possibilities would actually happen for any one offspring.

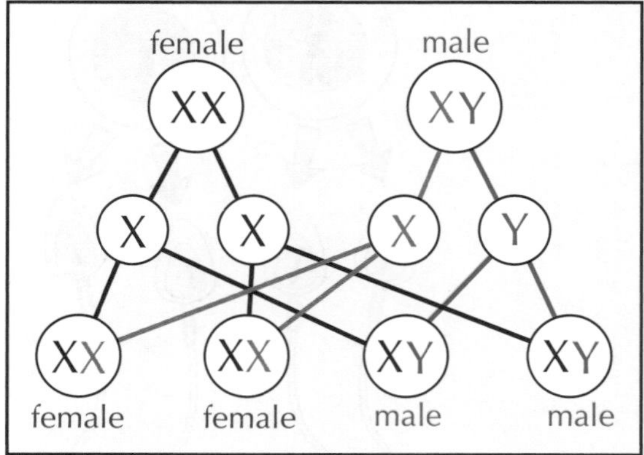

These diagrams aren't as scary as they look...

Most genetic diagrams you'll see in exams concentrate on a gene, instead of a chromosome. But the principle's the same. Don't worry — there are loads of other examples on the following pages.

Warm-Up and Exam Questions

There's only one way to do well in the exam — learn the facts and then practise lots of exam questions to see what it'll be like on the big day. We couldn't have made it easier for you — so do it.

Warm-Up Questions

1) What does cell 'differentiation' mean?
2) Give one example of a condition that could be treated with embryonic stem cells.
3) What combination of X and Y chromosomes does: a) a male have? b) a female have?

Exam Questions

1 Read the passage below about stem cell research.

> Stem cell research has been widely debated over the past few years. Adult stem cells have already been used to cure disorders, and it is thought that embryonic stem cells have the potential to treat many more disorders.
>
> One of the most controversial issues surrounds the technique used to create embryonic stem cells. Current legislation in the UK means that production of stem cells by human reproductive cloning is illegal. Research can only be carried out on embryos produced in the laboratory and surplus embryos created for use in *in vitro* fertilisation (IVF).

(a) What are stem cells?

(2 marks)

(b) Describe how stem cells could be used to treat disorders.

(1 mark)

(c) Explain why embryonic stem cells have the potential to treat more disorders than adult stem cells.

(1 mark)

(d) Give **one** place where adult stem cells are found in the body.

(1 mark)

(e) *In this question you will be assessed on the quality of your English, the organisation of your ideas and your use of appropriate specialist vocabulary.*

Discuss why some people are in favour of using embryos to create stem cells for research, while others are against the idea.

(6 marks)

2 Karen and Frank have four children. They are all girls. Karen discovers that she is pregnant. What is the probability that the new baby will be a boy? Explain your answer.

(2 marks)

The Work of Mendel

Gregor Mendel was pretty much the founder of genetics. Here's a whole page on him.

Mendel Did Genetic Experiments with Pea Plants

1) Gregor Mendel was an Austrian monk who trained in mathematics and natural history at the University of Vienna. On his garden plot at the monastery, Mendel noted how characteristics in plants were passed on from one generation to the next.
2) The results of his research were published in 1866 and eventually became the foundation of modern genetics.
3) These diagrams show two crosses for height in pea plants that Mendel carried out...

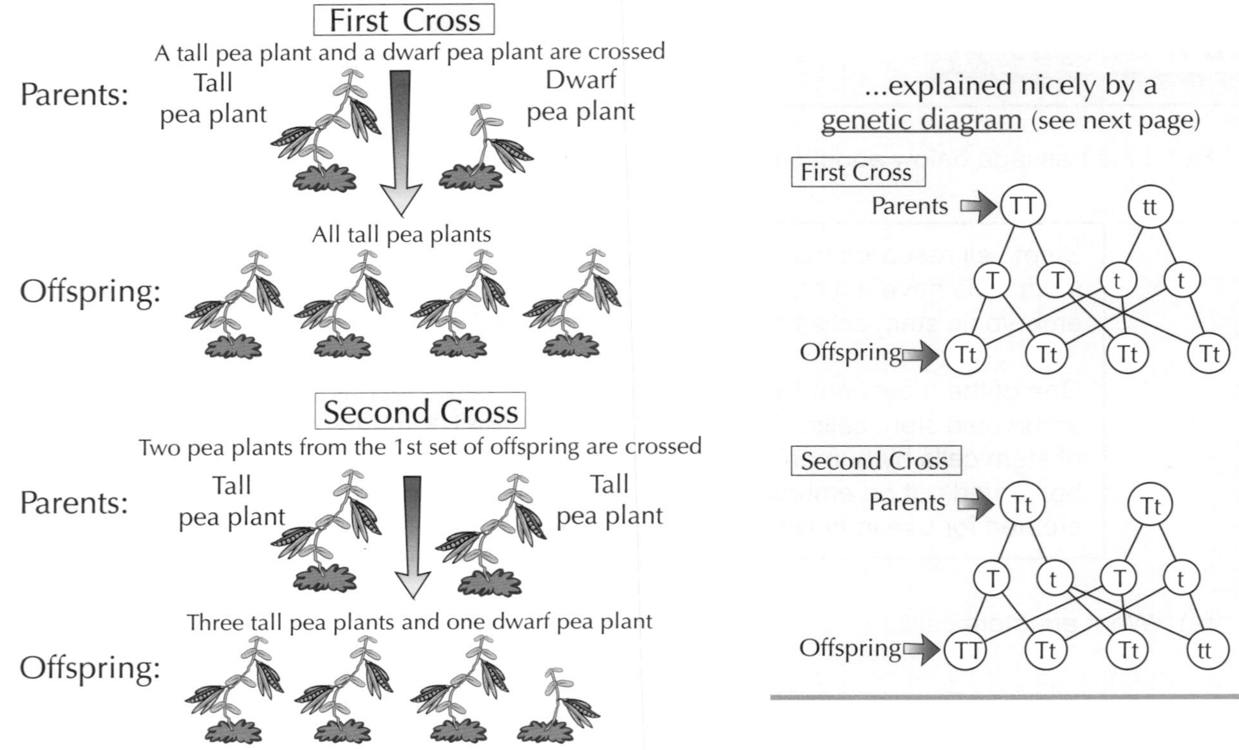

Mendel had shown that the height characteristic in pea plants was determined by separately inherited "hereditary units" passed on from each parent. The ratios of tall and dwarf plants in the offspring showed that the unit for tall plants, T, was dominant over the unit for dwarf plants, t.

Mendel Reached Three Important Conclusions

Mendel reached these three important conclusions about heredity in plants:

1) Characteristics in plants are determined by "hereditary units".
2) Hereditary units are passed on from both parents, one unit from each parent.
3) Hereditary units can be dominant or recessive — if an individual has both the dominant and the recessive unit for a characteristic, the dominant characteristic will be expressed.

We now know that the "hereditary units" are, of course, genes.

But in Mendel's time nobody knew anything about genes or DNA, and so the significance of his work was not to be realised until after his death.

Genetic Diagrams

When a single gene controls the inheritance of a characteristic, you can work out the odds of getting it...

Genetic Diagrams Show the Possible Genes of Offspring

1) Alleles are different versions of the same gene.
2) In genetic diagrams letters are usually used to represent alleles.
3) If an organism has two alleles for a particular gene the same, then it's HOMOZYGOUS. If its two alleles for a particular gene are different, then it's HETEROZYGOUS.
4) If the two alleles are different, only one can determine what characteristic is present. The allele for the characteristic that's shown is called the dominant allele (use a capital letter for dominant alleles — e.g. 'C'). The other one is called recessive (and you show these with small letters — e.g. 'c').
5) For an organism to display a recessive characteristic, both its alleles must be recessive (e.g. cc). But to display a dominant characteristic the organism can be either CC or Cc, because the dominant allele overrules the recessive one if the plant/animal/other organism is heterozygous.

Remember, gametes only have one allele, but all the other cells in an organism have two.

You Need to be Able to Interpret, Explain and Construct Them

Imagine you're cross-breeding hamsters, some with normal hair and a mild disposition and others with wild scratty hair and a leaning towards crazy acrobatics.

Let's say that the gene which causes the crazy nature is recessive, so we use a small "b" for it, whilst normal (boring) behaviour is due to a dominant gene, so we represent it with a capital "B".

1) A crazy hamster must have the genotype bb. However, a normal hamster could have two possible genotypes — BB or Bb.
2) Here's what happens if you breed from two homozygous hamsters:

Parents' phenotypes: Normal Crazy
Parents' genotypes: BB bb
Gametes' genotypes: B B b b
Offspring's genotypes: Bb Bb Bb Bb
Offspring's phenotypes: All the offspring are normal (boring).

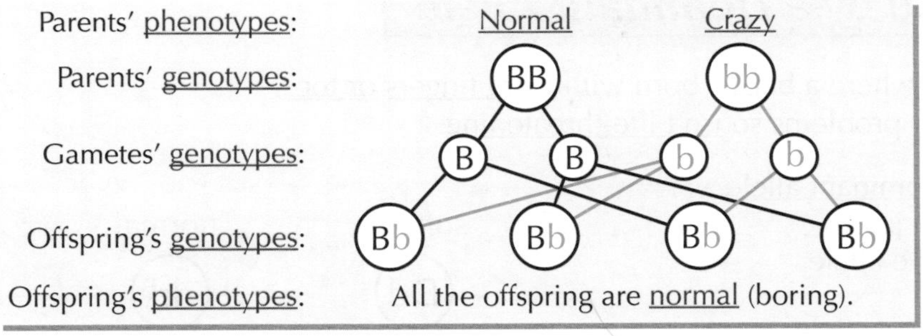

3) If two of these offspring now breed, you'll get the next generation:

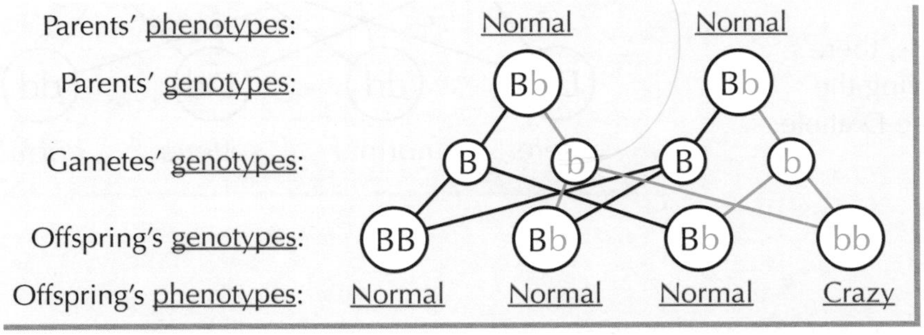

Parents' phenotypes: Normal Normal
Parents' genotypes: Bb Bb
Gametes' genotypes: B b B b
Offspring's genotypes: BB Bb Bb bb
Offspring's phenotypes: Normal Normal Normal Crazy

4) This gives a 3:1 ratio of normal to crazy offspring in this generation. Remember that "results" like this are only probabilities — they don't say definitely what'll happen.

Genotype means what alleles you have. Phenotype means the actual characteristic.

When you cross two parents to look at just one characteristic, it's called a monohybrid cross.

Genetic Disorders

It's not just characteristics that are passed on — some disorders are inherited. You need to learn these two.

Cystic Fibrosis is Caused by a Recessive Allele

Cystic fibrosis is a genetic disorder of the cell membranes. It results in the body producing a lot of thick sticky mucus in the air passages and in the pancreas.

1) The allele which causes cystic fibrosis is a recessive allele, 'f', carried by about 1 person in 25.
2) Because it's recessive, people with only one copy of the allele won't have the disorder — they're known as carriers.
3) For a child to have the disorder, both parents must be either carriers or sufferers.
4) There's a 1 in 4 chance of a child having the disorder if both parents are carriers:

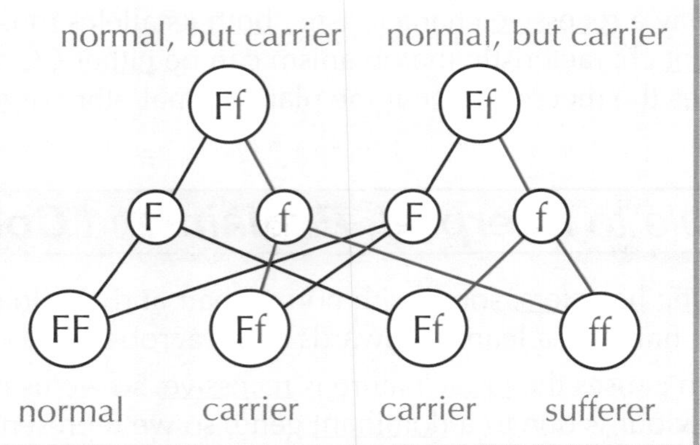

Polydactyly is Caused by a Dominant Allele

Polydactyly is a genetic disorder where a baby's born with extra fingers or toes. It doesn't usually cause any other problems so isn't life-threatening.

1) The disorder is caused by a dominant allele, 'D', and so can be inherited if just one parent carries the defective allele.
2) The parent that has the defective allele will be a sufferer too since the allele is dominant.
3) As the genetic diagram shows, there's a 50% chance of a child having the disorder if one parent has the D allele.

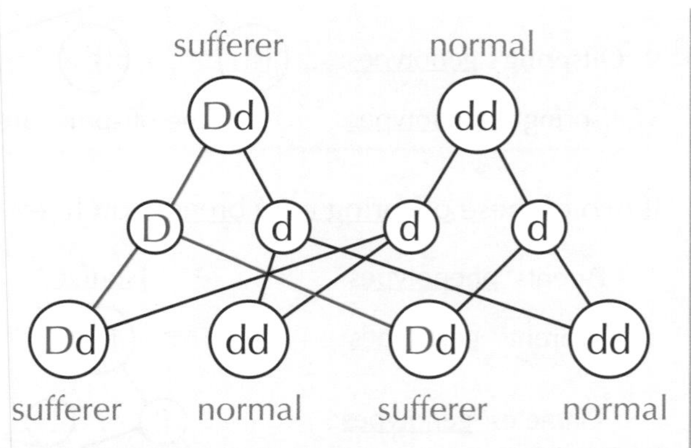

That's four genetic diagrams in two pages — get scribbling...

Genetic diagrams look pretty confusing at first, but they're really not. The important thing to get clear in your head is whether the characteristic is caused by a dominant or recessive allele.

Screening for Genetic Disorders

In vitro fertilisation (IVF) is quite widely used now by people who have problems conceiving naturally. Part of the process involves screening for genetic disorders, but some people are unhappy about this.

Embryos Can Be Screened for Genetic Disorders

1) During *in vitro* fertilisation (IVF), embryos are fertilised in a laboratory, and then implanted into the mother's womb. More than one egg is fertilised, so there's a better chance of the IVF being successful.
2) Before being implanted, it's possible to remove a cell from each embryo and analyse its genes.
3) Many genetic disorders could be detected in this way, such as cystic fibrosis.
4) Embryos with 'good' alleles would be implanted into the mother — the ones with 'bad' alleles destroyed.

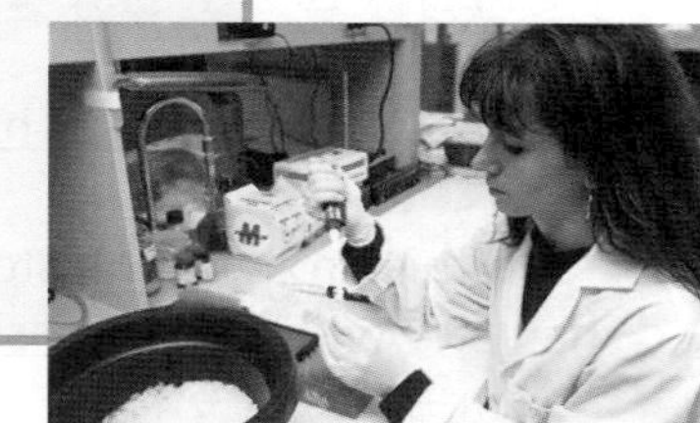

There is a huge debate raging about embryonic screening. Here are some arguments for and against it.

Against Embryonic Screening

1) There may come a point where everyone wants to screen their embryos so they can pick the most 'desirable' one, e.g. they want a blue-eyed, blond-haired, intelligent boy.
2) The rejected embryos are destroyed — they could have developed into humans.
3) It implies that people with genetic problems are 'undesirable' — this could increase prejudice.
4) Screening is expensive.

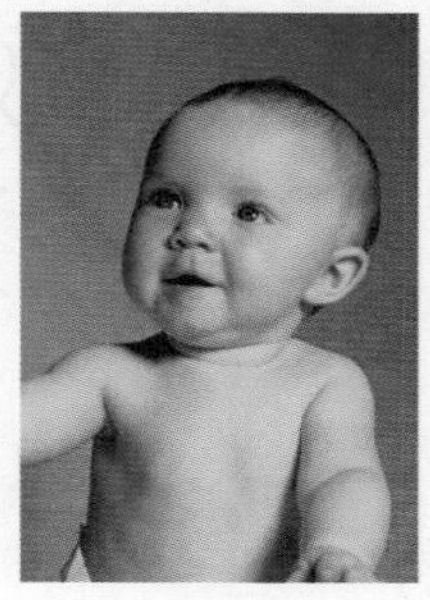

For Embryonic Screening

1) It will help to stop people suffering.
2) There are laws to stop it going too far. At the moment parents cannot even select the sex of their baby (unless it's for health reasons).
3) During IVF, most of the embryos are destroyed anyway — screening just allows the selected one to be healthy.
4) Treating disorders costs the Government (and the taxpayers) a lot of money.

Many people think that embryonic screening isn't justified for genetic disorders that don't affect a person's health, such as polydactyly (see page 122).

Embryonic screening — it's a tricky one...

In the exam you may be asked to compare the issues for and against embryonic screening for different disorders. Make sure you can apply the pros and cons above to different disorders and you'll be fine.

More Genetic Diagrams

In the exam they could ask about the inheritance of any kind of characteristic that's controlled by a single gene, because the principle's always the same. So here's a bit more on genetic diagrams...

You Should be able to *Predict* and *Explain* the Outcomes of Crosses

If you've got your head round all this, you should be able to draw a genetic diagram and work out the outcomes of crosses between individuals for each possible combination of dominant and recessive alleles of a gene. But it'll make it easier for you if you've seen all the different types before. So get ready for a couple of pages of examples...

All the Offspring are *Normal*

Let's take another look at the crazy hamster example from page 121:

In this cross, a hamster with two dominant alleles (BB) is crossed with a hamster with two recessive alleles (bb). All the offspring are normal (boring).

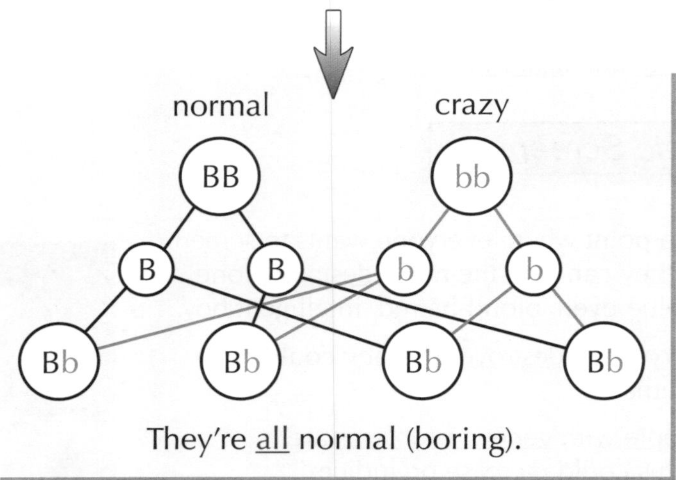

But, if you crossed a hamster with two dominant alleles (BB) with a hamster with a dominant and a recessive allele (Bb), you would also get all normal (boring) offspring.

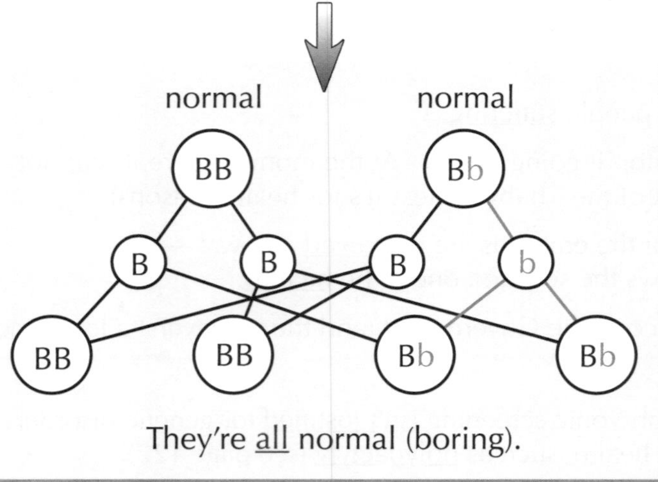

To find out which it was you'd have to breed the offspring together and see what kind of ratio you got that time — then you'd have a good idea. If it was 3:1, it's likely that you originally had BB and bb.

More Genetic Diagrams

One more example of a genetic cross diagram coming up on this page. Then a little bit about another type of genetic diagram that you need to know how to interpret — called a family tree...

There's a 1:1 Ratio in the Offspring

1) A cat with long hair was bred with another cat with short hair.
2) The long hair is caused by a dominant allele 'H', and the short hair by a recessive allele 'h'.

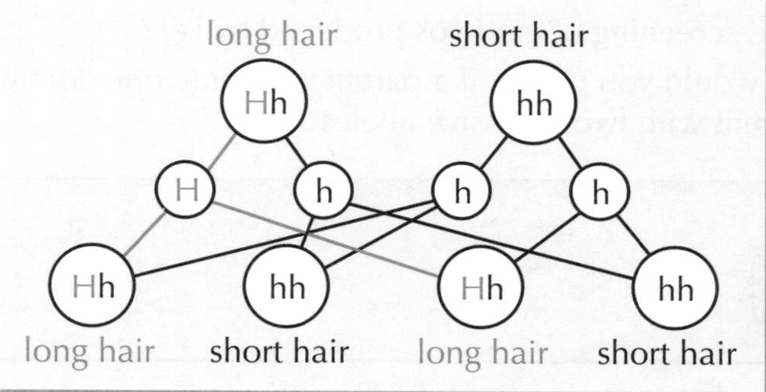

3) They had 8 kittens — 4 with long hair and 4 with short hair.
4) This is a 1:1 ratio — it's what you'd expect when a parent with only one dominant allele (Hh) is crossed with a parent with two recessive alleles (hh).

You Need to be Able to Interpret Family Trees

Knowing how inheritance works can help you to interpret a family tree — this is one for cystic fibrosis.

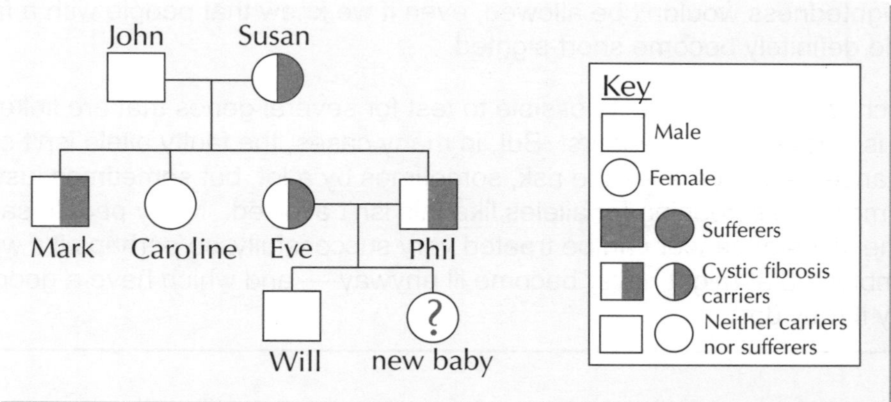

1) From the family tree, you can tell that the allele for cystic fibrosis isn't dominant because plenty of the family carry the allele but aren't sufferers.
2) There is a 25% chance that the new baby will be a sufferer and a 50% chance that it will be a carrier, as both of its parents are carriers but not sufferers. The case of the new baby is just the same as the genetic diagram on page 122 — so the baby could be normal (FF), a carrier (Ff) or a sufferer (ff).

It's enough to make you go cross-eyed...

If you see a family tree showing the inheritance of a dominant allele, it won't have any carriers on it (everyone who carries the allele is a sufferer). A good way to work out a family tree is to write the genotype of each person onto it — try copying the one above and writing the genotypes on for practice.

Warm-Up and Exam Questions

There's no better preparation for exam questions than doing... err... practice exam questions. Hang on, what's this I see...

Warm-Up Questions

1) What are alleles?
2) Explain how it's possible to be a carrier of cystic fibrosis without knowing.
3) What is polydactyly?
4) What is meant by the **screening** of embryos produced by IVF?
5) What offspring ratio would you expect if a parent with only one dominant allele is crossed with a parent with two recessive alleles?

Exam Questions

1 Read this passage about embryo screening.

> Embryo screening already happens in the UK for genetic disorders like cystic fibrosis. A genetic test can be done during IVF treatment — so that doctors can select a healthy embryo to implant in the mother. The other embryos are discarded.
>
> At the moment, regulations say that embryo screening is only allowed when there is "a significant risk of a serious genetic condition being present in the embryo." In other words, it is only allowed when a child of the person carrying the faulty allele would be likely to suffer from the disorder, and the disorder is serious. So screening for short-sightedness wouldn't be allowed, even if we knew that people with a faulty allele would definitely become short-sighted.
>
> Medical technology has made it possible to test for several genes that are linked to very serious illnesses, e.g. cancers. But, in many cases, the faulty allele isn't certain to cause cancer — it increases the risk, sometimes by a lot, but sometimes just slightly. So, at the moment, screening for alleles like this isn't allowed. Many people say this is right. Some kinds of cancer can be treated very successfully, so perhaps it's wrong to destroy embryos that might never become ill anyway — and which have a good chance of recovery if they do.

(a) Could embryos be screened for polydactyly under the current regulations? Explain your answer.

(1 mark)

(b) Cancer is a serious illness that kills thousands of people each year in the UK. Why is cancer not included in embryo screening?

(3 marks)

(c) Give **one** reason why a person might be opposed to screening embryos for genetic conditions.

(1 mark)

Exam Questions

2 In one of Gregor Mendel's experiments, he crossed thoroughbred purple-flowered pea plants with thoroughbred white-flowered plants. The first generation of offspring were all purple-flowered.

(a) In Mendel's experiment, which characteristic is recessive?

(1 mark)

(b) Using the symbols **F** and **f** to represent the alleles for purple and white, write down the combination of alleles (genetic make-up) of each of the following:

(i) the original purple-flowered parent plant

(1 mark)

(ii) the original white-flowered parent plant

(1 mark)

(iii) the first generation of purple-flowered offspring

(1 mark)

3 Cystic fibrosis is a disease caused by recessive alleles.

F = the normal allele
f = the faulty allele that leads to cystic fibrosis

The genetic diagram below shows the possible inheritance of cystic fibrosis from one couple.

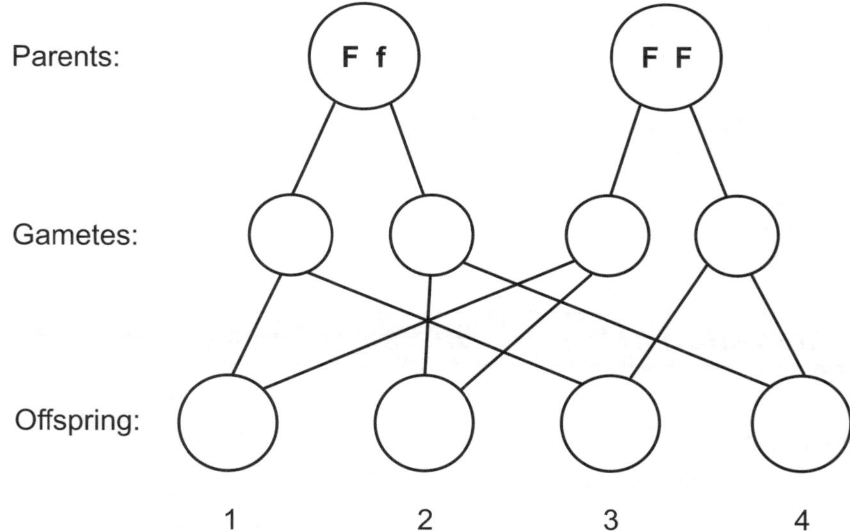

(a) Copy and complete the genetic diagram.

(2 marks)

(b) Which of the possible offspring will be sufferers and which will be unaffected?

(1 mark)

(c) (i) What proportion of the possible offspring are homozygous?

(1 mark)

(ii) Which of the possible offspring are carriers of the disease?

(1 mark)

Fossils and Extinction

Fossils can be really useful — if they're well preserved, they can show you what creatures that have been dead for millions of years might have looked like.

Fossils are the Remains of Plants and Animals

Fossils are the remains of organisms from many years ago, which are found in rocks.
Fossils provide the evidence that organisms lived ages ago.

Fossils form in rocks in one of three ways:

1) From Gradual Replacement by Minerals

Most fossils happen this way...

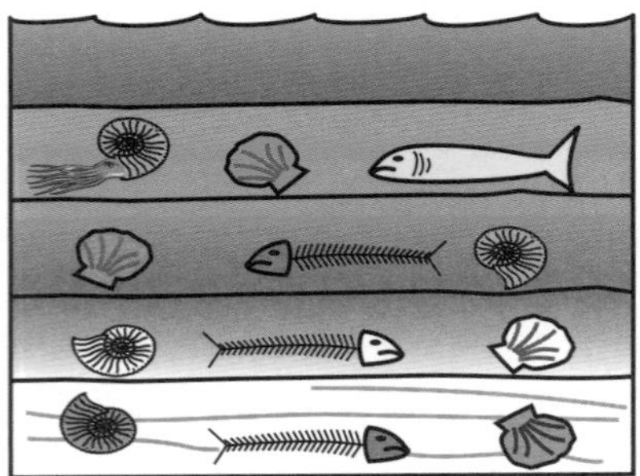

1) Things like teeth, shells, bones etc., which don't decay easily, can last a long time when buried.
2) They're eventually replaced by minerals as they decay, forming a rock-like substance shaped like the original hard part.
3) The surrounding sediments also turn to rock, but the fossil stays distinct inside the rock and eventually someone digs it up.

2) From Casts and Impressions

1) Sometimes, fossils are formed when an organism is buried in a soft material like clay. The clay later hardens around it and the organism decays, leaving a cast of itself.

   An animal's burrow or a plant's roots can be preserved as casts.

2) Things like footprints can be pressed into these materials when soft, leaving an impression when it hardens.

3) From Preservation in Places Where No Decay Happens

1) In amber (a clear yellow 'stone' made from fossilised resin) and tar pits there's no oxygen or moisture so decay microbes can't survive.

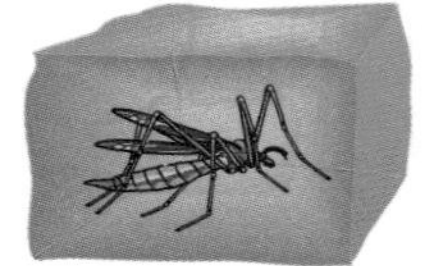

2) In glaciers it's too cold for the decay microbes to work.

3) Peat bogs are too acidic for decay microbes.

Fossils give us information about ancient animals and plants

It's amazing that fossils of organisms can still exist millions of years after they died. You need to know the three ways that fossils form — cover the page and scribble them down till you're sure you've got it.

Fossils and Extinction

Fossils can also help us to work out how life on Earth has evolved. Evolution leads to the development of lots of different species. But not every species is still around today...

No One Knows How Life Began...

Fossils show how many of today's species have evolved (changed and developed) over millions of years. But where did the first living thing come from...

1) There are various hypotheses suggesting how life first came into being, but no one really knows.
2) Maybe the first life forms came into existence in a primordial swamp (or under the sea) here on Earth. Maybe simple organic molecules were brought to Earth on comets — these could have then become more complex organic molecules, and eventually very simple life forms.
3) These hypotheses can't be supported or disproved because there's a lack of valid and reliable evidence.
4) There's a lack of evidence because scientists believe many early organisms were soft-bodied, and soft tissue tends to decay away completely. So the fossil record is incomplete.
5) Plus, fossils that did form millions of years ago may have been destroyed by geological activity, e.g. the movement of tectonic plates may have crushed fossils already formed in the rock.

Validity and reliability are explained on page 3.

Extinction Happens if You Can't Evolve Quickly Enough

The fossil record contains many species that don't exist any more — these species are said to be extinct. Dinosaurs and mammoths are extinct animals, with only fossils to tell us they existed at all.

Species become extinct for these reasons:

1) The environment changes too quickly (e.g. destruction of habitat).
2) A new predator kills them all (e.g. humans hunting them).
3) A new disease kills them all.
4) They can't compete with another (new) species for food.
5) A catastrophic event happens that kills them all (e.g. a volcanic eruption or a collision with an asteroid).
6) A new species develops (this is called speciation — see page 130).

Dodos are now extinct. Humans not only hunted them, but introduced other animals which ate all their eggs, and we destroyed the forest where they lived — they really didn't stand a chance...

Species evolve — or become extinct...

We don't really know how life on Earth began — there are plenty of hypotheses, but we won't really know unless we find valid and reliable evidence. I'm afraid that's just science for you...

Speciation

If you've been wondering how a new species can spring up, this is the page for you.

Speciation is the Development of a New Species

1) A species is a group of similar organisms that can reproduce to give fertile offspring.
2) Speciation is the development of a new species.
3) Speciation occurs when populations of the same species become so different that they can no longer breed together to produce fertile offspring.

Isolation and Natural Selection Lead to Speciation

ISOLATION is where populations of a species are separated.

1) Isolation can happen due to a physical barrier. E.g. floods and earthquakes can cause barriers that geographically isolate some individuals from the main population.
2) Conditions on either side of the barrier will be slightly different, e.g. they may have different climates.
3) Because the environment is different on each side, different characteristics will become more common in each population due to natural selection:
   - Each population shows variation because they have a wide range of alleles.
   - In each population, individuals with characteristics that make them better adapted to their environment have a better chance of survival and so are more likely to breed successfully.
   - So the alleles that control the beneficial characteristics are more likely to be passed on to the next generation.
4) Eventually, individuals from the different populations will have changed so much that they won't be able to breed with one another to produce fertile offspring.
5) The two groups will have become separate species:

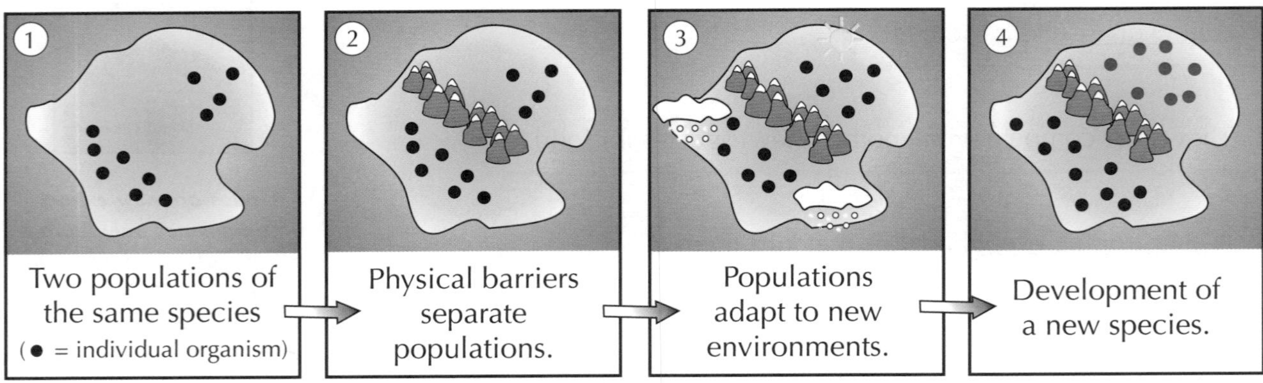
1
Two populations of the same species
(● = individual organism)
2
Physical barriers separate populations.
3
Populations adapt to new environments.
4
Development of a new species.

A new species can develop when populations become separated

So speciation happens if two or more populations of the same species change so much that they can no longer breed together to produce fertile offspring. It can be caused by populations becoming separated from each other. Now then, time to learn this page before moving on to more questions...

Warm-Up and Exam Questions

You need to test your knowledge with a few warm-up questions, followed by some exam questions...

Warm-Up Questions

1) What are fossils?
2) Give an example of something that can be preserved as a cast.
3) Some fossils of early organisms did form in ancient rocks.
   Explain why many of these fossils have not survived to the present day.
4) What is an extinct species?
5) What does the term 'isolation' mean in the context of speciation?

Exam Questions

1 The fossils of an extinct species of insect is found preserved inside a piece of amber.

(a) Explain why the remains of the insect have been preserved so well inside the amber.

(2 marks)

(b) This particular species of insect became extinct because a catastrophic event wiped out every member of the species at once.

Give **one** example of the kind of catastrophic event that could wipe out a species.

(1 mark)

2 The picture on the right shows what scientists believe the dinosaur **Stegosaurus** looked like.

(a) Fossils of Stegosaurus teeth have been discovered.

Briefly explain how the fossils of the Stegosaurus teeth were formed.

(2 marks)

(b) Scientists cannot be completely sure what Stegosaurus looked like because of a lack of evidence.

Suggest why there is not enough evidence to show exactly what Stegosaurus looked like.

(1 mark)

3 Two different species of birds are found on two nearby islands.
The two species were originally just one species living on one of the islands.

Suggest an explanation for how the two different bird species developed.

(5 marks)

Revision Summary for Biology 2b

Wow, that was quite a long section. First there was all the stuff about enzymes and then came all the genetics bits. And just to finish off, some questions. Use these to find out what you know about it all — and what you don't. Then look back and learn the bits you don't know.
Then try the questions again, and again...

1) State four functions of proteins in living cells.
2) Explain why an enzyme-catalysed reaction stops when the reaction mixture is heated above a certain temperature.
3) In which three places in the body is amylase produced?
4) Where in the body is bile: a) produced? b) stored? c) used?
5) Explain why the stomach produces hydrochloric acid.
6) Write down the word equation for aerobic respiration.
7) Give two examples of how an animal uses the energy released by aerobic respiration.
8) What is anaerobic respiration? Which acid does anaerobic respiration produce in humans?
9) Explain how you repay an oxygen debt.
10) Give two kinds of enzyme that would be useful in a biological washing powder.
11) Discuss the advantages and disadvantages of using enzymes in industry.
12) Explain how DNA controls the activities of a cell.
13) Explain how DNA fingerprinting is used in forensic science.
14) What is mitosis used for in the human body? Describe the four steps in mitosis.
15) Name the other type of cell division that isn't mitosis.
16) Which chromosome in the human body causes male characteristics?
17) Copy and complete the diagrams to show what happens to the X and Y chromosomes during reproduction.
18) List three important conclusions that Mendel reached following his experiments with pea plants.

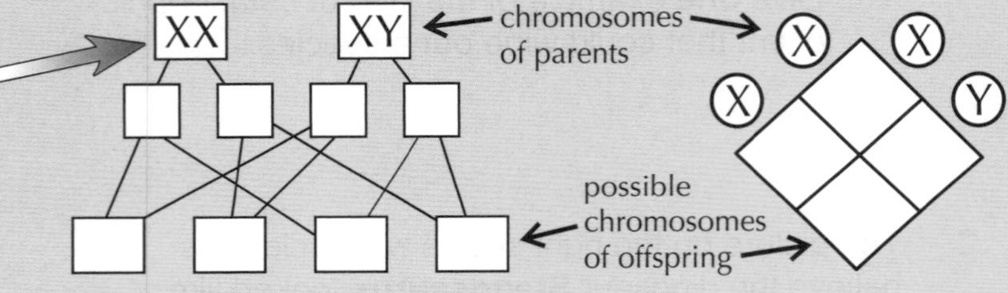

19) The significance of Mendel's work was not realised until 1900, 16 years after Mendel died. Suggest why the importance of the work wasn't understood at the time.
20) What is meant by an organism being heterozygous? What about homozygous?
21) Describe the basic difference between a recessive allele and a dominant one.
22) What is cystic fibrosis?
23) If both parents carry the recessive allele for cystic fibrosis, what is the probability of their child being a carrier?
24)*Blue colour in a plant is carried on a recessive allele, b. The dominant allele, B, gives white flowers. In the first generation after a cross, all the flowers are white. These are bred together and the result is a ratio of 54 white : 19 blue. What were the alleles of the flowers used in the first cross?
25) Name the three ways that fossils can form.
26) Give three reasons why some species become extinct.
27) What is speciation?

* Answers on page 234.

Osmosis

If you've got your head round diffusion, osmosis will be a breeze. If not, have another look at page 82.

Osmosis is a *Special Case* of *Diffusion*, That's All

Learn this definition of osmosis:

> OSMOSIS is the movement of water molecules across a partially permeable membrane from a region of high water concentration to a region of low water concentration.

1) A partially permeable membrane is just one with very small holes in it. So small, in fact, only tiny molecules (like water) can pass through them, and bigger molecules (e.g. sucrose) can't.

2) The water molecules actually pass both ways through the membrane during osmosis. This happens because water molecules move about randomly all the time.

3) But because there are more water molecules on one side than on the other, there's a steady net flow of water into the region with fewer water molecules, i.e. into the stronger sugar solution.

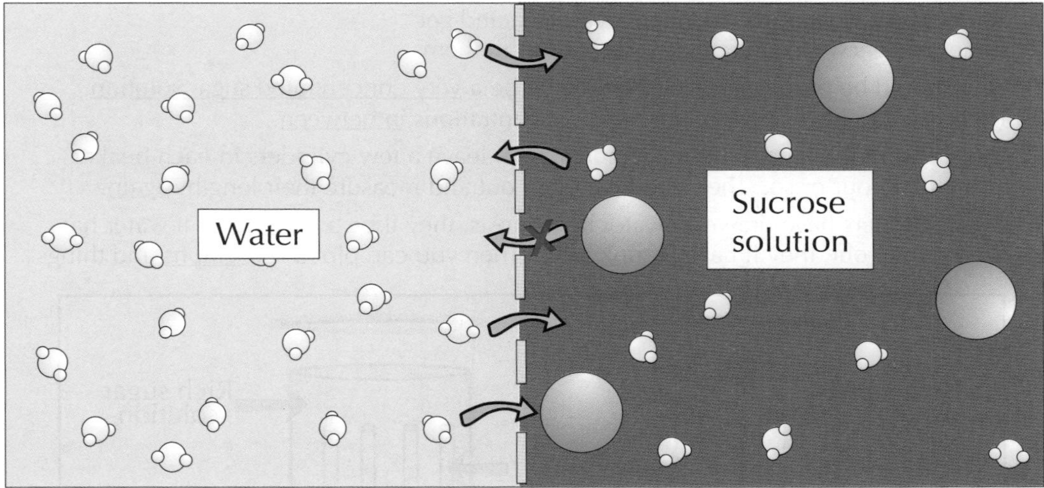

4) This means the strong sugar solution gets more dilute. The water acts like it's trying to "even up" the concentration either side of the membrane.

5) Osmosis is a type of diffusion — passive movement of water particles from an area of high water concentration to an area of low water concentration.

Osmosis

You're not learning about osmosis just for fun — it's how water moves into and out of cells, so it's pretty important in biology.

Water Moves Into and Out of **Cells** by **Osmosis**

1) Tissue fluid surrounds the cells in the body — it's basically just water with oxygen, glucose and stuff dissolved in it. It's squeezed out of the blood capillaries to supply the cells with everything they need.

2) The tissue fluid will usually have a different concentration to the fluid inside a cell. This means that water will either move into the cell from the tissue fluid, or out of the cell, by osmosis.

3) If a cell is short of water, the solution inside it will become quite concentrated. This usually means the solution outside is more dilute, and so water will move into the cell by osmosis.

4) If a cell has lots of water, the solution inside it will be more dilute, and water will be drawn out of the cell and into the fluid outside by osmosis.

Osmosis Experiment

There's an experiment you can do to show osmosis at work.

1) You cut up a potato into identical cylinders, and get some beakers with different sugar solutions in them.
2) One should be pure water, another should be a very concentrated sugar solution. Then you can have a few others with concentrations in between.
3) You measure the length of the cylinders, then leave a few cylinders in each beaker for half an hour or so. Then you take them out and measure their lengths again.
4) If the cylinders have drawn in water by osmosis, they'll be a bit longer. If water has been drawn out, they'll have shrunk a bit. Then you can plot a few graphs and things.

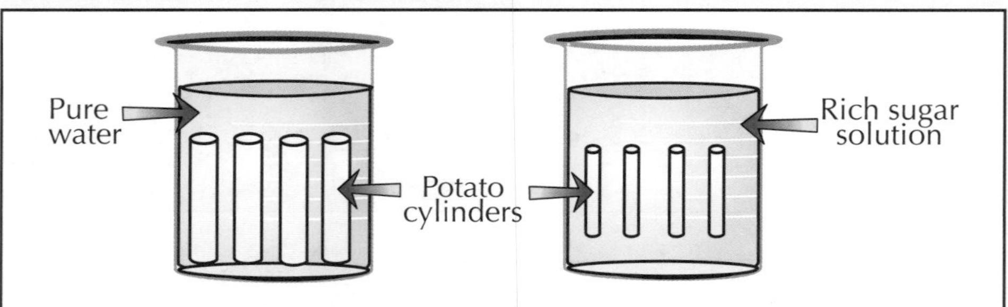

The dependent variable is the chip length and the independent variable is the concentration of the sugar solution. All other variables (volume of solution, temperature, time, type of sugar used, etc. etc.) must be kept the same in each case or the experiment won't be a fair test.

Water always moves into the more concentrated solution

That's why it's bad to drink sea-water. The high salt content means you end up with a much lower water concentration in your blood and tissue fluid than in your cells. All the water is sucked out of your cells by osmosis and they shrivel and die. So next time you're stranded at sea, remember this...

Gas and Solute Exchange

The processes that keep organisms alive won't happen without the right raw materials in the right places.

Substances Move by **Diffusion**, **Osmosis** and **Active Transport**

1) Life processes need gases or other dissolved substances before they can happen.
2) For example, for photosynthesis to happen, carbon dioxide and water have to get into plant cells. And for respiration to take place, glucose and oxygen both have to get inside cells.
3) Waste substances also need to move out of the cells so that the organism can get rid of them.
4) These substances move to where they need to be by diffusion, osmosis and active transport:

- Diffusion is where particles move from an area of high concentration to an area of low concentration. For example, gases can just diffuse through one another, like a smell spreading through a room. Alternatively, dissolved particles can diffuse in and out of cells through cell membranes — see p.82.

- You've just learned all about osmosis on the previous two pages.

- Diffusion and osmosis both involve stuff moving from an area where there's a high concentration of it, to an area where there's a lower concentration of it. Sometimes substances need to move in the other direction — which is where active transport comes in — see page 140.

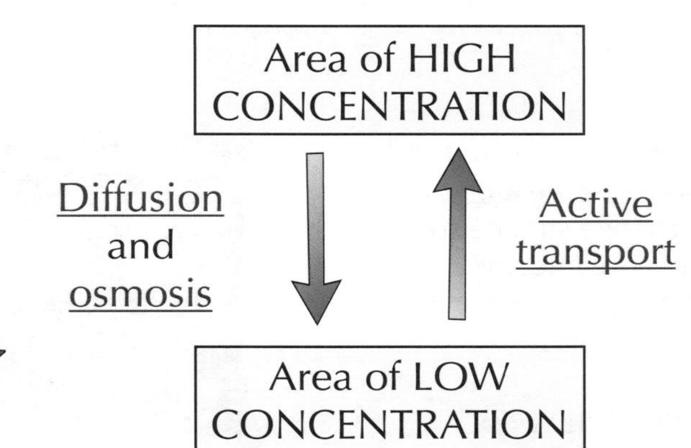

5) In life processes, the gases and dissolved substances have to move through some sort of exchange surface. The exchange surface structures have to allow enough of the necessary substances to pass through.

Exchange Surfaces are **Adapted** to **Maximise Effectiveness**

Exchange surfaces are adapted in the following ways:

1) They are thin, so substances only have a short distance to diffuse.
2) They have a large surface area so lots of a substance can diffuse at once.
3) Exchange surfaces in animals have lots of blood vessels, to get stuff into and out of the blood quickly.
4) Gas exchange surfaces in animals (e.g. alveoli, p.139) are often ventilated too — air moves in and out.

Exchanging substances gets more difficult in bigger and more complex organisms — the place where the substances are needed (or the waste is made) ends up being a long way away from exchange surfaces.

Gas and Solute Exchange

The **Structure of Leaves** Lets Gases **Diffuse** In and Out of Cells

Carbon dioxide diffuses into the air spaces within the leaf, then it diffuses into the cells where photosynthesis happens. The leaf's structure is adapted so that this can happen easily:

1) The underneath of the leaf is an exchange surface. It's covered in biddy little holes called stomata which the carbon dioxide diffuses in through.

2) Oxygen (produced in photosynthesis) and water vapour also diffuse out through the stomata. (Water vapour is actually lost from all over the leaf surface, but most of it is lost through the stomata.)

3) The size of the stomata are controlled by guard cells — see page 83. These close the stomata if the plant is losing water faster than it is being replaced by the roots. Without these guard cells the plant would soon wilt.

4) The flattened shape of the leaf increases the area of this exchange surface so that it's more effective.

5) The walls of the cells inside the leaf form another exchange surface. The air spaces inside the leaf increase the area of this surface so there's more chance for carbon dioxide to get into the cells.

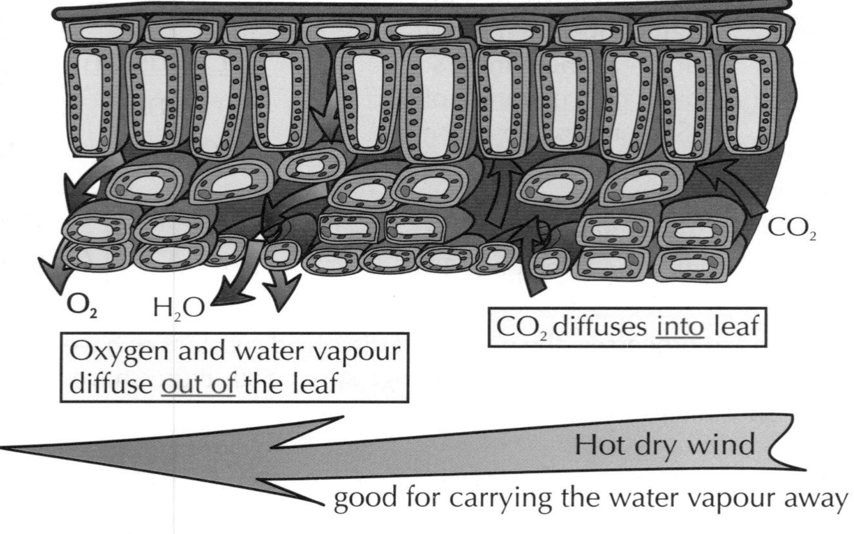

The water vapour evaporates from the cells inside the leaf. Then it escapes by diffusion because there's a lot of it inside the leaf and less of it in the air outside. Evaporation is quickest in hot, dry, windy conditions.

Interesting fact — stomata is the plural of stoma...

The cells on the stem of a cactus photosynthesise and have stomata-like holes to let gases in. The cacti don't want to lose much water, so the holes only open at night when it's cooler. The cacti are adapted so that they can store the CO_2 that diffuses in at night until daylight when it's used for photosynthesis.

The Breathing System

You need to get <u>oxygen</u> from the air into your bloodstream so that it can get to your cells for <u>respiration</u>. You also need to get rid of <u>carbon dioxide</u> in your blood. This all happens inside the <u>lungs</u>.

The Lungs Are in the **Thorax**

1) The <u>thorax</u> is the top part of your 'body'.
2) It's separated from the lower part of the body (the <u>abdomen</u>) by the <u>diaphragm</u>.
3) The lungs are like big pink <u>sponges</u> and are protected by the <u>ribcage</u>.
4) The air that you breathe in goes through the <u>trachea</u>. This splits into two tubes called '<u>bronchi</u>' (each one is 'a bronchus'), one going to each lung.
5) The bronchi split into progressively smaller tubes called <u>bronchioles</u>.
6) The bronchioles finally end at small bags called <u>alveoli</u> where the gas exchange takes place.

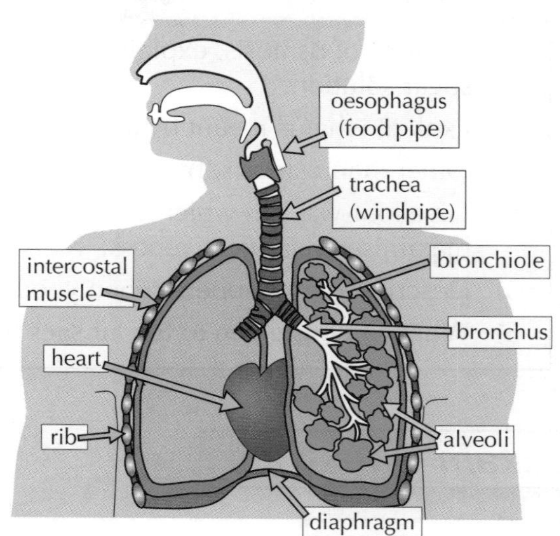

Ventilation is **Breathing In...**

1) <u>Intercostal muscles</u> and <u>diaphragm contract</u>.
2) Thorax volume <u>increases</u>.
3) This <u>decreases</u> the pressure, drawing air <u>in</u>.

air goes in

muscles between ribs pull ribcage and sternum up and out

sternum

in

in

ribcage

diaphragm flattens out

...and **Breathing Out**

1) <u>Intercostal muscles</u> and <u>diaphragm relax</u>.
2) Thorax volume <u>decreases</u>.
3) This <u>increases</u> the pressure, so air is forced <u>out</u>.

The fancy way of defining <u>ventilation</u> is "the movement of air into and out of the lungs". Remember, ventilation is different from <u>respiration</u> (p.105).

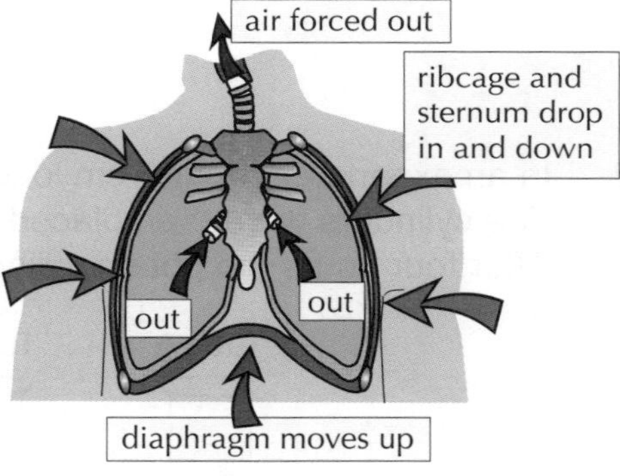

Artificial Ventilators Help People to **Breathe**

1) <u>Ventilators</u> are machines that move air (often with extra oxygen) <u>into</u> or <u>out of</u> the <u>lungs</u>. They help people who <u>can't breathe</u> by themselves, e.g. if they're under <u>general anaesthetic</u>, or have a <u>lung injury</u> or <u>disease</u>.
2) They used to be a <u>giant case</u> (an '<u>iron lung</u>') from the neck to the abdomen, with only the patient's head poking out. Air was <u>pumped out</u> of the case, pressure <u>dropped</u>, the lungs <u>expanded</u> and so air was <u>drawn into</u> the lungs. Air pumped <u>into</u> the case had the opposite effect, forcing air <u>out</u> of the lungs. However, they could interfere with <u>blood flow</u> to the lower body.
3) Nowadays, most ventilators work by <u>pumping air into</u> the lungs. This <u>expands</u> the ribcage — when they stop pumping, the ribcage <u>relaxes</u> and pushes air back <u>out</u> of the lungs. This <u>doesn't</u> interfere with blood flow, but it can occasionally cause <u>damage</u> (e.g. <u>burst alveoli</u>) if the lungs can't cope with the artificial air flow.

Warm-Up and Exam Questions

Question time again — warm-up first, then exam (or the other way round if you want to be different).

Warm-Up Questions

1) In terms of osmosis, explain what will happen if an animal cell is placed in a concentrated sugar solution.
2) Explain what is meant by a partially permeable membrane.
3) Other than osmosis, by what two processes do substances move across exchange surfaces?
4) Give four ways in which exchange surfaces in animals are adapted to maximise their effectiveness.
5) Describe what happens when you breathe out.
6) What name is given to the air sacs in the lungs where gas exchange happens?

Exam Questions

1 Our lungs allow us to breathe in and out.

(a) Describe the changes that take place in the thorax when breathing air into the lungs.

(4 marks)

Some people can't breathe on their own and have to use an artificial ventilator.

(b) How does an artificial ventilator work?

(2 marks)

(c) Give **one** potential disadvantage of using an artificial ventilator.

(1 mark)

2 In an experiment, four 5 cm long cylinders were cut from a fresh potato. The cylinders were then placed in different sugar solutions, as shown in the diagram. After four hours the potato cylinders were removed and measured.

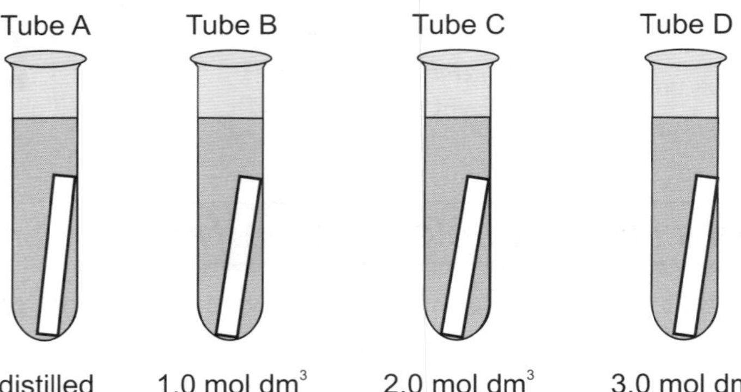

(a) Which potato cylinder would you expect to be shortest after four hours? Explain your answer.

(2 marks)

(b) The potato cylinder in tube A increased in length during the four hours. Explain why this happened.

(2 marks)

Diffusion Through Cell Membranes

This page is about how two different parts of the human body are adapted so that substances can diffuse through them most effectively. The first bit is about how gases in the lungs get into and out of the blood. The second is about how digested food gets from the gut to the blood.

Gas Exchange Happens in the Lungs

1) The job of the lungs is to transfer oxygen to the blood and to remove waste carbon dioxide from it.
2) To do this the lungs contain millions of little air sacs called alveoli where gas exchange takes place.

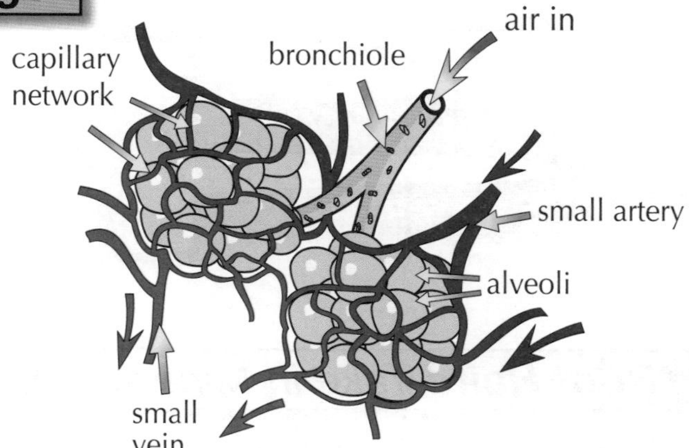

Blue = blood with carbon dioxide.
Red = blood with oxygen.

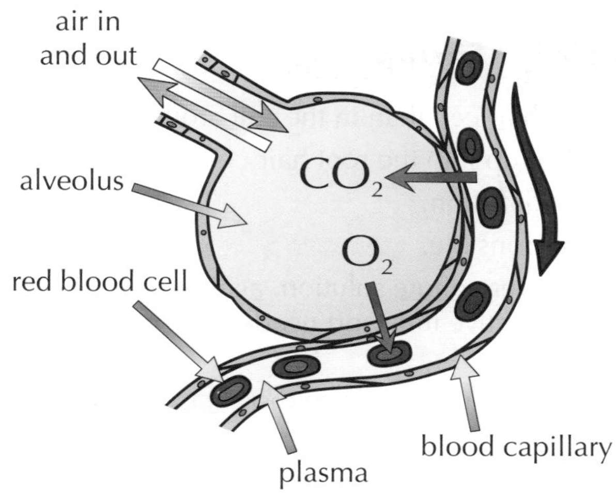

3) The alveoli are specialised to maximise the diffusion of oxygen and CO_2. They have:
   - An enormous surface area (about 75 m^2 in humans).
   - A moist lining for dissolving gases.
   - Very thin walls.
   - A good blood supply.

The Villi Provide a Really Big Surface Area

1) The inside of the small intestine is covered in millions and millions of these tiny little projections called villi.
2) They increase the surface area in a big way so that digested food is absorbed much more quickly into the blood.
3) Notice they have:
   - a single layer of surface cells
   - a very good blood supply to assist quick absorption.

The digested food moves into the blood by diffusion and by active transport *(see page 140)**.*

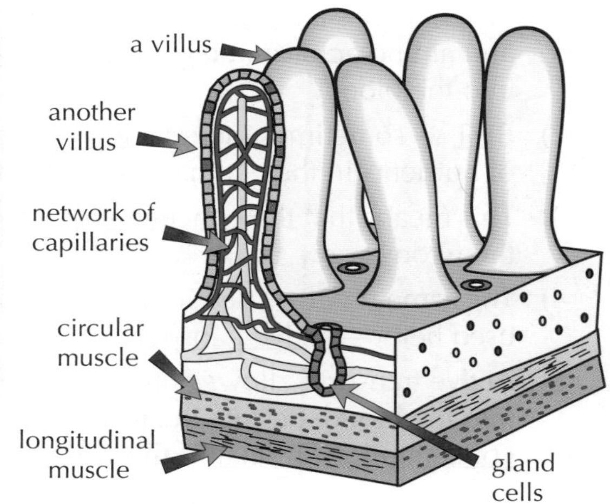

Alveoli and villi are both exchange surfaces

Living organisms are really well adapted for getting the substances they need to their cells. A large surface area is a key way that organisms' exchange surfaces are made more effective — molecules can only diffuse through a membrane when they're right next to it, and a large surface area means that a lot more molecules are close to the membrane.

Active Transport

Sometimes substances need to be absorbed against a concentration gradient, i.e. from a lower to a higher concentration. This process is referred to as active transport.

Root Hairs are Specialised for Absorbing Water and Minerals

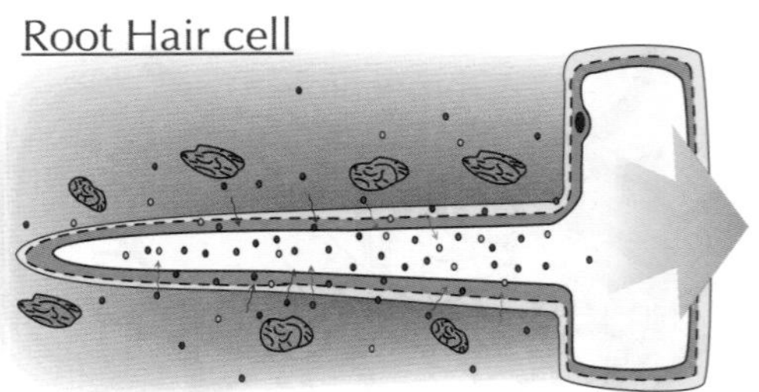

1) The cells on the surface of plant roots grow into long "hairs" which stick out into the soil.
2) This gives the plant a big surface area for absorbing water and mineral ions from the soil.
3) Most of the water and mineral ions that get into a plant are absorbed by the root hair cells.

Root Hairs Take in Minerals Using Active Transport

1) The concentration of minerals is usually higher in the root hair cell than in the soil around it.
2) So normal diffusion doesn't explain how minerals are taken up into the root hair cell.
3) They should go the other way if they followed the rules of diffusion.
4) The answer is that a process called "active transport" is responsible.
5) Active transport allows the plant to absorb minerals from a very dilute solution, against a concentration gradient. This is essential for its growth. But active transport needs energy from respiration to make it work.
6) Active transport also happens in humans, for example in taking glucose from the gut (see below), and from the kidney tubules.

We Need Active Transport to Stop Us Starving

Active transport is used in the gut when there is a low concentration of nutrients in the gut, but a high concentration of nutrients in the blood.

1) When there's a higher concentration of glucose and amino acids in the gut they diffuse naturally into the blood.
2) BUT — sometimes there's a lower concentration of nutrients in the gut than there is in the blood.
3) This means that the concentration gradient is the wrong way.
4) The same process used in plant roots is used here — active transport.
5) Active transport allows nutrients to be taken into the blood, despite the fact that the concentration gradient is the wrong way.

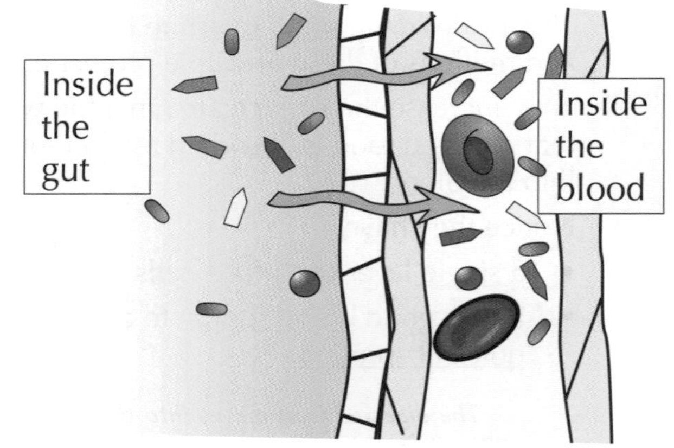

Active transport uses energy

An important difference between active transport and diffusion is that active transport uses energy. Imagine a pen of sheep in a field. If you open the pen, the sheep will happily diffuse from the area of high sheep concentration into the field, which has a low sheep concentration — you won't have to do a thing. To get them back in the pen though, you'll have to put in quite a bit of energy.

Water Flow Through Plants

Flowering plants have two separate types of vessel — xylem and phloem — for transporting stuff around. Both types of vessel go to every part of the plant, but they are totally separate.

Phloem Tubes Transport Food:

1) Made of columns of living cells with small holes in the ends to allow stuff to flow through.

2) They transport food substances (mainly dissolved sugars) made in the leaves to growing regions (e.g. new shoots) and storage organs (e.g. root tubers) of the plant.

3) The transport goes in both directions.

Xylem Tubes Take Water UP:

1) Made of dead cells joined end to end with no end walls between them and a hole down the middle.

2) They carry water and minerals from the roots to the stem and leaves in the transpiration stream (see page 142).

Xylem vessels carry water, phloem vessels carry sugars

You probably did that really dull experiment at school where you stick a piece of celery in a beaker of water with red food colouring in it. Then you stare at it for half an hour, and once the time is up, the red has reached the top of the celery. That's because it travelled there in the xylem.

Water Flow Through Plants

If you don't water a house plant for a few days it starts to go all droopy. Plants need water.

Transpiration is the Loss of Water from the Plant

1) Transpiration is caused by the evaporation and diffusion (see page 82) of water from inside the leaves.

2) This creates a slight shortage of water in the leaf, and so more water is drawn up from the rest of the plant through the xylem vessels to replace it.

3) This in turn means more water is drawn up from the roots, and so there's a constant transpiration stream of water through the plant.

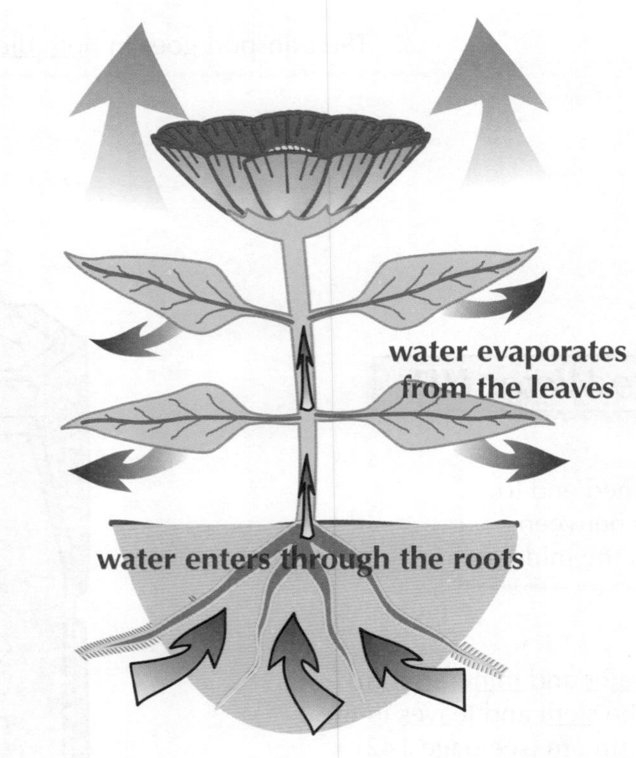

4) Transpiration is just a side-effect of the way leaves are adapted for photosynthesis. They have to have stomata in them so that gases can be exchanged easily. Because there's more water inside the plant than in the air outside, the water escapes from the leaves through the stomata.

Transpiration involves evaporation and diffusion

A big tree loses about a thousand litres of water from its leaves every single day — it's a fact. That's as much water as the average person drinks in a whole year, so the roots have to be very effective at drawing in water from the soil. Which is why they have all those root hairs, you see.

Warm-Up and Exam Questions

Right, I'm looking at five warm-up questions and two exam questions... better get cracking.

Warm-Up Questions

1) Name two exchange surfaces in humans.
2) If there's a low concentration of glucose in the gut and a high concentration in the blood, what process is used to absorb glucose into the blood?
3) For each of the transport systems, xylem and phloem, answer the following questions:
   (a) What substances does it transport?
   (b) From where and to where does it transport these substances?
4) Name the two processes involved in transpiration.
5) Where are the main places that a plant: (a) absorbs water? (b) loses water?

Exam Questions

1 The diagram shows a villus from the small intestine.
Glucose and other products of digestion are absorbed into the blood through the villi.

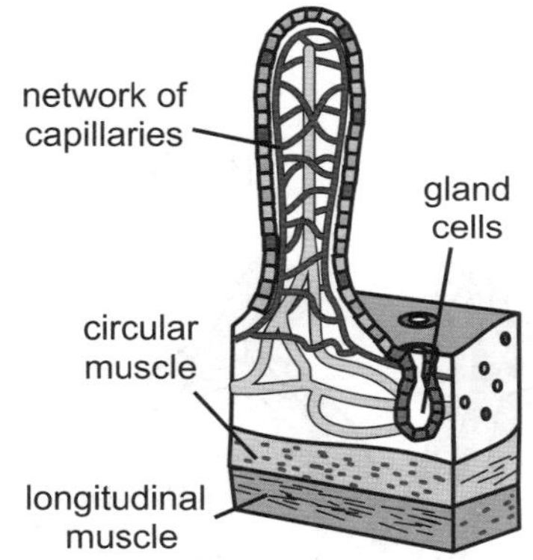

(a) Describe how the products of digestion move into the blood.

(2 marks)

(b) Explain, as fully as you can, how the structure of a villus is related to its function.

(3 marks)

2 The diagram shows a root hair cell.

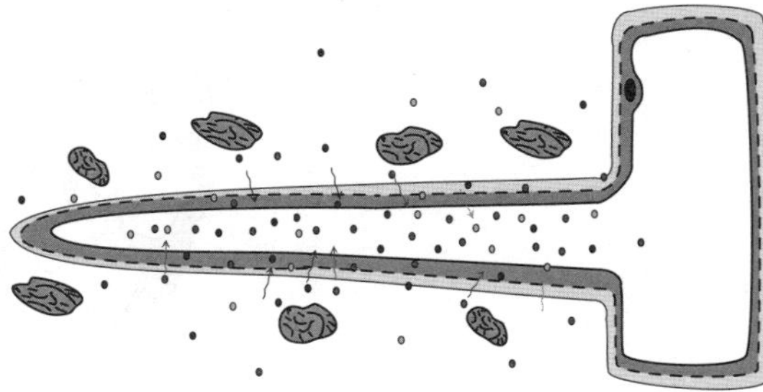

(a) Describe how the structure of a root hair cell is adapted to carry out its function.

(1 mark)

(b) Explain how mineral ions are absorbed into the root hair cell.

(3 marks)

Circulatory System — The Heart

The circulatory system's main function is to get food and oxygen to every cell in the body. As well as being a delivery service, it's also a waste collection service — it carries waste products like carbon dioxide and urea to where they can be removed from the body.

It's a DOUBLE Circulatory System

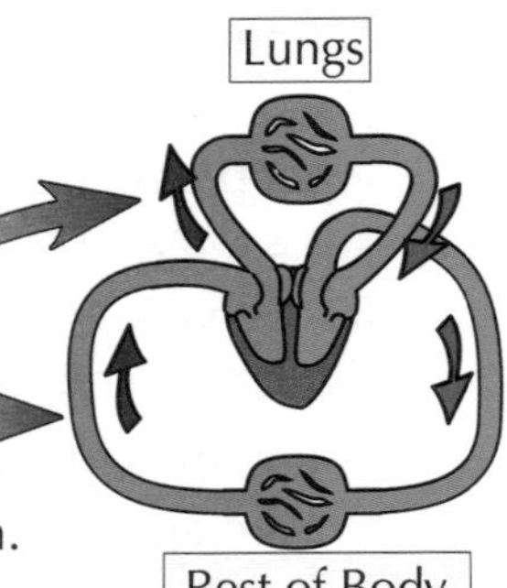

Humans have a double circulatory system — two circuits joined together:

1) The first one pumps deoxygenated blood (blood without oxygen) to the lungs to take in oxygen. The blood then returns to the heart.
2) The second one pumps oxygenated blood around all the other organs of the body. The blood gives up its oxygen at the body cells and the deoxygenated blood returns to the heart to be pumped out to the lungs again.

The Heart Contracts to Pump Blood Around The Body

1) The heart is a pumping organ that keeps the blood flowing around the body. The walls of the heart are mostly made of muscle tissue.
2) The heart has valves to make sure that blood goes in the right direction — they prevent it flowing backwards.
3) This is how the heart uses its four chambers (right atrium, right ventricle, left atrium and left ventricle) to pump blood around:

   1) Blood flows into the two atria from the vena cava and the pulmonary vein.
   2) The atria contract, pushing the blood into the ventricles.
   3) The ventricles contract, forcing the blood into the pulmonary artery and the aorta, and out of the heart.
   4) The blood then flows to the organs through arteries (see p.145), and returns through veins (see p.146).
   5) The atria fill again and the whole cycle starts over.

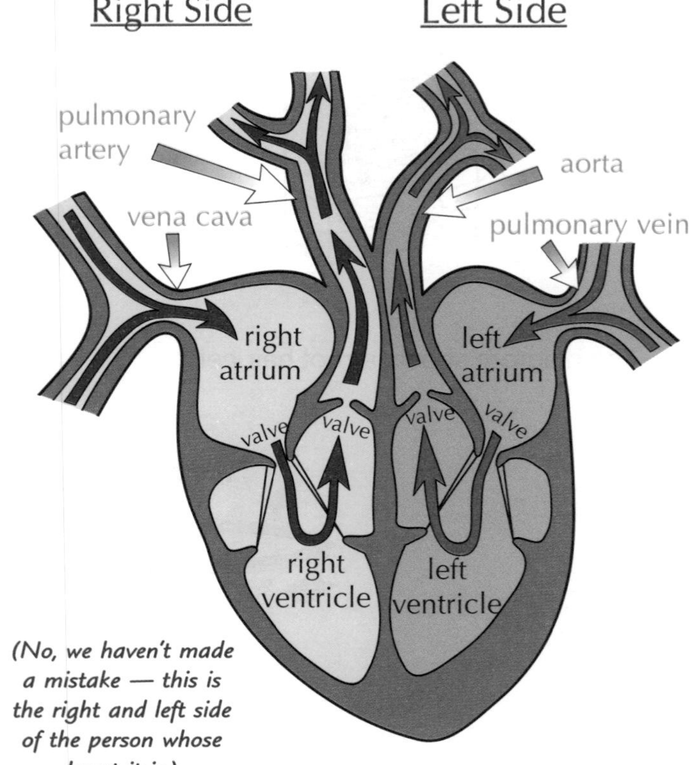

(No, we haven't made a mistake — this is the right and left side of the person whose heart it is.)

The heart has valves to prevent blood flowing backwards

The human heart beats 100 000 times a day on average. You can feel a pulse in your wrist or neck (where the vessels are close to the surface). This is the blood being pushed along by another beat. Doctors use a stethoscope to listen to your heart — it's actually the valves closing that they hear.

Circulatory System — Blood Vessels

Blood is pumped around the body in different types of blood vessels.

Blood Vessels are Designed for Their Function

There are three different types of blood vessel:

1) ARTERIES — these carry the blood away from the heart.

2) CAPILLARIES — these are involved in the exchange of materials at the tissues.

3) VEINS — these carry the blood to the heart.

Arteries Carry Blood Under Pressure

1) The heart pumps the blood out at high pressure so the artery walls are strong and elastic.

2) The walls are thick compared to the size of the hole down the middle (the "lumen").

3) They contain thick layers of muscle to make them strong, and elastic fibres to allow them to stretch and spring back.

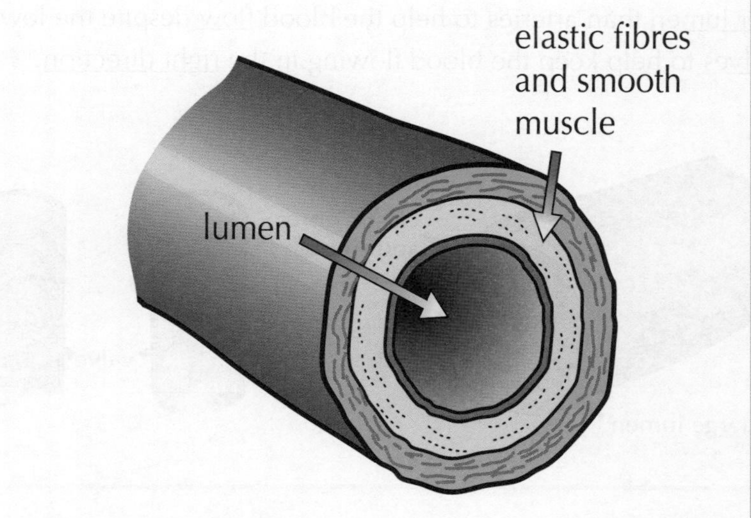

ARTERIES carry blood AWAY from the heart...

... you need to remember that. You also need to remember that their walls are made of thick muscle and are elastic to withstand the high pressure of the blood being pumped out of the heart.

Circulatory System — Blood Vessels

This page is about the other two types of blood vessel — capillaries and veins.

Capillaries are Really Small

1) Arteries branch into capillaries.
2) Capillaries are really tiny — too small to see.
3) They carry the blood really close to every cell in the body to exchange substances with them.
4) They have permeable walls, so substances can diffuse in and out.
5) They supply food and oxygen, and take away waste like CO_2.
6) Their walls are usually only one cell thick. This increases the rate of diffusion by decreasing the distance over which it occurs.

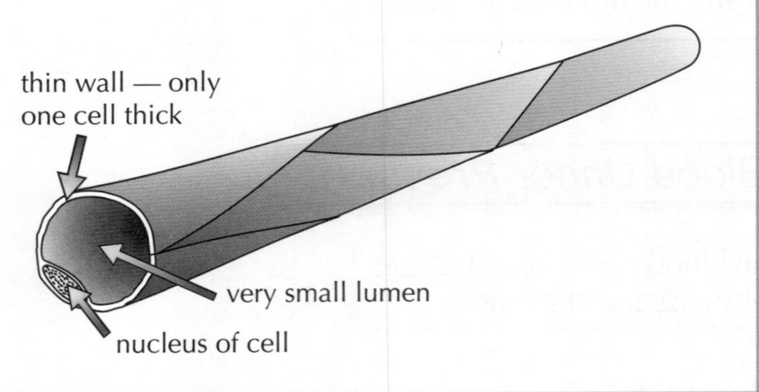

Veins Take Blood Back to the Heart

1) Capillaries eventually join up to form veins.
2) The blood is at lower pressure in the veins so the walls don't need to be as thick as artery walls.
3) They have a bigger lumen than arteries to help the blood flow despite the lower pressure.
4) They also have valves to help keep the blood flowing in the right direction.

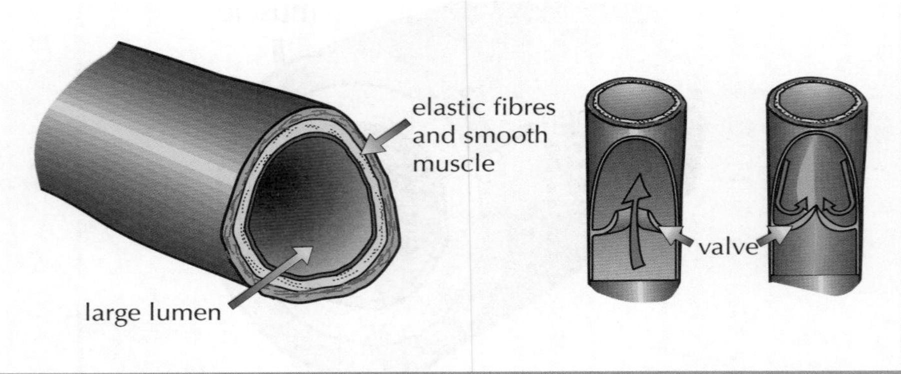

Make sure you know the features of arteries, capillaries and veins

Here's an interesting fact for you — your body contains about 60 000 miles of blood vessels. That's about six times the distance from London to Sydney in Australia. Of course, capillaries are really tiny, which is how there can be such a big length — they can only be seen with a microscope.

Circulatory System — The Blood

Blood is a tissue. It's part of a huge transport system. There are four main things in blood...

Red Blood Cells Carry Oxygen

1) The job of red blood cells is to carry oxygen from the lungs to all the cells in the body.
2) They have a biconcave shape to give a large surface area for absorbing oxygen.
3) They don't have a nucleus — this allows more room to carry oxygen.
4) They contain a red pigment called haemoglobin.
5) In the lungs, haemoglobin combines with oxygen to become oxyhaemoglobin. In body tissues, the reverse happens — oxyhaemoglobin splits up into haemoglobin and oxygen, to release oxygen to the cells.

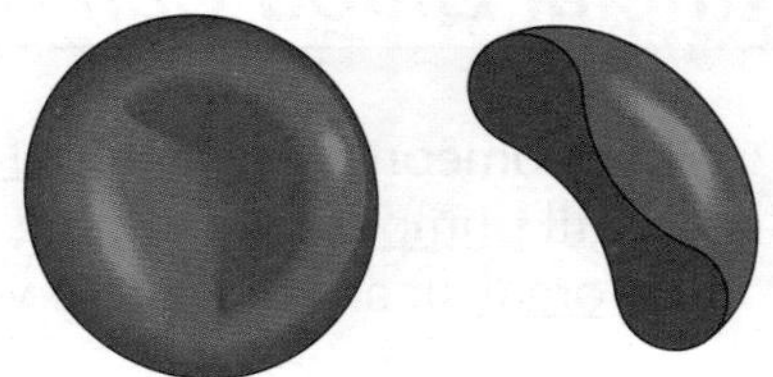

The more red blood cells you've got, the more oxygen can get to your cells. At high altitudes there's less oxygen in the air — so people who live there produce more red blood cells to compensate.

White Blood Cells Defend Against Disease

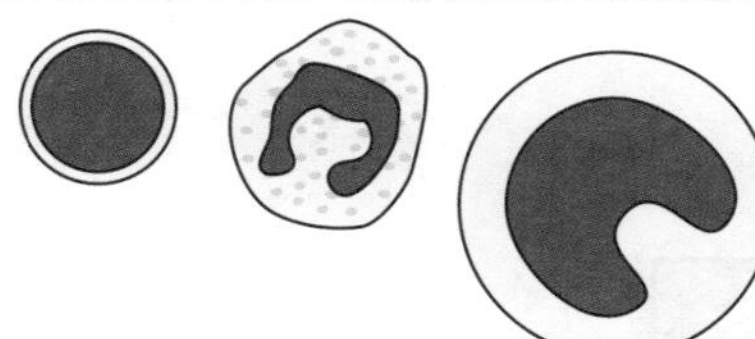

1) They can change shape to engulf unwelcome microorganisms.
2) They produce antibodies to fight microorganisms, as well as antitoxins to neutralise any toxins produced by the microorganisms.
3) Unlike red blood cells, they do have a nucleus.

Platelets Help Blood Clot

1) These are small fragments of cells. They have no nucleus.
2) They help the blood to clot at a wound — to stop all your blood pouring out and to stop microorganisms getting in.
3) Lack of platelets can cause excessive bleeding and bruising.

Plasma is the Liquid That Carries Everything in Blood

This is a pale straw-coloured liquid which carries just about everything:

1) Red and white blood cells and platelets.
2) Nutrients like glucose and amino acids. These are the soluble products of digestion which are absorbed from the gut and taken to the cells of the body.
3) Carbon dioxide from the organs to the lungs.
4) Urea from the liver to the kidneys.
5) Hormones.
6) Antibodies and antitoxins produced by the white blood cells.

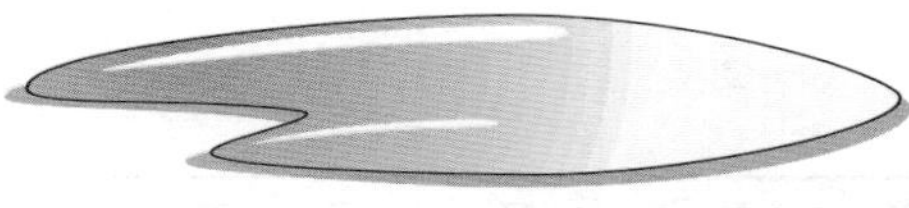

Blood — red blood cells, white blood cells, platelets and plasma

When you're ill the doctor often takes a blood sample for analysis. Blood tests can be used to diagnose loads of things — not just disorders of the blood. This is because the blood transports so many chemicals produced by so many organs... and it's easy to take a sample of blood.

Circulation Aids

This page is about artificial blood, artificial hearts and artificial heart valves — all life-saving things.

Artificial Blood Can Keep You Alive In An Emergency

1) When someone loses a lot of blood, e.g. in an accident, their heart can still pump the remaining red blood cells around (to get oxygen to their organs), as long as the volume of their blood can be topped up.

2) Artificial blood is a blood substitute, e.g. a salt solution ("saline"), which is used to replace the lost volume of blood. It's safe (if no air bubbles get into the blood) and can keep people alive even if they lose 2/3 of their red blood cells. This may give the patient enough time to produce new blood cells. If not, the patient will need a blood transfusion.

3) Ideally, an artificial blood product would replace the function of the red blood cells, so that there's no need for a blood transfusion. These are being developed but currently have problems with side-effects.

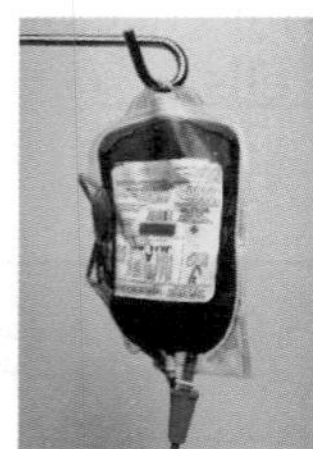

An artificial blood product that carries oxygen would replace the need for a blood transfusion from another person. This would have advantages such as decreasing the risk of diseases being passed on.

The Heart Can Be Replaced With Artificial Parts

1) Artificial hearts are mechanical devices that are put into a person to pump blood if their own heart fails. They're usually used as a temporary fix, to keep a person alive until a donor heart can be found. In some cases they're used as a permanent fix, which reduces the need for a donor heart.

2) The main advantage of artificial hearts is that they're not rejected by the body's immune system. This is because they're made from metals or plastics, so the body doesn't recognise them as 'foreign' and attack in the same way as it does with living tissue.

3) But surgery to fit an artificial heart can lead to bleeding and infection. Also, artificial hearts don't work as well as healthy natural ones — parts of the heart could wear out or the electrical motor could fail. Blood doesn't flow through artificial hearts as smoothly, which can cause blood clots and lead to strokes. The patient has to take drugs to thin their blood and make sure this doesn't happen, which can cause problems with bleeding if they're hurt in an accident.

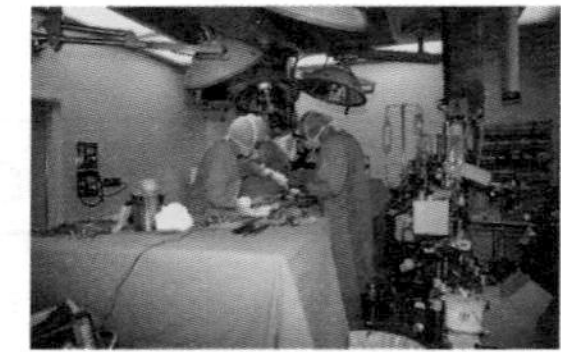

Replacing a person's heart with an artificial one is major surgery, which has risks.

The Heart Can Be Repaired With Artificial Valves

1) If it's just the heart valves (p.144) that are defective, they can be replaced with mechanical valves.
2) Replacing a valve is a much less drastic procedure than a whole heart transplant.
3) However, fitting artificial valves is still major surgery and there can still be problems with blood clots.

Circulation Aids

Stents (tiny tube things that keep arteries open) are another life-saving invention.

Coronary Heart Disease is Life-Threatening

Coronary heart disease is when the arteries that supply the blood to the muscle of the heart get blocked by fatty deposits.

This causes the arteries to become narrow and blood flow is restricted — this can result in a heart attack.

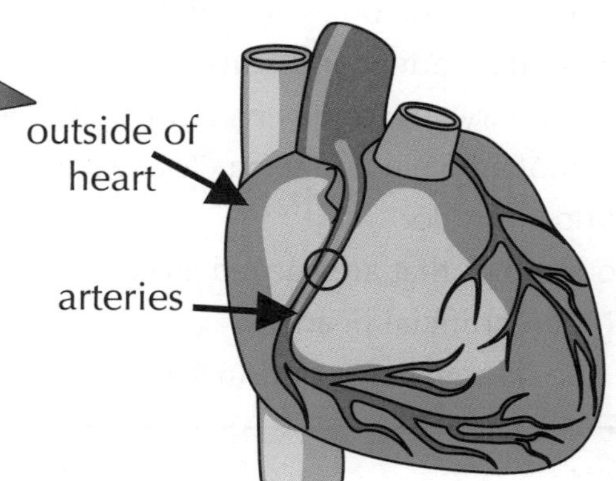

Stents Keep Arteries Open

1) Stents are tubes that are inserted inside arteries. They keep them open, making sure blood can pass through to the heart muscles. This keeps the person's heart beating (and the person alive).

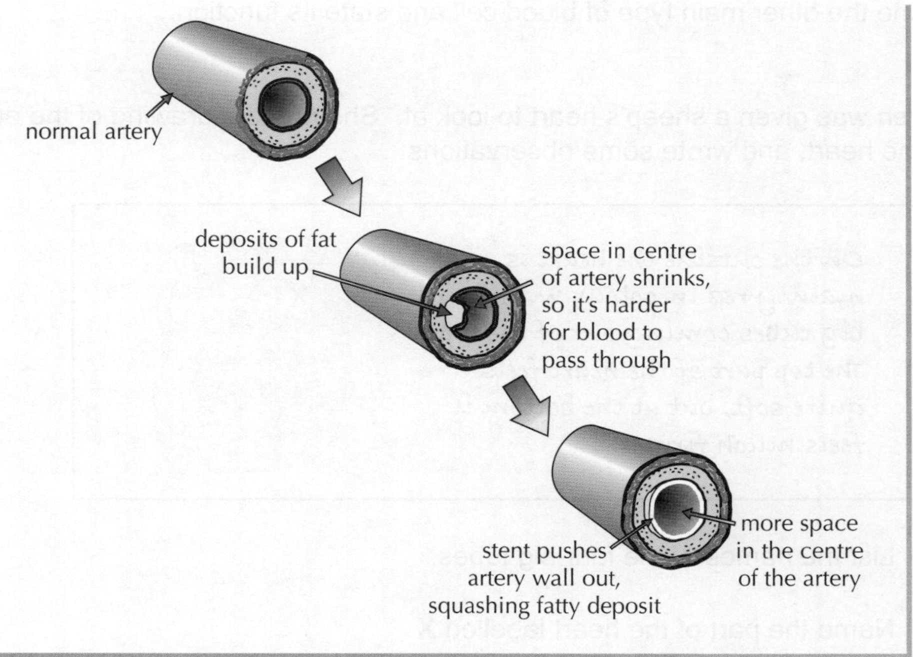

2) Stents are a way of lowering the risk of a heart attack in people with coronary heart disease.
3) But over time, the artery can narrow again as stents can irritate the artery and make scar tissue grow. The patient also has to take drugs to stop blood clotting on the stent.

You need to know the pros and cons...

In your exam they may ask you to consider the advantages and disadvantages of artificial blood, artificial hearts, artificial valves, and stents. Obviously, if you're really ill, you're not going to turn down any of these treatments — but they're certainly not perfect.

Warm-Up and Exam Questions

Hopefully I've persuaded you by now that it's a good idea to try these questions. So off you go...

Warm-Up Questions

1) From the following options, which one correctly describes the flow of blood through the heart?
   A pulmonary artery and aorta, atria, ventricles, pulmonary vein and vena cava
   B pulmonary vein and vena cava, ventricles, atria, pulmonary artery and aorta
   C pulmonary vein and vena cava, atria, ventricles, pulmonary artery and aorta
2) What do veins do?
3) List four things that are carried around the body in the blood plasma.
4) What is an artificial heart?
5) Give one disadvantage of using stents.

Exam Questions

1 Red blood cells carry oxygen around the body.

(a) Describe **three** ways in which red blood cells are adapted for carrying out their function.

(3 marks)

(b) Name the other main type of blood cell and state its function.

(2 marks)

2 (a) Karen was given a sheep's heart to look at. She made a drawing of the outside of the heart, and wrote some observations.

On the outside the heart is mainly red in colour, with four big tubes coming out of the top. The top part of the heart feels quite soft, but at the bottom it feels much firmer.

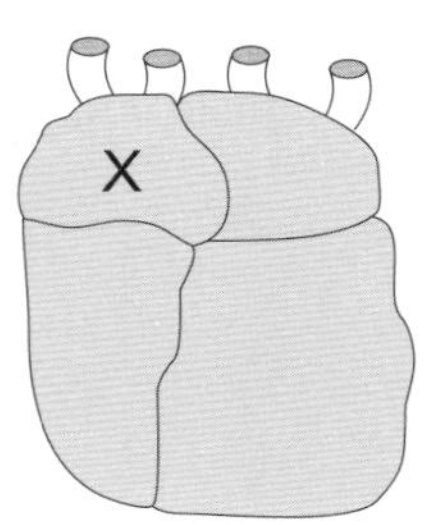

(i) List the names of the four big tubes.

(4 marks)

(ii) Name the part of the heart labelled **X**.

(1 mark)

(b) Karen then dissected the heart. Inside she found the heart chambers, and some flaps between the chambers.

(i) How many heart chambers would you expect her to find?

(1 mark)

(ii) What were the flaps she found between the chambers?

(1 mark)

(iii) What is their function?

(1 mark)

Homeostasis

Homeostasis is a fancy word. It covers lots of things, so I guess it has to be. Homeostasis covers all the functions of your body which try to maintain a "constant internal environment". Learn that definition:

HOMEOSTASIS is the maintenance of a constant internal environment.

There Are *Six* Main Things That Need to Be *Controlled*

The first four are all things you need, but at just the right level — not too much and not too little.

1) The body temperature can't get too hot or too cold (see below).

2) Water content mustn't get too high or low, or too much water could move into or out of cells and damage them. There's more on controlling water content on page 154.

3) If the ion content of the body is wrong, the same thing could happen. See page 153.

4) The blood sugar level needs to stay within certain limits (see page 160).

The last two are waste products — they're constantly produced in the body and you need to get rid of them.

5) Carbon dioxide is a product of respiration. It's toxic in high quantities so it's got to be removed. It leaves the body by the lungs when you breathe out.

6) Urea is a waste product made from excess amino acids. There's more about it on page 153.

Body Temperature Must Be Carefully Controlled

All enzymes work best at a certain temperature (see page 101). The enzymes within the human body work best at about 37 °C. If the body gets too hot or too cold, the enzymes won't work properly and some really important reactions could be disrupted. In extreme cases, this can even lead to death.

The next page is all about how the human body controls temperature.

Homeostasis

Body Temperature is kept at About 37 °C

1) There is a thermoregulatory centre in the brain which acts as your own personal thermostat.
2) It contains receptors that are sensitive to the temperature of the blood flowing through the brain.
3) The thermoregulatory centre also receives impulses from the skin, giving info about skin temperature.
4) If you're getting too hot or too cold, your body can respond to try and cool you down or warm you up:

When you're TOO HOT:

1) Hairs lie flat.

2) Sweat is produced by sweat glands and evaporates from the skin, which removes heat.

3) The blood vessels supplying the skin dilate so more blood flows close to the surface of the skin. This makes it easier for heat to be transferred from the blood to the environment.

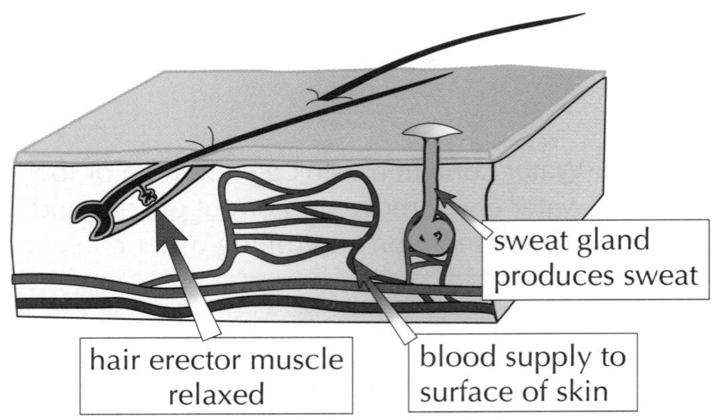

When you're TOO COLD:

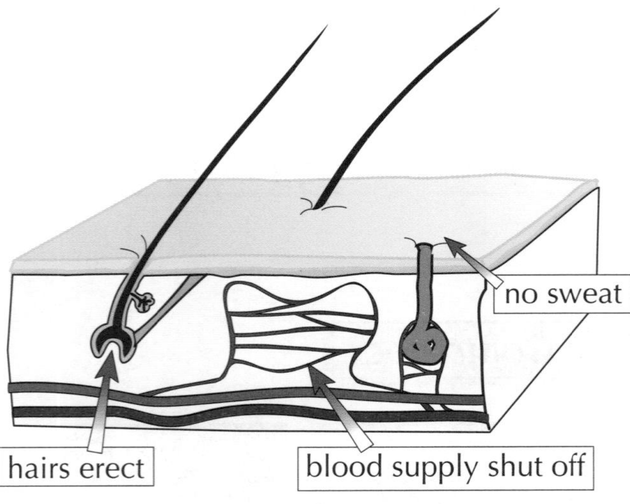

1) Hairs stand up to trap an insulating layer of air.

2) No sweat is produced.

3) Blood vessels supplying skin capillaries constrict to close off the skin's blood supply.

When you're cold you shiver too (your muscles contract automatically). This needs respiration, which releases some energy to warm the body.

Goose bumps — the result of hairs standing up when you're cold

People who are exposed to extreme cold for long time periods without protection can get frostbite — the blood supply to the fingers and toes is cut off to save heat (this kills the cells, so they go black).

The Kidneys and Homeostasis

The kidneys are really important in homeostasis — they control the content of the blood.

Kidneys Basically Act as Filters to "Clean the Blood"

The kidneys perform three main roles:

1) Removal of urea from the blood.

2) Adjustment of ions in the blood.

3) Adjustment of water content of the blood.

1) Removal of Urea

1) Proteins can't be stored by the body — so any excess amino acids are converted into fats and carbohydrates, which can be stored.
2) This process occurs in the liver. Urea is produced as a waste product from the reactions.
3) Urea is poisonous. It's released into the bloodstream by the liver. The kidneys then filter it out of the blood. It's temporarily stored in the bladder in urine and excreted from the body.

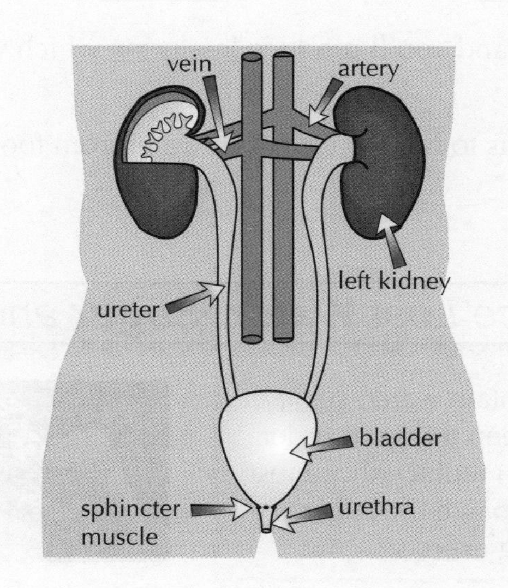

2) Adjustment of Ion Content

1) Ions such as sodium are taken into the body in food, and then absorbed into the blood.
2) If the ion (or water) content of the body is wrong, this could upset the balance between ions and water, meaning too much or too little water is drawn into cells by osmosis (see page 133). Having the wrong amount of water can damage cells or mean they don't work as well as normal.
3) Excess ions are removed by the kidneys. For example, a salty meal will contain far too much sodium and so the kidneys will remove the excess sodium ions from the blood.
4) Some ions are also lost in sweat (which tastes salty, you may have noticed).
5) But the important thing to remember is that the balance is always maintained by the kidneys.

The Kidneys and Homeostasis

Urine contains water as well as urea and ions, to help keep the balance right in the body.

3) Adjustment of *Water Content*

Water is taken into the body as food and drink and is lost from the body in three main ways:

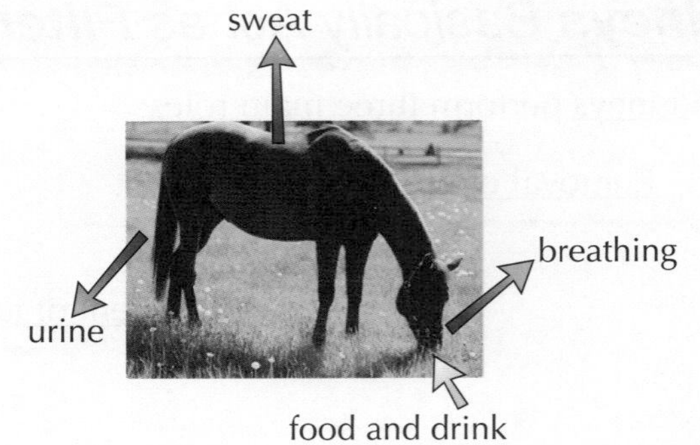

1) In urine
2) In sweat
3) In the air we breathe out.

The body has to constantly balance the water coming in against the water going out. Our bodies can't control how much we lose in our breath, but we do control the other factors. This means the water balance is between:

1) Liquids consumed
2) Amount sweated out
3) Amount excreted by the kidneys in the urine.

On a cold day, if you don't sweat, you'll produce more urine which will be pale and dilute.

On a hot day, you sweat a lot, and you'll produce less urine which will be dark-coloured and concentrated.

The water lost when it is hot has to be replaced with water from food and drink to restore the balance.

Sports Drinks Replace Lost *Water*, *Sugar* and *Ions*

Sports drinks (which usually contain water, sugar and ions) can help your body keep things in order. The water and ions (e.g. sodium) replace those lost in sweat, while the sugar can replace the sugar that's used up by muscles during exercise.

Some sports drink manufacturers claim that their products will rehydrate you faster than plain water, or improve your endurance (how long you can keep exercising for). To judge whether you can believe claims like these or not, you need to watch out for all the same things as with other health claims — so make sure you look again at page 22.

Adjusting water content involves blood, sweat and urine

Scientists have made a machine which does the same job as the kidneys — a kidney dialysis machine. People with kidney failure have to use it for 3-4 hours, three times a week, which makes life difficult as it can't be carried around. More on kidney failure and dialysis is coming up after some questions...

Warm-Up and Exam Questions

Without a good warm-up you're likely to strain a brain cell or two. So take the time to run through these simple questions and get the basic facts straight before plunging into the exam questions.

Warm-Up Questions

1) Name two waste products produced in the body that need to be removed.
2) Name the part of the brain that controls body temperature.
3) Describe two ways that the brain monitors body temperature.
4) Describe three ways in which the body responds to a rise in temperature.
5) State the three main functions of the kidneys.

Exam Questions

1 The diagram shows the human urinary system.

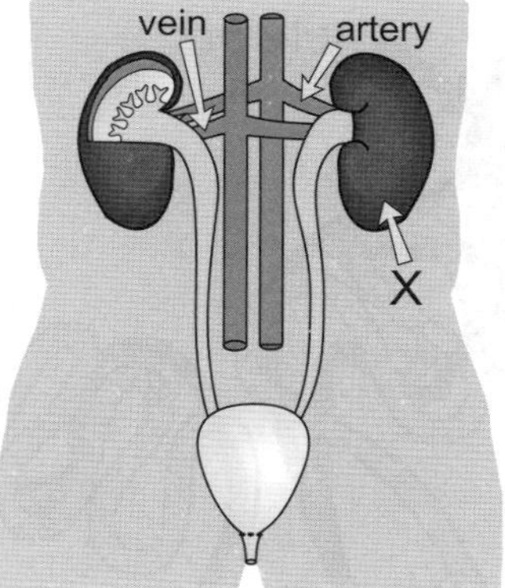

(a) Name the structure labelled X.

(1 mark)

(b) What is the function of the bladder?

(1 mark)

2 Describe **three** ways in which the body responds to a drop in temperature.

(3 marks)

3 If someone's kidneys fail they may be given a kidney transplant, or they can use a dialysis machine. A dialysis machine does the job of the kidneys and filters the blood.

(a) What **three** substances would you expect a dialysis machine to remove from the blood?

(1 mark)

(b) Suggest a reason why people with kidney failure are often advised to eat low-salt diets.

(2 marks)

4 One of the substances that sports drinks contain is water.
Give **two** other substances that sports drinks contain.
For each of these substances, explain why they are present in sports drinks.

(4 marks)

Kidney Function

In case you've forgotten since page 153, the kidneys get rid of toxic waste like urea as well as adjusting the amount of dissolved ions and water in the blood. Here's the rest of the stuff you need to know.

Nephrons Are the Filtration Units in the Kidneys

1) Ultrafiltration:

1) A high pressure is built up which squeezes water, urea, ions and sugar out of the blood and into the Bowman's capsule.
2) The membranes between the blood vessels and the Bowman's capsule act like filters, so big molecules like proteins and blood cells are not squeezed out. They stay in the blood.

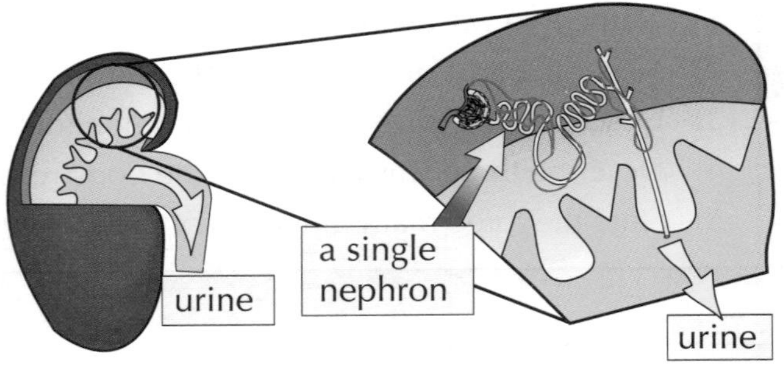

Enlarged View of a Single Nephron

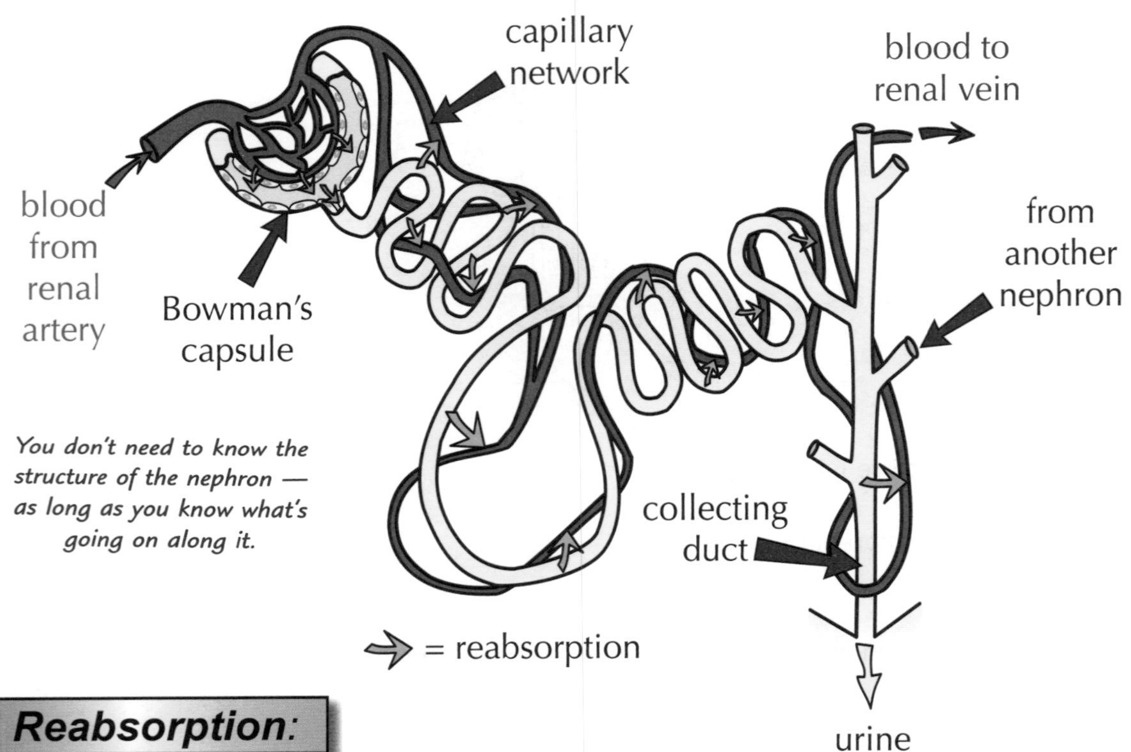

You don't need to know the structure of the nephron — as long as you know what's going on along it.

2) Reabsorption:

As the liquid flows along the nephron, useful substances are reabsorbed back into the blood:

1) All the sugar is reabsorbed. This involves the process of active transport against the concentration gradient.
2) Sufficient ions are reabsorbed. Excess ions are not. Active transport is needed.
3) Sufficient water is reabsorbed.

3) Release of wastes:

The remaining substances (including urea) continue out of the nephron, into the ureter and down to the bladder as urine.

Each kidney contains about one million nephrons

The kidneys are pretty complicated organs as you can see. Luckily you don't have to learn all the ins and outs of the diagram — but you do have to make sure you know exactly what happens in each of the three stages. Learn what's filtered, what's reabsorbed and what's released as urine.

Kidney Failure

If someone's kidneys stop working, there are basically two treatments — regular dialysis or a transplant.

The Kidneys Remove **Waste Substances** from the Blood

1) If the kidneys don't work properly, waste substances build up in the blood and you lose your ability to control the levels of ions and water in your body. Eventually, this results in death.

2) People with kidney failure can be kept alive by having dialysis treatment — where machines do the job of the kidneys. Or they can have a kidney transplant.

The kidneys are incredibly important — if they don't work as they should, you can get problems in the heart, bones, nervous system, stomach, mouth, etc.

Dialysis Machines **Filter** the Blood

1) Dialysis has to be done regularly to keep the concentrations of dissolved substances in the blood at normal levels, and to remove waste substances.

2) In a dialysis machine the person's blood flows alongside a selectively permeable barrier, surrounded by dialysis fluid. It's permeable to things like ions and waste substances, but not big molecules like proteins (just like the membranes in the kidney).

3) The dialysis fluid has the same concentration of dissolved ions and glucose as healthy blood.

4) This means that useful dissolved ions and glucose won't be lost from the blood during dialysis.

5) Only waste substances (such as urea) and excess ions and water diffuse across the barrier.

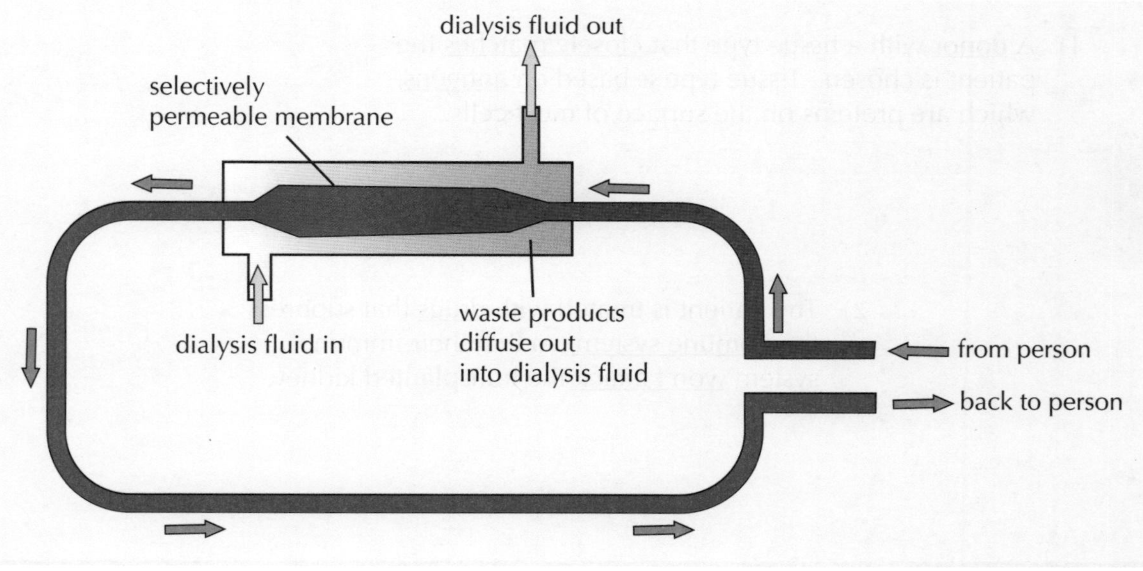

6) Many patients with kidney failure have to have a dialysis session three times a week. Each session takes 3-4 hours — not much fun.

7) Plus, dialysis may cause blood clots or infections.

Kidney Failure

Getting a kidney transplant sounds like the ideal treatment for kidney failure — but it's not that simple.

Transplanted Organs can be Rejected by the Body

1) At the moment, the only cure for kidney disease is to have a kidney transplant.

2) Healthy kidneys are usually transplanted from people who have died suddenly, say in a car accident, and who are on the organ donor register or carry a donor card (provided their relatives give the go-ahead).

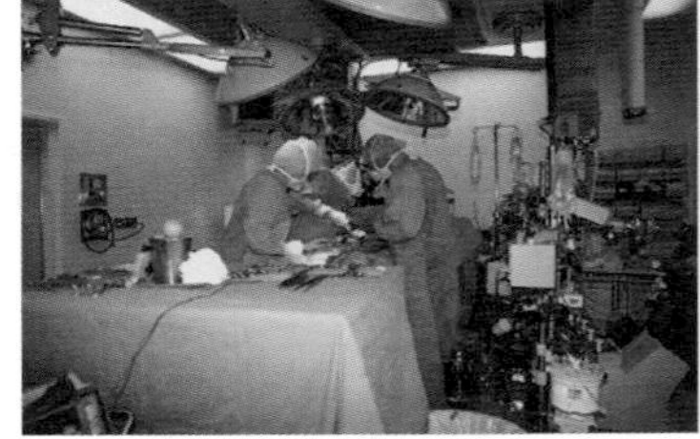

The first successful kidney transplant was carried out in 1954.

3) But kidneys can also be transplanted from people who are still alive — as we all have two of them.

The donor kidney can be rejected by the patient's immune system — the foreign antigens (see page 25) on the donor kidney are attacked by the patient's antibodies.
To help prevent this happening, precautions are taken:

1) A donor with a tissue type that closely matches the patient is chosen. Tissue type is based on antigens, which are proteins on the surface of most cells.

2) The patient is treated with drugs that suppress the immune system, so that their immune system won't attack the transplanted kidney.

Dialysis or transplant — both have their downsides...

Kidney dialysis machines are expensive things for the NHS to run — and dialysis is not a pleasant experience. Transplants are cheaper and can put an end to the hours spent on dialysis, but there are long waiting lists for kidneys. Even if one with a matching tissue type is found, there's the possibility that it'll be rejected. And taking drugs that suppress the immune system means the person is vulnerable to other illnesses.

Warm-Up and Exam Questions

Just a few simple warm-up questions and a few slightly harder exam questions stand between you and controlling blood glucose...

Warm-Up Questions

1) What is a nephron?
2) Explain what happens if a person's kidneys don't work properly.
3) Roughly how often does kidney dialysis have to be carried out?
4) Give two precautions that are taken to prevent the rejection of a transplanted kidney.

Exam Questions

1 The table shows the concentrations of some different substances in the fluid inside a nephron of a kidney — in the Bowman's capsule, and in the collecting duct.

Substance	Conc. in Bowman's capsule (g/100 ml)	Conc. in urine (g/100 ml)
water	99	96
protein	0	0
glucose	0.10	0
urea	0.04	2.0
salt	0.70	0.30

Explain why the liquid in the Bowman's capsule does not contain any proteins.

(2 marks)

2 Mary has kidney failure. She has dialysis three times a week.

(a) (i) Explain how the dialysis machine removes urea from Mary's blood.

(2 marks)

(ii) Explain why Mary does not lose glucose from her blood during dialysis.

(2 marks)

(b) Mary is hoping that she will soon have a kidney transplant.

(i) Suggest **one** reason why this form of treatment may be preferable to dialysis.

(1 mark)

(ii) One disadvantage of a kidney transplant is that the donor kidney can be rejected by the body. Explain why this is.

(1 mark)

3 *In this question you will be assessed on the quality of your English, the organisation of your ideas and your use of appropriate specialist vocabulary.*

Our kidneys produce urine. Describe the stages involved in the production of urine and explain what happens at each stage.

(6 marks)

Controlling Blood Glucose

Blood sugar is also controlled as part of homeostasis. Insulin and glucagon are hormones that control how much sugar there is in your blood. Learn how they do it:

Insulin and *Glucagon* Control *Blood Glucose* Level

1) Eating foods containing carbohydrate puts glucose (a type of sugar) into the blood from the gut.
2) The normal metabolism of cells removes glucose from the blood.
3) Vigorous exercise removes much more glucose from the blood.
4) Levels of glucose in the blood must be kept steady. Changes in blood glucose are monitored and controlled by the pancreas, using the hormones insulin and glucagon, as shown:

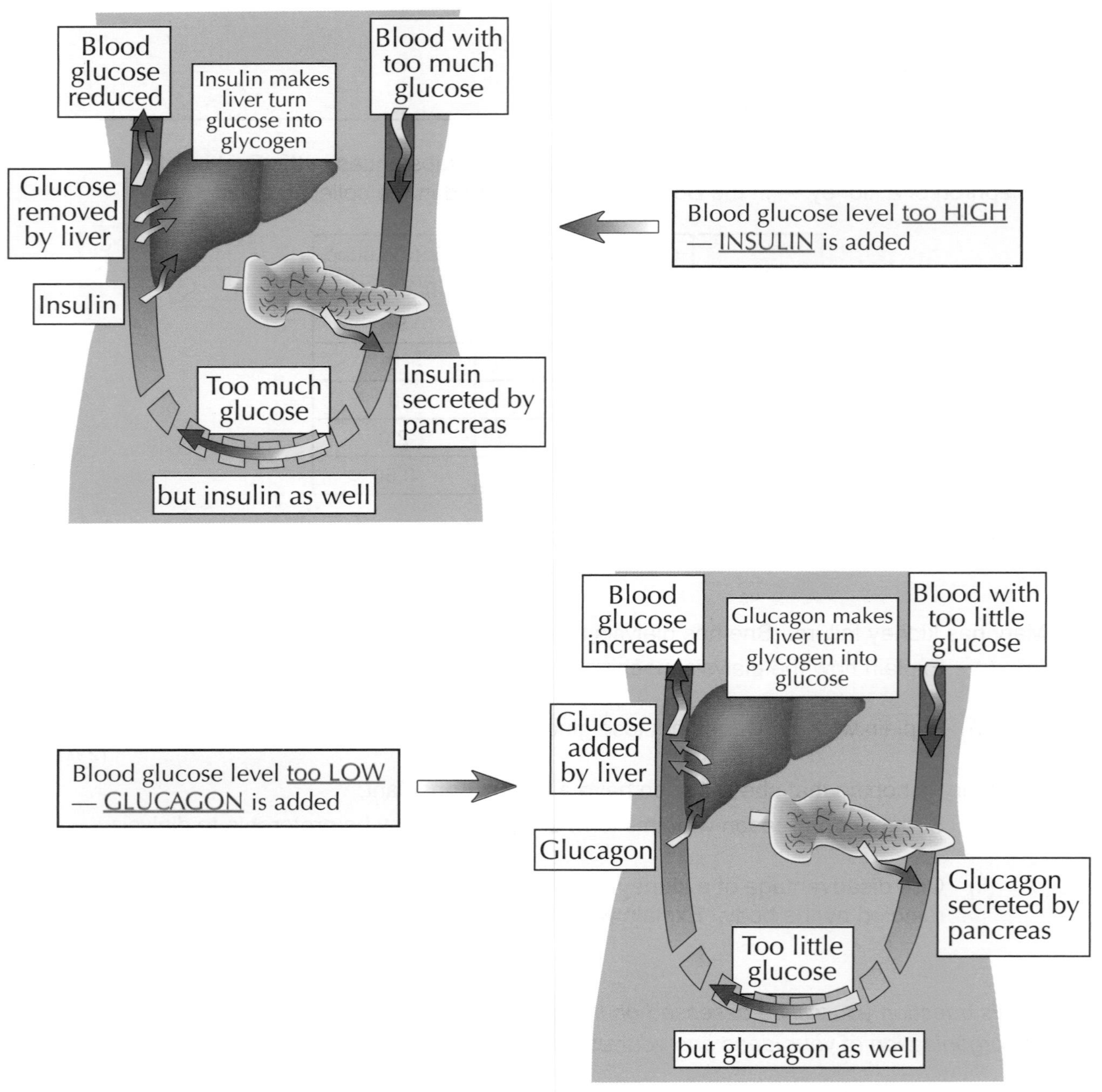

So now you know what your pancreas is for...

Learn these two diagrams and you shouldn't have any problems answering questions about how blood sugar is controlled. Don't forget that only carbohydrate foods put the blood sugar level up.

Controlling Blood Glucose

The system described on the last page shows how insulin and glucagon control the blood glucose level. In people who suffer from diabetes this system does not function properly.

Type 1 Diabetes — Caused by a Lack of Insulin

1) Type 1 diabetes is a condition where the pancreas produces little or no insulin.
2) The result is that a person's blood glucose can rise to a level that can kill them.
3) The problem can be controlled in two ways:

Remember, insulin reduces blood glucose level.

Method 1: Avoiding foods rich in simple carbohydrates
i.e. sugars

The digestion of simple carbohydrates causes glucose levels to rise rapidly.

It can also be helpful to take exercise after eating to try and use up the extra glucose produced during digestion — but this isn't usually very practical.

Method 2: Injecting insulin into the blood at mealtimes
(especially if the meal is high in simple carbohydrates).

This will make the liver remove the glucose as soon as it enters the blood from the gut, when the food is being digested.

This stops the level of glucose in the blood from getting too high and is a very effective treatment.

4) The amount of insulin that needs to be injected depends on the person's diet and how active they are.

Treatments for Diabetes Have Improved

1) Insulin used to be extracted from the pancreases of pigs or cows, but now human insulin is made by genetic engineering. This human insulin doesn't cause adverse reactions in patients, like animal insulin did.
2) Insulin injections help to control a person's blood glucose level, but it can't be controlled as accurately as having a normal working pancreas, so they may still have long-term health problems.

Insulin used to be extracted from pigs and purified.

3) Diabetics can have a pancreas transplant. A successful operation means they won't have to inject themselves with insulin again. But as with any organ transplant, your body can reject the tissue. If this happens you have to take costly immunosuppressive drugs, which often have serious side-effects.
4) Modern research into artificial pancreases and stem cell research may mean the elimination of organ rejection, but there's a way to go yet (see page 116).

Insulin is used to control type 1 diabetes

Insulin can't be taken in a pill or tablet — the enzymes in the stomach completely destroy it before it reaches the bloodstream. That's why diabetics have to inject it, which isn't much fun.

Warm-Up and Exam Questions

Right then, another section down. Now there's just the small matter of answering some questions...

Warm-Up Questions

1) Where does the sugar in your blood come from?
2) Name the organ that monitors and controls your blood sugar level.
3) What does insulin do?
4) (a) Before genetically engineered insulin was available, where did we get insulin from?
   (b) Give one problem with getting insulin from this source.

Exam Questions

1 The diagram below shows how blood sugar level is regulated in humans.

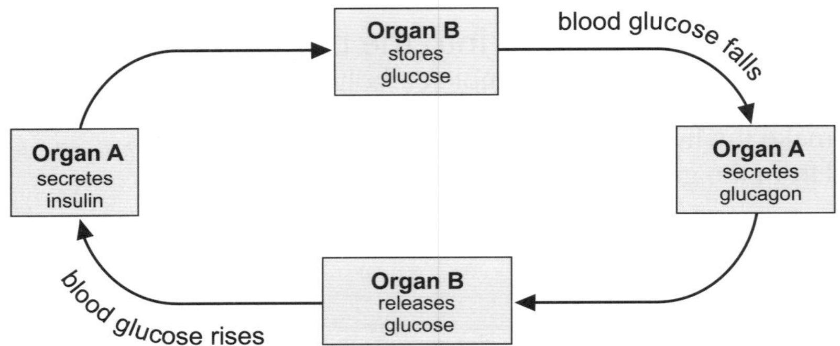

(a) From the diagram, identify:

(i) organ A *(1 mark)*

(ii) organ B *(1 mark)*

(b) (i) Suggest a reason why blood glucose might rise. *(1 mark)*

(ii) What process constantly removes glucose from the blood? *(1 mark)*

(iii) What would cause blood glucose levels to fall rapidly? *(1 mark)*

(iv) Describe what the hormone glucagon does. *(1 mark)*

2 Some people suffer from type 1 diabetes.

(a) Explain what type 1 diabetes is and what it can result in. *(2 marks)*

(b) Type 1 diabetes can be treated using insulin injections or by a pancreas transplant. Suggest **one** advantage and **one** disadvantage of treating diabetes with a pancreas transplant rather than insulin injections. *(2 marks)*

Revision Summary for Biology 3a

So you think you've learnt all these important processes, eh... Well, there's only one way to really find out. And you know what that is, I'll bet. It's obvious... I mean, there's a whole load of questions staring you in the face — chances are, it's got to involve those in some way. And sure enough, it does. Just write down the answers to all these questions. Then go back over the section and see if you got any wrong. If you did, then you need a bit more revision, so go back and have another read of the section and then have another go. It's the best way to make sure you actually know your stuff.

1) A solution of pure water is separated from a concentrated sugar solution by a partially permeable membrane. In which direction will molecules flow, and what substance will these molecules be?
2) Explain how leaves are adapted to maximise the amount of carbon dioxide that gets to their cells.
3) Name the main substances that diffuse out of leaves.
4) What conditions does evaporation of water from leaves happen most quickly in?
5) Define ventilation.
6) Give four ways that the alveoli's structure is ideal for gas exchange.
7) Draw a diagram of a root hair cell.
8) Give the two main differences between active transport and diffusion.
9) What is the transpiration stream?
10) Explain why our circulation system is called a double circulation system.
11) Give the function of the following parts of the heart: a) atria b) ventricles
12) Why do arteries need very muscular, elastic walls?
13) Explain how capillaries are adapted to their function.
14) What's the substance in red blood cells called? What is it called when it combines with oxygen?
15) What are the cell fragments called that help blood to clot? Why is it important that blood can clot?
16) Explain how artificial blood products can help keep people alive.
17) State one part of the heart that can be replaced with artificial parts, and give one potential complication.
18) What does a stent do?
19) Define homeostasis.
20) Write down four things that the body needs to keep fairly constant.
21) Where in the body is urea produced?
22) How is water taken into the body?
23) Give three ways in which water is lost from the body.
24) Explain why your urine is likely to be more concentrated on a hot day.
25) Explain why sugar doesn't simply diffuse back into the blood from the nephrons.
26) Give two ways in which kidney failure can be treated.
27) Describe what happens when blood glucose level is too high.
28) Give two ways in which type 1 diabetes can be controlled.

Human Impact on the Environment

We have an impact on the world around us — and the more humans there are, the bigger the impact.

There are Over Six Billion People in the World...

1) The population of the world is currently rising very quickly, and it's not slowing down — look at the graph...

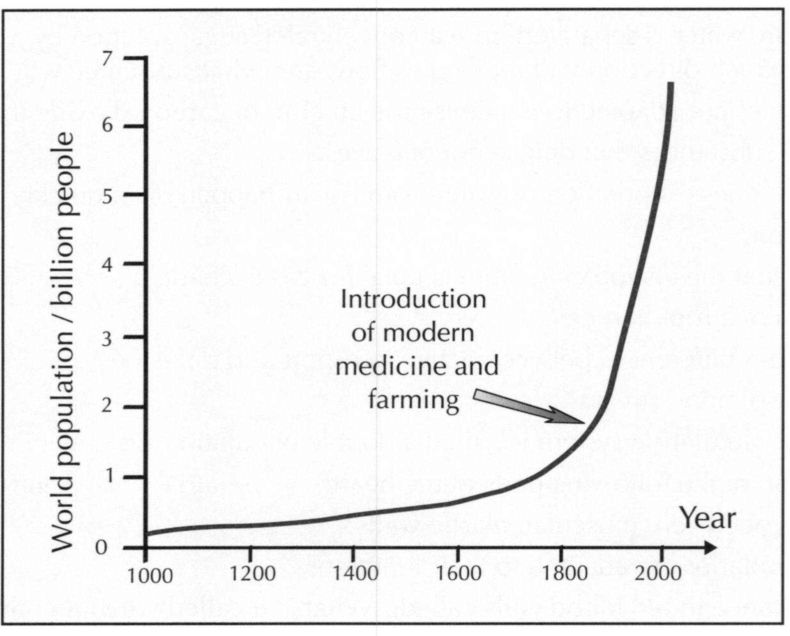

2) This is mostly due to modern medicine and farming methods, which have reduced the number of people dying from disease and hunger.
3) This is great for all of us humans, but it means we're having a bigger effect on the environment we live in.

...With Increasing Demands on the Environment

When the Earth's population was much smaller, the effects of human activity were usually small and local. Nowadays though, our actions can have a far more widespread effect.

1) Our increasing population puts pressure on the environment, as we take the resources we need to survive.

2) But people around the world are also demanding a higher standard of living (and so demand luxuries to make life more comfortable — cars, computers, etc.). So we use more raw materials (e.g. oil to make plastics), but we also use more energy for the manufacturing processes. This all means we're taking more and more resources from the environment more and more quickly.

3) Unfortunately, many raw materials are being used up quicker than they're being replaced. So if we carry on like we are, one day we're going to run out.

Human Impact on the Environment

We humans are producing an awful lot of rubbish — and the more of us there are, the more land we're using too...

We're Also Producing **More Waste**

As we make more and more things we produce more and more waste. And unless this waste is properly handled, more harmful pollution will be caused. This affects water, land and air.

Water

Sewage and toxic chemicals from industry can pollute lakes, rivers and oceans, affecting the plants and animals that rely on them for survival (including humans). And the chemicals used on land (e.g. fertilisers) can be washed into water.

Land

We use toxic chemicals for farming (e.g. pesticides and herbicides). We also bury nuclear waste underground, and we dump a lot of household waste in landfill sites.

Air

Smoke and gases released into the atmosphere can pollute the air, e.g. sulfur dioxide can cause acid rain.

More People Means **Less Land** for Plants and Other Animals

Humans also reduce the amount of land and resources available to other animals and plants. The four main human activities that do this are:

1) Building

2) Farming

3) Dumping Waste

4) Quarrying for metal ores

More people, more mess, less space, fewer resources...

Well, I don't know about you, but I feel a bit guilty. We're destroying the planet because there are loads more of us than before, and we're demanding a higher standard of living. In the exam you might be given some data about environmental impact, so make sure you understand what's going on...

Carbon Dioxide and the Greenhouse Effect

The increasing amount of carbon dioxide in our atmosphere is starting to cause us trouble...

Too Much Carbon Dioxide in the Air Causes Problems

1) Carbon is present in the atmosphere as carbon dioxide (CO_2).
2) Many processes lead to CO_2 being released, e.g. burning fossil fuels.
3) Too much CO_2 in the atmosphere causes global warming (see page 167).

Luckily There Are Natural Stores of Carbon Dioxide

CO_2 can be sequestered ('locked up') in natural stores, including:

Oceans, lakes and ponds.

Green plants, where it's stored as carbon compounds.

Green plants remove CO_2 from the atmosphere during photosynthesis.

Peat bogs (see page 169).

Storing CO_2 in these ways is really important because it means CO_2 is removed from the atmosphere.

Natural stores of CO_2 reduce the amount in the atmosphere

We really need to look after our natural stores of carbon dioxide because they help to remove it from the atmosphere. But, unfortunately, some of these natural stores are being destroyed by human activity (see pages 168-69) — and that could be really bad news for the environment.

Carbon Dioxide and the Greenhouse Effect

The greenhouse effect is always in the news. We need it, since it makes Earth a suitable temperature for living on. But unfortunately it's starting to trap more heat than is necessary.

Carbon Dioxide and Methane Trap Heat from the Sun

1) The temperature of the Earth is a balance between the heat it gets from the Sun and the heat it radiates back out into space.

2) Gases in the atmosphere naturally act like an insulating layer. They absorb most of the heat that would normally be radiated out into space, and re-radiate it in all directions (including back towards the Earth).

This is what happens in a greenhouse. The sun shines in, and the glass helps keeps some of the heat in.

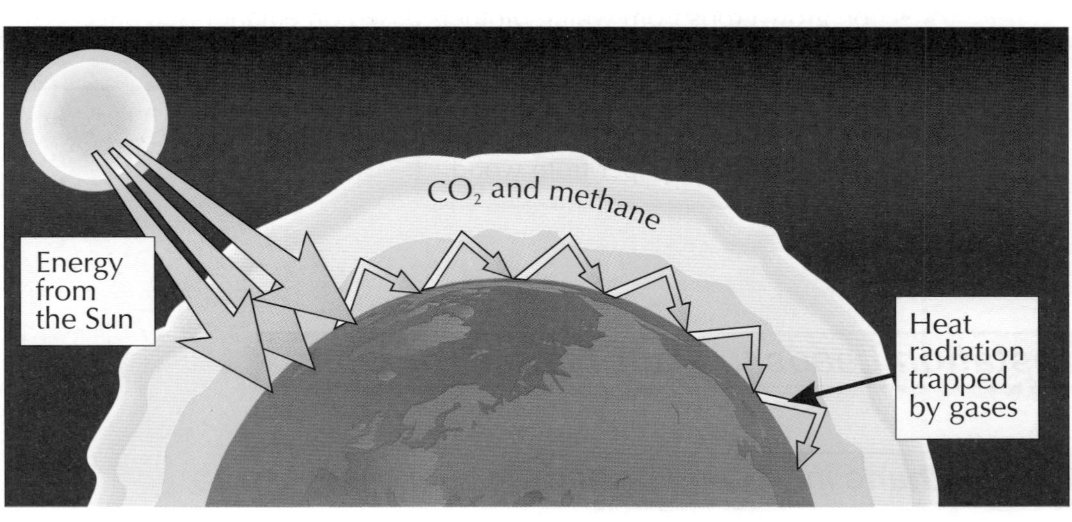

3) If this didn't happen, then at night there'd be nothing to keep any heat in, and we'd quickly get very cold indeed. But recently we've started to worry that this effect is getting a bit out of hand...

4) There are several different gases in the atmosphere which help keep the heat in. They're called "greenhouse gases" and the main ones whose levels we worry about are carbon dioxide and methane — because the levels of these two gases are rising quite sharply.

5) The Earth is gradually heating up because of the increasing levels of greenhouse gases — this is global warming. Global warming is a type of climate change and causes other types of climate change, e.g. changing rainfall patterns.

We need greenhouse gases in the atmosphere, but not too much

Global warming is rarely out of the news these days. Scientists accept that it's happening and that human activity has caused most of the recent warming. However, they still don't really know exactly what the effects of global warming will be (see page 170).

Deforestation and the Destruction of Peat Bogs

Trees and peat bogs trap carbon dioxide and lock it up. The problems start when it escapes...

Deforestation means Chopping Down Trees

Deforestation is the cutting down of forests.
This causes big problems when it's done on a large scale, such as cutting down rainforests.

It's done for various reasons:

1) To provide timber to use as building material.

2) To clear more land for farming, which is important to:
   - provide more food, e.g. from more rice fields or farming more cattle,
   - or, grow crops from which biofuels based on ethanol (see page 174) can be produced.

3) To produce paper from wood.

Deforestation Leads to Four Main Problems:

1) More Methane in the Atmosphere

1) Rice is grown in warm, waterlogged conditions — ideal for decomposers. These organisms produce methane, so more is released into the atmosphere.
2) Cattle produce methane and rearing cattle means that more methane is released.

It's the cows' "pumping" that's the problem, believe it or not...

2) More Carbon Dioxide in the Atmosphere

1) Carbon dioxide is released when trees are burnt to clear land. (Carbon in wood doesn't contribute to atmospheric pollution until it's released by burning.)
2) Microorganisms feeding on bits of dead wood release carbon dioxide as a waste product of respiration.

Deforestation and the Destruction of Peat Bogs

3) Less Carbon Dioxide Taken In

Cutting down loads of trees means that the amount of carbon dioxide removed from the atmosphere during photosynthesis is reduced.

More CO_2 in the atmosphere causes global warming (page 167), which leads to climate change (page 170).

4) Less Biodiversity

1) BIODIVERSITY is the variety of different species in a habitat — the more species, the greater the biodiversity.
2) Habitats like tropical rainforests can contain a huge number of different species, so when they are destroyed there is a danger of many species becoming extinct — biodiversity is reduced.
3) This causes a number of lost opportunities, e.g. there are probably lots of useful products that we will never know about because the organisms that produced them have become extinct. Newly discovered plants and animals are a great source of new foods, new fibres for clothing and new medicines.

Destroying Peat Bogs Adds More CO_2 to the Atmosphere

1) Bogs are areas of land that are acidic and waterlogged. Plants that live in bogs don't fully decay when they die, because there's not enough oxygen. The partly-rotted plants gradually build up to form peat.
2) So the carbon in the plants is stored in the peat instead of being released into the atmosphere.
3) However, peat bogs are often drained so that the area can be used as farmland, or the peat is cut up and dried to use as fuel. Peat is also sold to gardeners as compost.

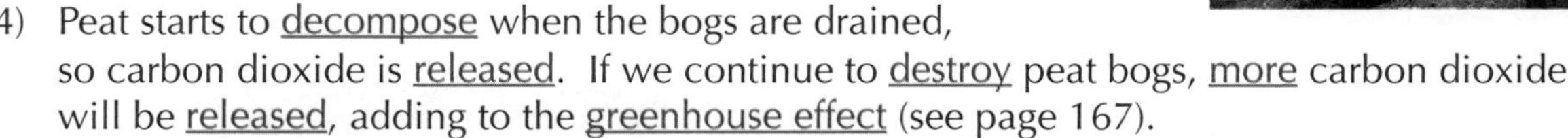

4) Peat starts to decompose when the bogs are drained, so carbon dioxide is released. If we continue to destroy peat bogs, more carbon dioxide will be released, adding to the greenhouse effect (see page 167).
5) So one way people can do their bit is by buying peat-free compost for their gardens (e.g. manure, leaf mould or bark chippings) to reduce the demand for peat.

Fewer trees and fewer peat bogs = bad news for the environment

Cutting down trees and digging up peat is increasing the amount of CO_2 in our atmosphere. Add in methane from farming and falling biodiversity, and you've got the makings of big environmental trouble.

Climate Change

The Earth is getting warmer. Climate scientists are now trying to work out what the effects of global warming might be — sadly, it's not as simple as everyone having nicer summers.

*The **Consequences** of **Global Warming** Could be Pretty **Serious***

There are several reasons to be worried about global warming. Here are a few:

1) As the sea gets warmer, it expands, causing sea level to rise. Sea level has risen a little bit over the last 100 years. If it keeps rising it'll be bad news for people living in low-lying places like the Netherlands, East Anglia and the Maldives — they'd be flooded.

2) Higher temperatures make ice melt. Water that's currently 'trapped' on land (as ice) runs into the sea, causing sea level to rise even more.

3) Global warming has changed weather patterns in many parts of the world. It's thought that many regions will suffer more extreme weather because of this, e.g. longer, hotter droughts. Hurricanes form over water that's warmer than 27 °C — so with more warm water, you'd expect more hurricanes. However, the climate is a very complicated system. It's hard to predict exactly what will happen, but lots of people are working on it, and it's not looking too good.

4) The distribution of many wild animal and plant species may change. Some species may become more widely distributed, e.g. species that need warmer temperatures may spread further as the conditions they thrive in exist over a wider area. Other species may become less widely distributed, e.g. species that need cooler temperatures may have smaller ranges as the conditions they thrive in exist over a smaller area.

5) Biodiversity (see page 169) could be reduced if some species are unable to survive a change in the climate, so become extinct.

6) There could be changes in migration patterns, e.g. some birds may migrate further north, as more northern areas are getting warmer.

Global warming = rising sea level and changing climate

Global warming could cause some very big problems for us all. Make sure you learn what they are. You can test yourself by turning over the page and seeing if you can write them all down.

Climate Change

At GCSE level, it's not as simple as just learning all the facts any more (if that was ever simple). Sometimes you've got to be able to look at the scientific evidence and judge how useful it really is.

Scientists Collect **Evidence** to Show How the **Climate** is **Changing**

To find out how our climate is changing, scientists are busy collecting data about the environment.

1) Satellites are used to monitor snow and ice cover.
2) Satellites can also be used to measure the temperature of the sea surface.
3) The temperature and speed of ocean currents are monitored for any changes.
4) Automatic weather stations are constantly recording atmospheric temperatures.

You Need to **Weigh** the **Evidence** Before **Making Judgements**

All this data is only useful if it covers a wide enough area and a long enough time scale.

AREA

Generally, observations of a very small area aren't much use. Noticing that your local glacier seems to be melting does not mean that ice everywhere is melting, and it's certainly not a valid way to show that global temperature is changing. (That would be like going to Wales, seeing a stripy cow and concluding that all the cows in Wales are turning into zebras.) Looking at the area of ice cover over a whole continent, like Antarctica, would be better.

TIME

The same thing goes for time. It's no good going to the Arctic, seeing four polar bears one week but only two the next week and concluding that polar bears are dying out because the ice is disappearing. You need to do your observations again and again, year after year.

Scientists can make mistakes — so don't take one person's word for something, even if they've got a PhD. But if lots of scientists get the same result using different methods, it's probably right. That's why most governments around the world are starting to take climate change seriously.

To find out how the climate is changing, look at the evidence

Many people, and some governments, think we ought to start cleaning up the environmental problems we have caused. Scientists can help, mainly in understanding the problems and suggesting solutions, but it's society as a whole that has to do something.

Warm-Up and Exam Questions

Now's your chance to practise some incredibly life-like exam questions — but do the warm-up first — you don't want to end up straining something.

Warm-Up Questions

1) Give two reasons why the amount of waste produced by humans is increasing.
2) Give one way in which humans pollute land.
3) What does the term 'sequestered' mean in relation to carbon dioxide?
4) What is meant by the 'greenhouse effect'?
5) What are the two main gases that are causing an increase in the greenhouse effect?
6) Explain why using peat-free compost is better for the environment than using compost that contains peat.

Exam Questions

1 The graph shows the carbon dioxide concentration in the Earth's atmosphere between AD 1000 and AD 2000.

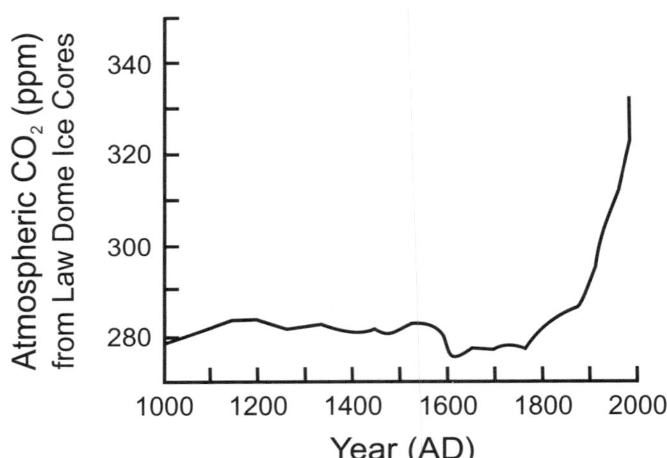

(a) Describe the trend in atmospheric carbon dioxide concentration between AD 1000 and AD 2000.

(2 marks)

(b) Name **two** human activities that may have caused the changes in concentration between AD 1850 and AD 2000.

(2 marks)

2 (a) Explain how global warming could lead to a rise in sea level.

(1 mark)

(b) Give **two** other possible consequences of global warming.

(1 mark)

Exam Questions

3 Some human activities damage the environment and can harm wildlife.

(a) Give **one** way in which human activity can cause water pollution.

(1 mark)

(b) Some industries increase the amount of sulfur dioxide in the air. Suggest why this is bad for the environment.

(1 mark)

(c) Some wild animals struggle to survive because humans have destroyed their natural habitats.

Name **two** human activities that reduce the amount of land that is available for wild animals to occupy.

(2 marks)

4 A scientist was examining some data to see if there is a link between the global human population and the carbon dioxide concentration in the atmosphere.

Here are the two graphs that the scientist examined.

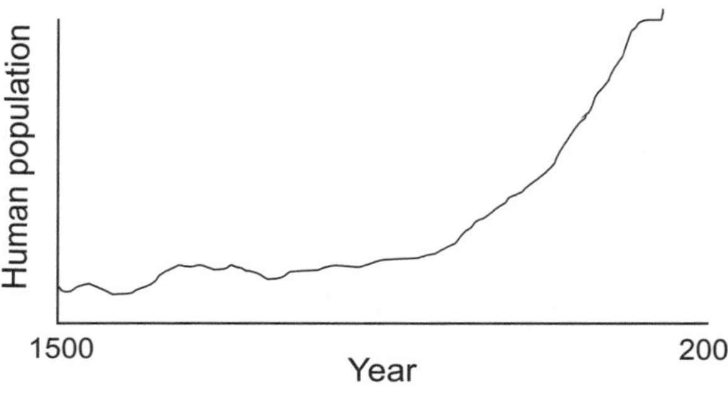

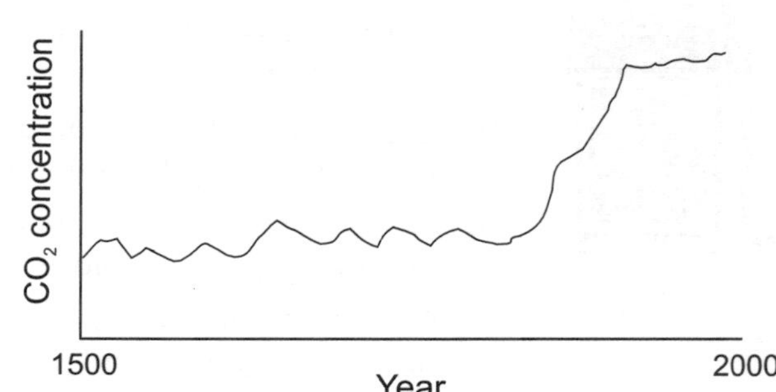

(a) The scientist said that there is a correlation between the two graphs. Explain what this means.

(1 mark)

(b) On their own, these graphs do not prove that the increased human population caused the increased carbon dioxide concentration. Explain why not.

(1 mark)

5 The tropical island of Hannaria has an area of approximately 2000 km^2. Most of the island is covered with tropical rainforest.

Some of the inhabitants of Hannaria want to clear large areas of the rainforest to create more farmland. Opponents say that this development will contribute to global warming.

(a) Explain how reducing the number of trees could contribute to global warming.

(2 marks)

(b) If the trees are cut down, they could be used as fuel or they could be used to make wooden buildings and furniture.

Which of these uses is likely to contribute more to global warming? Give a reason for your answer.

(1 mark)

Biofuels

There's too much carbon dioxide in the atmosphere, and burning fossil fuels (for energy) is making the problem worse. But luckily, there are some biofuels out there that we can use, which are 'carbon neutral' (see page 176). Many biofuels are made using microorganisms.

Fuels Can Be Made by Fermentation

1) Fuels can be made by fermentation of natural products — luckily enough, waste products can often be used.

Anaerobic respiration does not use oxygen.

2) Fermentation is when bacteria or yeast break sugars down by anaerobic respiration.

Ethanol is Made by Anaerobic Fermentation of Sugar

1) Yeast make ethanol when they break down glucose by anaerobic respiration.

Glucose → Ethanol + Carbon dioxide + Energy

2) Sugar cane juices can be used, or glucose can be derived from maize starch by the action of carbohydrase (an enzyme).
3) The ethanol is distilled to separate it from the yeast and remaining glucose before it's used.
4) In some countries, e.g. Brazil, cars are adapted to run on a mixture of ethanol and petrol — this is known as 'gasohol'.

Biogas is Made by Anaerobic Fermentation of Waste Material

1) Biogas is usually about 70% methane and 30% carbon dioxide.
2) Lots of different microorganisms are used to produce biogas. They ferment plant and animal waste, which contains carbohydrates. Sludge waste from, e.g. sewage works or sugar factories, is used to make biogas on a large scale.
3) It's made in a simple fermenter called a digester or generator.
4) Biogas generators need to be kept at a constant temperature to keep the microorganisms respiring away.
5) There are two types of biogas generators — batch generators and continuous generators. These are explained on the next page.
6) Biogas can't be stored as a liquid (it needs too high a pressure), so it has to be used straight away — for heating, cooking, lighting, or to power a turbine to generate electricity.

Biogas was used to power street lights in London

Fascinating stuff, this biogas. It makes a lot of sense, I suppose, to get energy from rubbish, sewage and pig poop instead of leaving it all to rot naturally — which would mean all that lovely methane just wafting away into the atmosphere. Remember — anaerobic respiration makes biofuels.

Biofuels

Here's more than you could ever have wanted to know about that magic stuff, biogas.

Fuel Production Can Happen on a **Large** or **Small Scale**

1) Large-scale biogas generators are now being set up in a number of countries. Also, in some countries, small biogas generators are used to make enough gas for a village or a family to use in their cooking stoves and for heating and lighting.

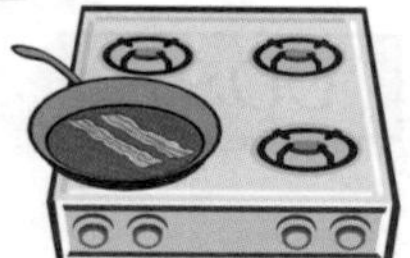

2) Human waste, waste from keeping pigs, and food waste (e.g. kitchen scraps) can be digested by bacteria to produce biogas.
3) By-products are used to fertilise crops and gardens.

Not All **Biogas Generators** Are the Same

There are two main types of biogas generator — batch generators and continuous generators.

Batch generators

Batch generators make biogas in small batches. They're manually loaded up with waste, which is left to digest, and the by-products are cleared away at the end of each session.

Continuous generators

Continuous generators make biogas all the time. Waste is continuously fed in, and biogas is produced at a steady rate. Continuous generators are more suited to large-scale biogas projects.

The diagram below shows a simple biogas generator.
Whether it's a continuous or batch generator, it needs to have the following:

1) an inlet for waste material to be put in,
2) an outlet for the digested material to be removed through,
3) an outlet so that the biogas can be piped to where it is needed.

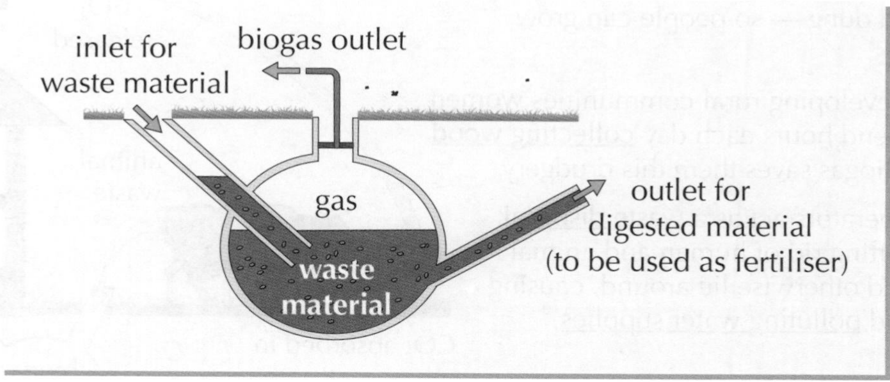

Biofuels

Four Factors to Consider When Designing a Generator:

When biogas generators are being designed, the following factors need to be considered:

COST: Continuous generators are more expensive than batch ones, because waste has to be mechanically pumped in and digested material mechanically removed all the time.

CONVENIENCE: Batch generators are less convenient because they have to be continually loaded, emptied and cleaned.

EFFICIENCY: Gas is produced most quickly at about 35 °C. If the temperature falls below this the gas production will be slower. Generators in some areas will need to be insulated or kept warm, e.g. by solar heaters. The generator shouldn't have any leaks or gas will be lost.

POSITION: The waste will smell during delivery, so generators should be sited away from homes. The generator is also best located fairly close to the waste source.

Using Biofuels Has Economic and Environmental Effects

1) Biofuels are a 'greener' alternative to fossil fuels. The carbon dioxide released into the atmosphere was taken in by plants which lived recently, so they're 'carbon neutral'.
2) The use of biofuels doesn't produce significant amounts of sulfur dioxide or nitrogen oxides, which cause acid rain.
3) Methane is a greenhouse gas and is one of those responsible for global warming. It's given off from untreated waste, which may be kept in farmyards or spread on agricultural land as fertiliser. Burning it as biogas means it's not released into the atmosphere.
4) The raw material is cheap and readily available.
5) The digested material is a better fertiliser than undigested dung — so people can grow more crops.
6) In some developing rural communities women have to spend hours each day collecting wood for fuel. Biogas saves them this drudgery.
7) Biogas generators act as a waste disposal system, getting rid of human and animal waste that'd otherwise lie around, causing disease and polluting water supplies.

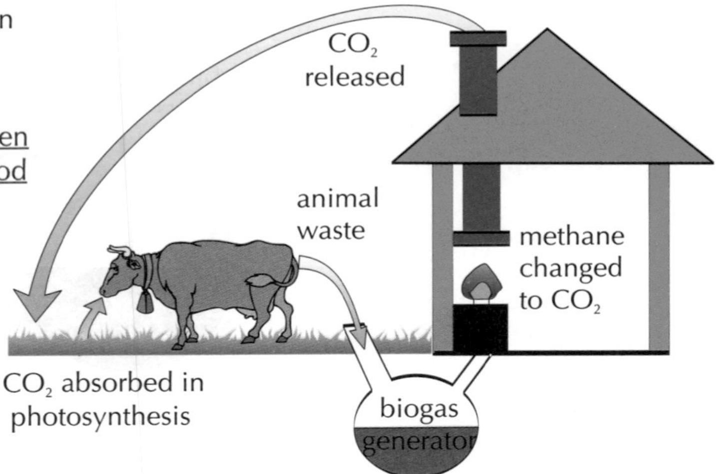

Warm-Up and Exam Questions

Yes, I know I've said it several times, but here are some more warm-up and exam questions...

Warm-Up Questions

1) Biogas is made by fermenting waste products. What is fermentation?
2) Other than biogas, give two examples of biofuels.
3) State four factors that need to be considered when designing a biogas generator.
4) Name three things that a biogas generator needs to have.
5) What will happen to the production of biogas if the temperature falls below 35 °C?

Exam Questions

1 (a) What is the main gas found in biogas?

(1 mark)

(b) Biogas can be made in continuous or batch generators.
Give **one** advantage and **one** disadvantage of continuous generators.

(2 marks)

(c) The table below shows the average temperatures in January and July for four countries.

	Average temperature (°C)	
	January	July
Nigeria	27	26
Brazil	27	26.5
England	4	18
Denmark	0	18

Use the data in the table to explain why the rate of biogas production, in a generator placed above ground, would be greater in Nigeria and Brazil than in England and Denmark.

(1 mark)

2 Some Chinese villages use biogas generators to provide energy.

(a) What sort of waste material can be used in a biogas generator?

(1 mark)

(b) Villagers usually site their generators some way from their houses and close to their agricultural fields. Suggest why:

(i) the generator is positioned away from the houses.

(1 mark)

(ii) the generator is sited close to the agricultural area.

(1 mark)

(c) Give **two** benefits of using a biogas generator instead of burning coal for energy.

(2 marks)

Managing Food Production

The human population is increasing — very quickly (see page 164) — so there are more mouths to feed. In order to make enough food, we need to produce it more efficiently. Here are some ways to do this...

The "Efficiency" of Food Production Can Be Improved by...

1) Reducing the Number of Stages in the Food Chain

1) There's less energy and less biomass every time you move up a stage in a food chain.

2) So for a given area of land, you can produce a lot more food (for humans) by growing crops rather than by having grazing animals. This is because you are reducing the number of stages in the food chain. Only 10% of what beef cattle eat becomes useful meat for people to eat.

3) However, people do need to eat a varied diet to stay healthy, and there's still a lot of demand for meat products. Also remember that some land is unsuitable for growing crops, e.g. moorland or hillsides. In these places, animals like sheep and deer might be the best way to get food from the land.

2) Restricting the Energy Lost by Farm Animals

1) In 'civilised' countries like the UK, animals such as pigs and chickens are often intensively farmed. They're kept close together indoors in small pens, so that they're warm and can't move about.

2) This saves them wasting energy on movement, and stops them giving out so much energy as heat. This makes the transfer of energy from the animal feed to the animal more efficient — so basically, the animals will grow faster on less food.

3) This makes things cheaper for the farmer, and for us when the animals finally turn up on supermarket shelves.

Many developed countries now actually produce too much food

The world produces enough food to feed the Earth's population, but there are still millions of undernourished people worldwide. The food is not equally distributed. Many people think that countries with food surpluses should give food to countries with food shortages (or sell it cheaply).

Managing Food Production

There's a third way that we can produce food more efficiently...

3) Developing **New Food Sources** like **Mycoprotein**

1) Mycoprotein means protein from fungi.

2) It's used to make meat substitutes for vegetarian meals, e.g. Quorn™.

3) A fungus called *Fusarium* is the main source of mycoprotein.

4) The fungus is grown in fermenters (see below), using glucose syrup as food. The glucose syrup is obtained by digesting maize starch with enzymes.

5) The fungus respires aerobically, so oxygen is supplied, together with nitrogen (as ammonia) and other minerals.

6) It's important to prevent other microorganisms growing in the fermenter. So the fermenter is initially sterilised using steam. The incoming nutrients are heat sterilised and the air supply is filtered.

7) The mycoprotein is then harvested and purified.

A fermenter

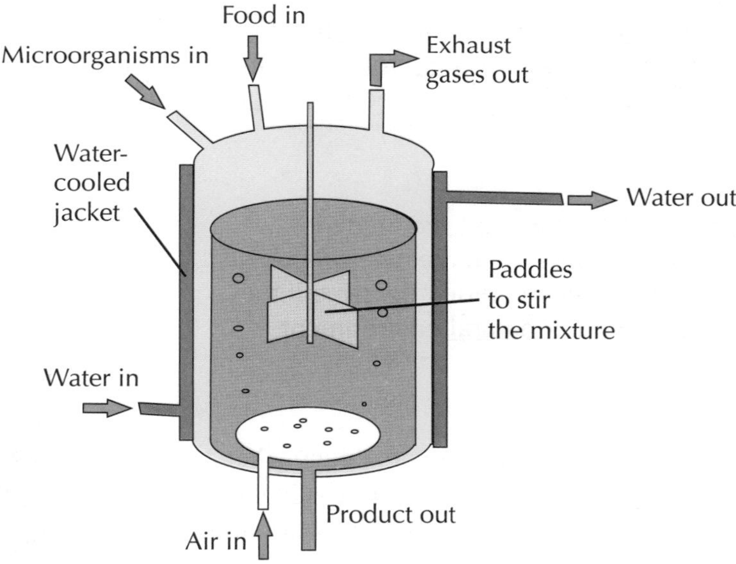

A fermenter is a big container full of liquid culture medium, which microorganisms can grow and reproduce in.

1) Food made from microorganisms mightn't sound very appetising, but there are definitely advantages to it.
2) In some developing countries it's difficult to find enough protein. Meat is a big source of protein, but animals need lots of space to graze, plenty of nice grass, etc.
3) Mycoprotein grown in a fermenter is an efficient way of producing protein to feed people.
4) The microorganisms grow very quickly, and don't need much space.
5) And they can even feed on waste material that would be no good for feeding animals.

Problems with Food Production and Distribution

Modern ways of producing food have advantages but also disadvantages.

Efficient Food Production Involves **Compromises** *and* **Conflict**

Improving the efficiency of food production is useful — it means cheaper food for us, and better standards of living for farmers. It also helps to feed an increasing human population. But it all comes at a cost.

Here are some examples of arguments against the intensive farming methods used to increase the efficiency of food production:

1) Some people think that forcing animals to live in unnatural and uncomfortable conditions is cruel. There's a growing demand for organic meat, which means the animals will not have been intensively farmed.

2) The crowded conditions on factory farms create a favourable environment for the spread of diseases, like avian flu and foot-and-mouth disease.

3) To try to prevent disease, animals are given antibiotics. When the animals are eaten these can enter humans. This allows microbes that infect humans to develop immunity to those antibiotics — so the antibiotics become less effective as human medicines.

4) The animals need to be kept warm to reduce the energy they lose as heat. This often means using power from fossil fuels — which we wouldn't be using if the animals were grazing in their natural environment.

5) Our fish stocks are getting low (see the next page). Yet a lot of fish goes on feeding animals that are intensively farmed — these animals wouldn't usually eat this source of food.

In an exam, you may be asked to give an account of the positive and negative aspects of food management. You will need to put both sides, whatever your personal opinion is. If you get given some information on a particular case, make sure you use it — they want to see that you've read it carefully.

People can be very passionate about where their food comes from

You may well have a strong opinion on some of the issues above — you might think cheap meat is great because it's cheap and more people can afford it, or you might be against it because of animal welfare concerns. Either way, in exams keep it to yourself and give a nice, balanced argument instead.

Problems with Food Production and Distribution

There are also problems with distributing food and fishing....

Food Distribution Also Causes Problems

1) Some food products have lots of 'food miles' — they're transported a long way from where they're produced to where they're sold, e.g. some green beans you buy in the UK have come from Kenya.
2) This can be expensive and it's also bad for the environment.

3) Planes, ships and trucks all burn scarce fossil fuels and release carbon dioxide into the atmosphere, contributing to global warming.

Overfishing is Decreasing Fish Stocks

1) Fish stocks are declining because we're fishing so much.
2) This means there's less fish for us to eat, the ocean's food chains are affected and some species of fish may disappear altogether in some areas.
3) To tackle this problem, we need to maintain fish stocks at a level where the fish continue to breed. This is sustainable food production — having enough food without using resources faster than they renew.
4) Fish stocks can be maintained (conserved) in these ways:

1) Fishing Quotas

1) There are limits on the number and size of fish that can be caught in certain areas.
2) This prevents certain species from being overfished.

2) Net Size

1) There are different limits on the mesh size of the fish net, depending on what's being fished.
2) This is to reduce the number of 'unwanted' and discarded fish — the ones that are accidently caught, e.g. shrimp caught along with cod. Using a bigger mesh size will let the 'unwanted' species escape.
3) It also means that younger fish will slip through the net, allowing them to reach breeding age.

Warm-Up and Exam Questions

Would you believe it, these are the last warm-up and exam questions in the book — congratulations... Unless for some reason you started with this section, in which case, welcome to the book.

Warm-Up Questions

1) What is a fermenter?
2) Give three advantages of producing mycoprotein in developing countries.
3) Give three arguments against intensive farming methods.
4) What is happening to our fish stocks?

Exam Questions

1 Growing mycoprotein is an example of efficient food production.

(a) What is mycoprotein used for?

(1 mark)

(b) Name the fungus that is the main source of mycoprotein.

(1 mark)

(c) A fermenter is used for growing mycoprotein.

(i) What is the food source of the fungus?

(1 mark)

(ii) Is the fungus grown under aerobic or anaerobic conditions?

(1 mark)

(iii) What process does the mycoprotein go through after it has been harvested?

(1 mark)

2 Three different food chains are shown below.

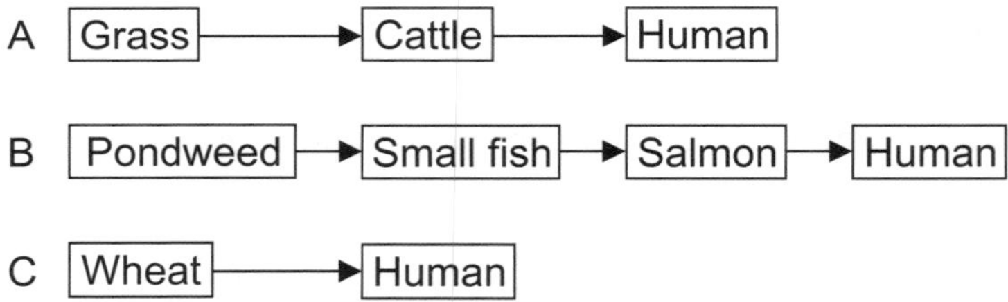

Explain which food chain shows the most efficient production of food for humans.

(2 marks)

3 Mr Bowman runs a farm in East Anglia. He raises cattle for milk and meat. He keeps the cattle in heated sheds and gives them regular injections of antibiotics, even if they're not ill.

(a) Suggest why Mr Bowman gives antibiotics to his cattle.

(1 mark)

(b) Explain the disadvantage of this practice.

(1 mark)

(c) Explain how keeping the cattle in heated sheds can improve the productivity of the farm.

(2 marks)

Revision Summary for Biology 3b

It's no good just reading the section through and hoping you've got it all — it'll only stick if you've learnt it properly. These questions are designed to really test whether you know all your stuff. If you get any wrong, read that bit through again, then have another go at the question.

1) What is happening to the world's population? What is largely responsible for this trend?
2) Name three stores of carbon.
3) Why is it so important to have stores of carbon?
4) Draw and label a diagram to explain the greenhouse effect.
5) Give three reasons why people chop down large areas of forest.
6) Explain the meaning of the term 'biodiversity'.
7) List the four main problems that deforestation can lead to.
8) How could growing rice contribute to global warming?
9) How is peat formed?
10)*Read the statement below and consider how valid it is.

> The Malaspina Glacier in Alaska is losing over 2.7 km^3 of water each year. This proves that global warming is happening.

11) Describe one way that scientists collect data about climate change.
12) Does fermentation involve aerobic or anaerobic respiration?
13) What are the two main components of biogas?
14)*Loompah is a small village. It's very hot in the summer but freezing cold in winter. The villagers keep goats and cows. They also try to grow crops, but the soil isn't very fertile, so it's difficult. The villagers currently rely on wood for fuel for heating and cooking. There's not much of this around, so they spend a lot of time collecting it, preventing them from practising their nail-art.
    a) How suitable do you think biogas would be for this village? Explain the advantages that using biogas would have for the village. What disadvantages or problems might there be?
    b) Loompah starts using biogas and uses the digested material as fertiliser. They compare their crops to the crops grown by the village of Moompah, which uses normal manure as a fertiliser. Loompah's crops are bigger, so they conclude that the digested material is a better fertiliser than manure. What do you think of the conclusion they've drawn?
15) A farmer has a field. He plans to grow corn in it and then feed the corn to his cows, which he raises for meat. How could the farmer use the field more efficiently to produce food for humans?
16) What is 'sustainable food production'?
17) What are fishing quotas? How do they help to conserve our fish stocks?
18) Describe how enforcing a net size limit helps to conserve fish stocks.

* Answers on page 237.

Practice Exams

Once you've been through all the questions in this book, you should feel pretty confident about the exams. As final preparation, here is a set of **practice exams** to really get you set for the real thing. The time allowed for each paper is 60 minutes. These papers are designed to give you the best possible preparation for your exams.

GCSE AQA Science

Unit Biology 1

Higher Tier

In addition to this paper you should have:
- A ruler.
- A calculator.

Centre name					
Centre number					
Candidate number					

Time allowed:
- 60 minutes

Surname
Other names
Candidate signature

Instructions to candidates
- Write your name and other details in the spaces provided above.
- Answer **all** questions in the spaces provided.
- Do all rough work on the paper.

Information for candidates
- The marks available are given in brackets at the end of each question.
- There are 9 questions in this paper.
- There are 60 marks available for this paper.
- You are allowed to use a calculator.
- You should answer Question 4(b) and Question 6(d) with continuous prose. You will be assessed on the quality of your English, the organisation of your ideas and your use of appropriate specialist vocabulary.

For examiner's use							
Q	Attempt Nº			Q	Attempt Nº		
	1	2	3		1	2	3
1				6			
2				7			
3				8			
4				9			
5							
				Total			

Advice to candidates
- In calculations show clearly how you worked out your answers.

Leave blank

Answer **all** questions in the spaces provided

1 Based on the results of a study, a nutritionist claims that a high protein, low carbohydrate diet helps people to lose weight.

Two hundred people took part in the six month long study — half followed a high protein, low carbohydrate diet and half continued their normal diet.

The participants were weighed before and after the study and were also asked general questions on their lifestyle.

The following results were obtained.

	Normal diet	**Study diet**
Percent overweight after study	35	26
Percent obese after study	10	9
Percent taking regular exercise throughout study	30	48
Percent with heart disease after study	8	10
Percent that are smokers	22	18

On average, the people who continued their normal diet lost -1% of their body weight.

On average, those that followed the study diet lost 4% of their body weight.

1 (a) Name **one** health problem that is more likely to occur in an obese person than in a person with a healthy body mass.

....

....

(1 mark)

1 (b) Can you be sure that the claim made by the nutritionist is valid? Explain your answer.

....

....

....

(2 marks)

3

2 Antibiotics can be used to kill bacteria and help a patient fight disease.

Scientists developing antibiotics were testing the effectiveness of three different antibiotics, X, Y and Z, against a bacterium. They grew the bacteria on agar jelly in 20 Petri dishes — forming a 'bacterial lawn' on the top of the agar.

They took four identical discs of paper and soaked each of them in different liquids:

Disc	Liquid soaked in
1	Antibiotic X
2	Antibiotic Y
3	Antibiotic Z
4	Distilled Water

The discs were then placed onto the agar in each dish. The dishes were kept in an incubator at 35 °C for two days, and then they were examined.

A typical dish is shown below.

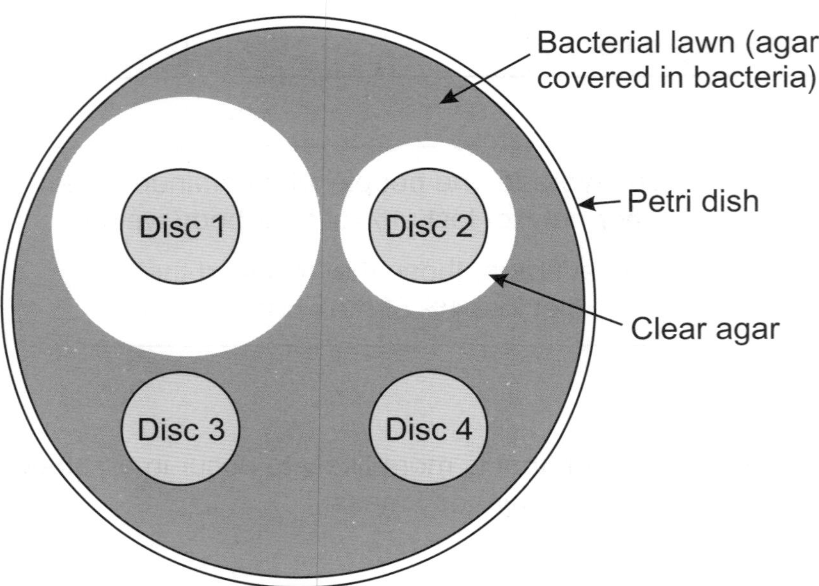

Leave blank

Leave blank

2 (a) Which antibiotic, **X**, **Y** or **Z**, was the most effective in killing the bacteria?

Explain your answer.

....

(1 mark)

2 (b) What was the dependent variable in this experiment?

....

....

(1 mark)

2 (c) The most effective antibiotic was manufactured and prescribed to patients.

Two years later scientists repeated the experiment with a fresh sample of the bacteria and found that no clear zone was produced around the disc soaked in this antibiotic.

Suggest an explanation for this observation and explain how this situation may have come about.

....

....

....

....

....

(4 marks)

$\overline{\ \ }$
6

Turn over for the next question

Leave blank

3 Exercise helps to keep your body fat low and strengthens your heart. Taking regular exercise can increase your resting metabolic rate.

The table lists some different activities and how much energy (in kJ per minute) they use up.

Activity	kJ/min
Sleeping	4.5
Active Office Work	16
Watching TV	7
Cycling (5 mph)	21
Aerobics	43
Swimming	35
Slow walking	14
Jogging (5 mph)	40

3 (a) What is meant by the term **metabolic rate**?

....

....

(1 mark)

3 (b) Jim watches TV for half an hour and then slowly walks to his friend's house, which takes him 10 minutes.

How much energy will he use up during these activities?

....

....

(2 marks)

3 (c) Jim eats a packet of crisps that contains 760 kJ of energy.

How many minutes will he have to jog (at 5 mph) for to burn off the same amount of energy?

....

....

(2 marks)

5

Leave blank

4 Vaccines, like the MMR vaccine, give people immunity to future infections.

4 (a) Which **three** diseases does the MMR vaccine protect against?

....

....

(1 mark)

4 (b) *In this question you will be assessed on the quality of your English, the organisation of your ideas and your use of appropriate specialist vocabulary.*

Explain how vaccination helps to protect the body against a disease.

....

....

....

....

....

....

....

....

....

....

....

(6 marks)

7

Turn over for the next question

Leave blank

5 Scientists tested the reflex actions of eight volunteers.

Each person was tapped just below the knee with a small rubber hammer. When the leg was tapped it automatically kicked outwards at the knee.

The scientists recorded how long it took each volunteer to respond to the stimulus of the tap on the leg. Each person did the test 20 times, and an average reaction time was calculated (to 2 decimal places).

The results are shown in the table.

Name	Average reaction time (s)
Mary	0.05
Tom	0.05
Phillip	0.04
Sarah	0.06
Christopher	0.04
Isobelle	0.06
Lucy	0.04
Ben	0.05

5 (a) How can you tell that the volunteers' response was a reflex? Give **two** reasons.

....

....

....

....

(2 marks)

5 (b) Another reflex is the response of moving your hand away from a painful stimulus.

Below is a diagram of the parts of the nervous system involved in this reflex.

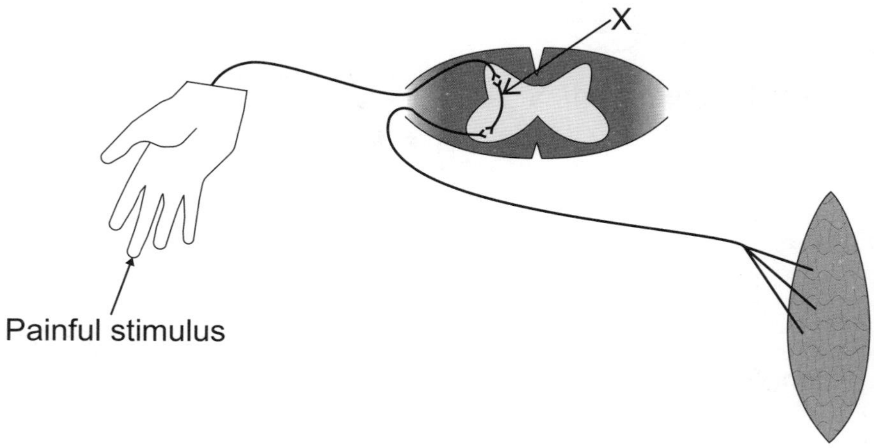

X

Painful stimulus

5 (b) (i) Name part **X** shown on the diagram.

....

(1 mark)

5 (b) (ii) Describe the path taken by a nervous impulse in this reflex, from stimulus to response.

....

....

....

....

....

....

....

....

....

....

(6 marks)

9

Turn over for the next question

6 The diagram below shows the first steps involved in adult cell cloning.

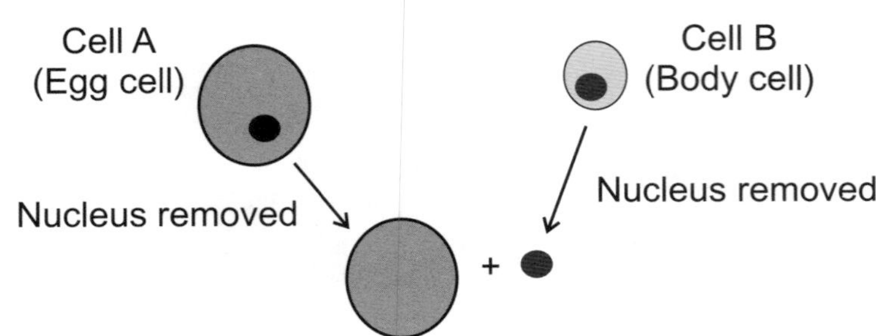

6 (a) What is a clone?

....

(1 mark)

6 (b) The new cell will be a clone of one of the original cells. Which one, **A** or **B**? ☐

Explain your answer.

....

(1 mark)

6 (c) Explain how an animal can be cloned using adult cell cloning.

....

....

....

....

....

....

....

(4 marks)

Leave blank

6 (d) *In this question you will be assessed on the quality of your English, the organisation of your ideas and your use of appropriate specialist vocabulary.*

Leave blank

Discuss some of the reasons for and against the cloning of animals.

....

....

....

....

....

....

....

....

....

(6 marks)

12

Turn over for the next question

Leave blank

7 The diagram below shows the amount of energy contained within an area of plants. It shows how much energy from the plants is transferred to each trophic level in a food chain.

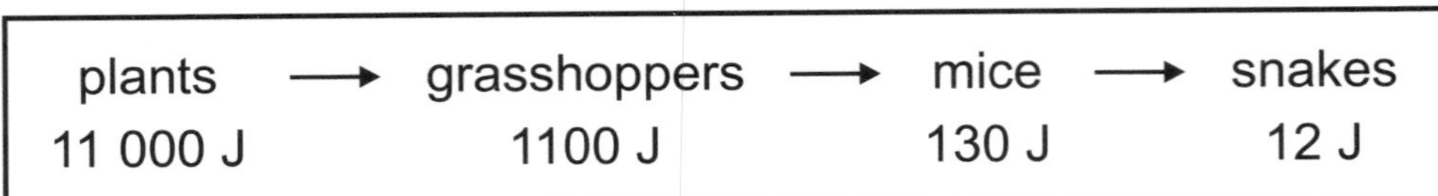

7 (a) Four pyramids of biomass are shown below.

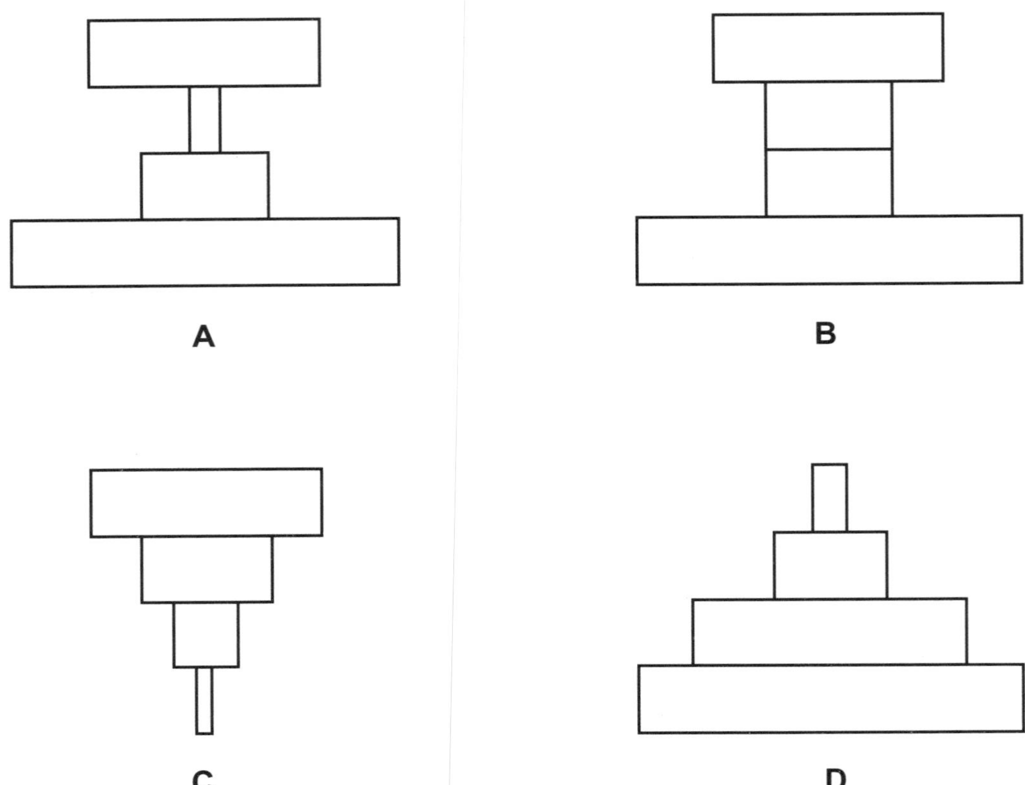

Which of the pyramids of biomass, **A**, **B**, **C** or **D**, represents the food chain? Give a reason for your answer.

....

....

(1 mark)

Leave blank

7 (b) Calculate the percentage of energy in the grasshoppers that is transferred to the mice. Show your working.

....

....

.... %

(2 marks)

7 (c) Give **two** ways in which energy is lost within a level of a food chain.

1. ....

2. ....

(2 marks)

7 (d) This food chain has four trophic levels. Most food chains have no more than five trophic levels. Explain why the length of food chains is limited in this way.

....

....

....

(2 marks)

$\overline{7}$

Turn over for the next question

Leave blank

8 Read the account of the peppered moth, and answer the questions that follow.

The peppered moth is an insect that lives on the trunks of trees in Britain. The moths are prey for birds such as thrushes.

The peppered moth exists in two varieties:

1. A light-coloured variety — they are better camouflaged on tree trunks in unpolluted areas.

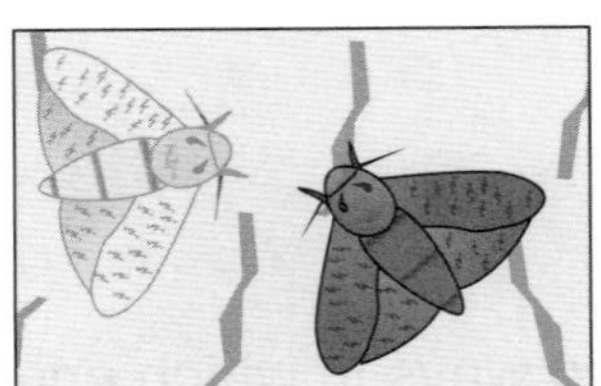

2. A dark-coloured variety — they are better camouflaged on sooty tree trunks in badly polluted areas.

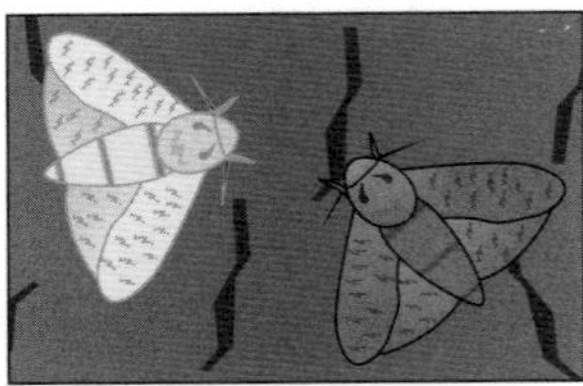

The dark variety of the moth was first recorded in the North of England in 1848. It became increasingly common in polluted areas until the 1960s, when the number of soot covered trees declined because of the introduction of new laws.

8 (a) (i) Which variety of moth has a better chance of survival in a soot polluted area?

....

(1 mark)

8 (a) (ii) Using the idea of natural selection, explain why this variety of moth became more common in soot polluted areas.

....

....

....

(2 marks)

Leave blank

8 (b) The bar chart shows the percentages of dark- and light-coloured peppered moths in two different towns.

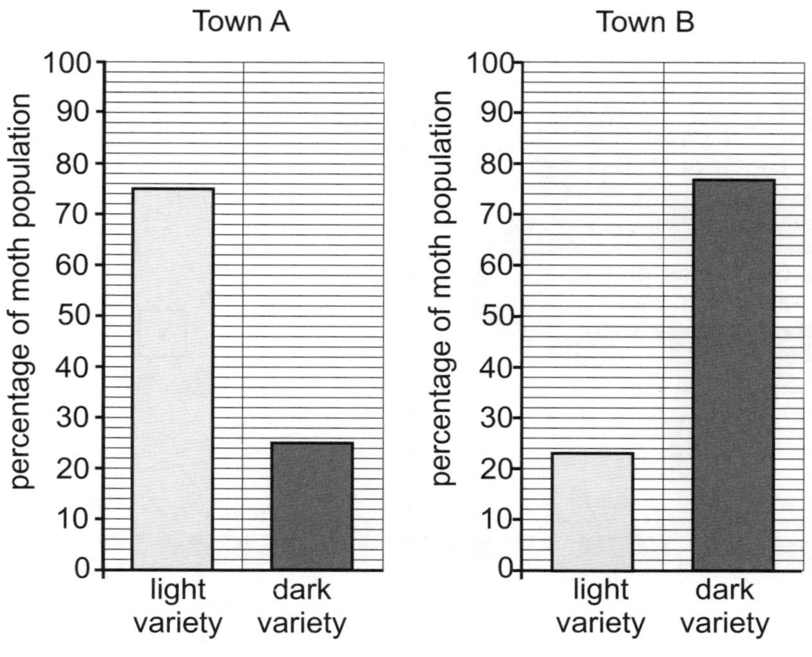

8 (b) (i) Which town is the most polluted, **A** or **B**? ☐

Explain your answer.

....

....

(1 mark)

8 (b) (ii) Calculate the percentage difference between the dark-coloured moth population in Town A and Town B.

....

....

(2 marks)

6

Turn over for the next question

Leave blank

9 The diagram below shows the carbon cycle.

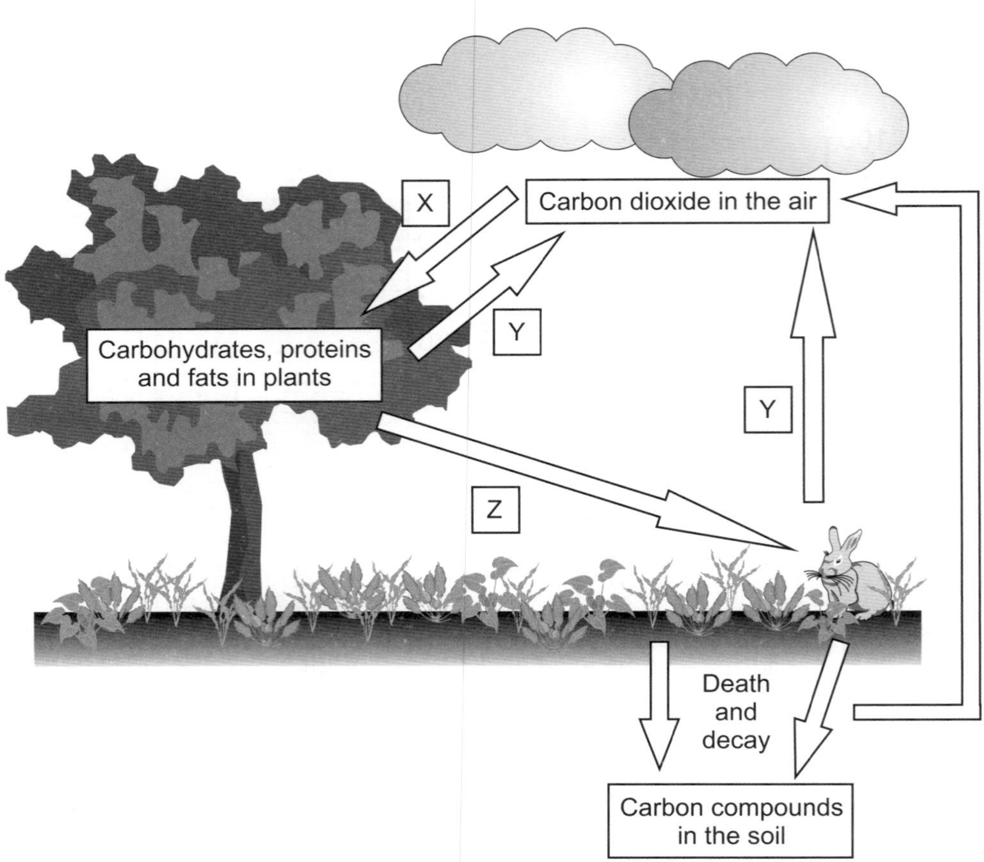

9 (a) Describe what is occurring at points **X**, **Y** and **Z** in the cycle.

....

....

....

....

....

(3 marks)

9 (b) How are microorganisms involved in the carbon cycle?

....

....

....

(2 marks)

5

END OF QUESTIONS

GCSE AQA Science

Unit Biology 2

Higher Tier

In addition to this paper you should have:
- A ruler.
- A calculator.

Centre name					
Centre number					
Candidate number					

Time allowed:
- 60 minutes

Surname
Other names
Candidate signature

Instructions to candidates
- Write your name and other details in the spaces provided above.
- Answer **all** questions in the spaces provided.
- Do all rough work on the paper.

Information for candidates
- The marks available are given in brackets at the end of each question.
- There are 7 questions in this paper.
- There are 60 marks available for this paper.
- You are allowed to use a calculator.
- You should answer Question 4(b) and Question 7(c) with continuous prose. You will be assessed on the quality of your English, the organisation of your ideas and your use of appropriate specialist vocabulary.

For examiner's use

Q	Attempt Nº 1	2	3	Q	Attempt Nº 1	2	3
1				5			
2				6			
3				7			
4							
				Total			

Advice to candidates
- In calculations show clearly how you worked out your answers.

Leave blank

Answer **all** questions in the spaces provided

1 Jeremy and Trisha investigated the organisms that live in a field next to their school.

1 (a) They each counted the number of plants in the area of the field they were standing in using a 1 m^2 quadrat. They got the following results.

	Number counted per m^2		
Plant	**Jeremy**	**Trisha**	**Mean per m^2**
Dandelions	5	7	6
Clover		96	89
Nettles	23	19	21
Buttercups	57	63	

1 (a) (i) Fill in the missing numbers in the results table above.

(2 marks)

1 (a) (ii) The field measures 50 m by 70 m. Use the data in the table to estimate the total population of dandelions in the field.

....

....

....

(2 marks)

1 (b) Suggest how Jeremy and Trisha could improve their investigation.

....

....

....

....

(2 marks)

Leave blank

6

Turn over for the next question

Leave blank

2 Some pondweed was used to investigate how the amount of light available affects the rate of photosynthesis.

The apparatus that was used for this experiment is shown below.

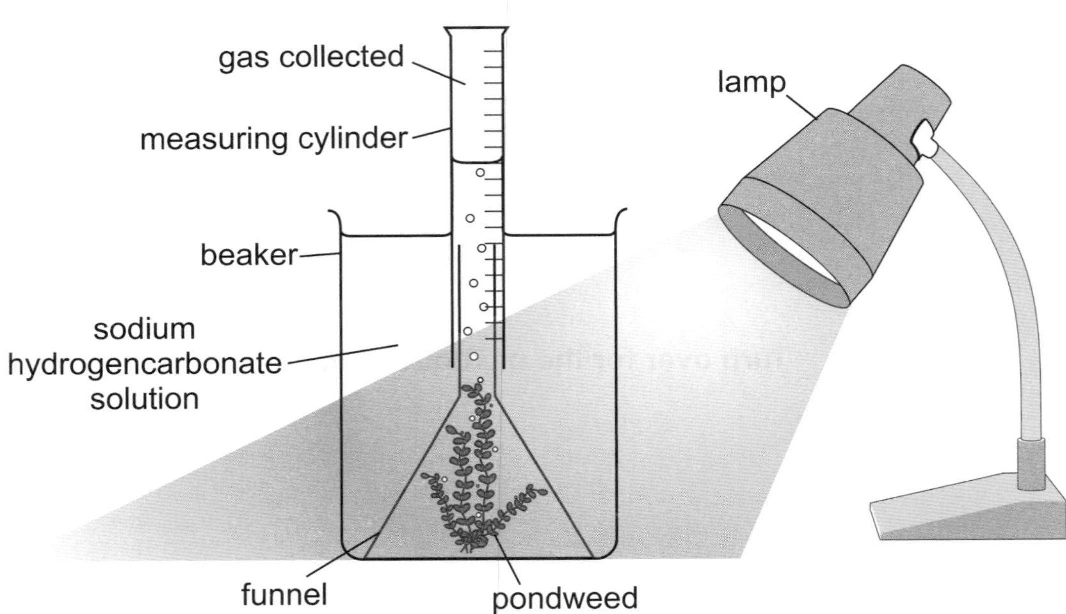

2 (a) What gas is being collected in the measuring cylinder?

....

(1 mark)

2 (b) What would happen to the volume of gas collected if the investigation was repeated with the lamp turned off? Give a reason for your answer.

....

....

....

(2 marks)

2 (c) Sodium hydrogen carbonate dissolves in water and releases carbon dioxide.

Suggest why sodium hydrogen carbonate was added to the water in this experiment.

....

....

....

(2 marks)

2 (d) Explain how temperature affects the rate of photosynthesis and suggest how this could be controlled in the experiment.

....

....

....

....

....

....

(3 marks)

2 (e) When plants photosynthesise they produce glucose.
Give **three** ways plants use the glucose they produce.

1. ....

2. ....

3. ....

(3 marks)

11

Turn over for the next question

Leave blank

3 The diagram below shows the stomach. The stomach is an organ. It is an important part of the digestive system.

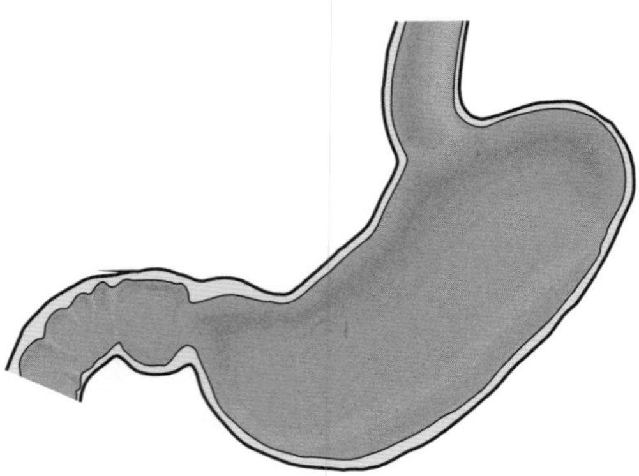

3 (a) State what is meant by the term **organ**.

....

....
(1 mark)

3 (b) The stomach contains different tissues.
Name **two** types of tissue found in the stomach and describe the role of each.

Tissue: ....

Role: ....

....

Tissue: ....

Role: ....

....
(4 marks)

5

Leave blank

4 The diagram below shows a single celled organism called *Euglena*, found in pond water.

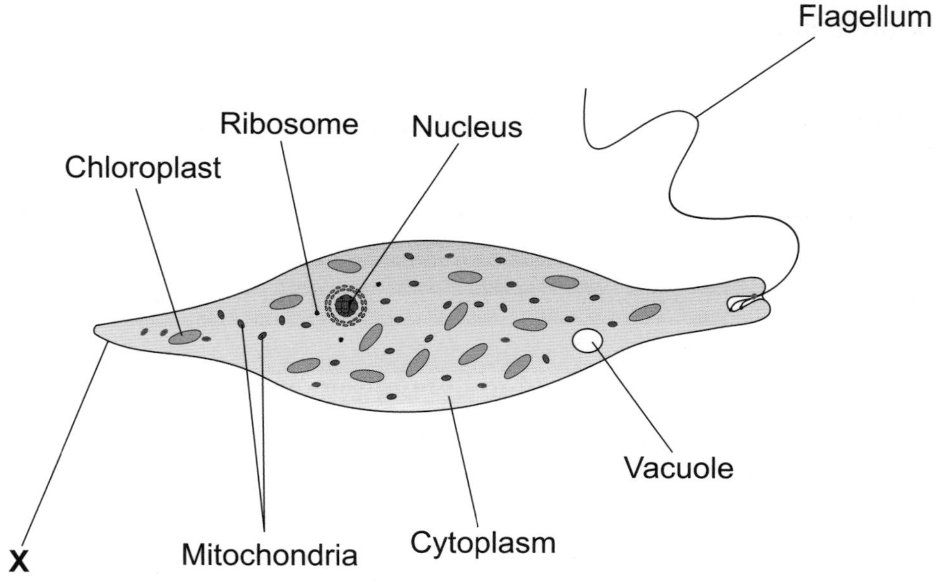

4 (a) Name part **X** and state its function.

....

....

(2 marks)

Question 4 continues on the next page

4 (b) *In this question you will be assessed on the quality of your English, the organisation of your ideas and your use of appropriate specialist vocabulary.*

When *Euglena* was first discovered, scientists disagreed over whether it was a plant or an animal.

Discuss the similarities and differences between plant and animal cells.

....

....

....

....

....

....

....

....

....

....

(6 marks)

Lea
blar

8

Leave blank

5 Gregor Mendel proposed the idea of separate 'hereditary units'.
In one experiment he investigated the inheritance of round or wrinkled seed coats in pea plants. The allele for round seed coats (R) is dominant over the allele for wrinkled seed coats (r).

Mendel first crossed pure-breeding round seed plants (RR) with pure-breeding wrinkled seed plants (rr). All the offspring had round seeds.

5 (a) Explain how the experiment shows that the allele for round seeds is dominant.

....

....
(2 marks)

5 (b) He then crossed the offspring together.

5 (b) (i) Draw a genetic diagram to show the predicted results of this cross.

(3 marks)

Question 5 continues on the next page

5 (b) (ii) When Mendel crossed the offspring, 7324 plants were produced. 5474 of these had round seed coats and the other 1850 had wrinkled seed coats.

Calculate the ratio of round to wrinkled seed coats in Mendel's results. Give your answer to **two** decimal places.

....

....

(2 marks)

5 (b) (iii) Explain why this ratio does not exactly match the ratio predicted by your genetic diagram.

....

....

(1 mark)

5 (c) Suggest **one** reason why Mendel's proposal was not recognised by scientists until after his death.

....

....

(1 mark)

Lea
blar

9

Leave blank

6 Nancy is a cyclist. A sports physiologist has produced a graph to show how the concentration of lactic acid in her blood changes with different work rates.

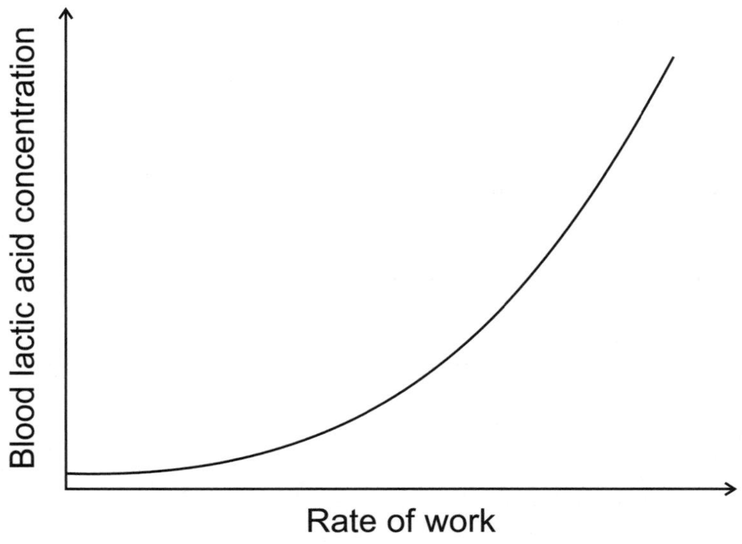

Blood lactic acid concentration

Rate of work

6 (a) (i) Describe the trend shown by the graph.

....

....

....

(2 marks)

6 (a) (ii) Suggest a reason for the trend you have described above.

....

....

....

....

....

(3 marks)

Question 6 continues on the next page

6 (b) Nancy takes part in a sprint race. Describe what will happen to Nancy's pulse rate and breathing rate immediately after her race, and explain why.

Leave blank

....

....

....

....

....

....

(3 marks)

8

Leave blank

7 Enzymes have many uses in the home and in industry.

7 (a) The enzyme amylase is often used in biological washing powders.

Asif did an experiment on the effect of temperature on the action of amylase. The graph below shows Asif's results.

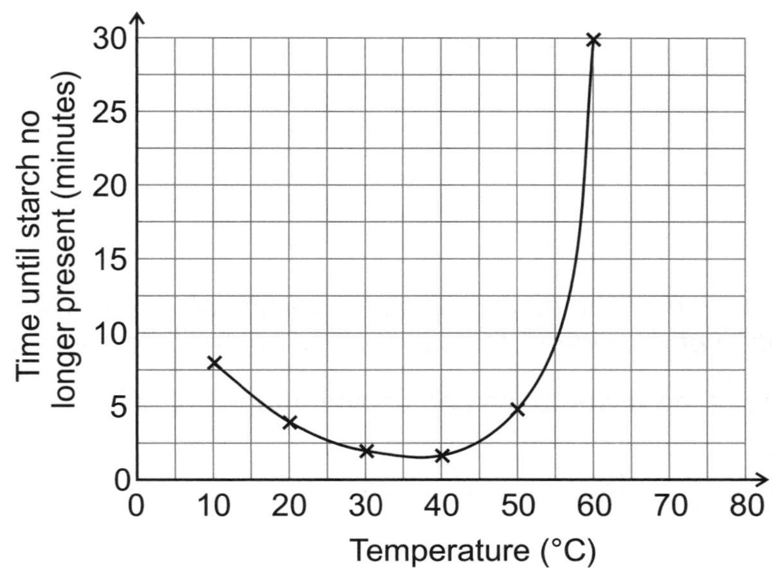

7 (a) (i) Use the graph to estimate the optimum temperature for this enzyme.

....
(1 mark)

7 (a) (ii) Explain the results between 50 °C and 60 °C.

....

....

....
(2 marks)

7 (a) (iii) Name **two** enzymes other than amylase that are often used in biological detergents.

1. ....

2. ....
(2 marks)

Question 7 continues on the next page

7 (b) Describe **two** ways that enzymes are used in the food industry.

Leave blank

1. ....

....

2. ....

....

(2 marks)

7 (c) *In this question you will be assessed on the quality of your English, the organisation of your ideas and your use of appropriate specialist vocabulary.*

Discuss some of the advantages and disadvantages of using enzymes in industry.

....

....

....

....

....

....

....

....

....

....

(6 marks)

13

END OF QUESTIONS

GCSE AQA Science

Unit Biology 3

Higher Tier

In addition to this paper you should have:
- A ruler.
- A calculator.

Centre name					
Centre number					
Candidate number					

Time allowed:
- 60 minutes

Surname
Other names
Candidate signature

Instructions to candidates
- Write your name and other details in the spaces provided above.
- Answer **all** questions in the spaces provided.
- Do all rough work on the paper.

Information for candidates
- The marks available are given in brackets at the end of each question.
- There are 10 questions in this paper.
- There are 60 marks available for this paper.
- You are allowed to use a calculator.
- You should answer Question 10(c) with continuous prose. You will be assessed on the quality of your English, the organisation of your ideas and your use of appropriate specialist vocabulary.

Advice to candidates
- In calculations show clearly how you worked out your answers.

For examiner's use

Q	Attempt Nº 1	2	3	Q	Attempt Nº 1	2	3
1				6			
2				7			
3				8			
4				9			
5				10			
				Total			

Leave blank

Answer **all** questions in the spaces provided

1 Read this extract from a report by a lifeboat crew member, then answer the questions that follow.

> "We were very concerned when we received news of a man lost overboard tonight because the sea is extremely cold at this time of year. Fortunately, we found him quickly and were able to rescue him before he suffered any serious ill effects. His skin was very cold when we picked him up, but his core body temperature was normal."

1 (a) What is the normal core body temperature of a human?

....

(1 mark)

1 (b) Describe how the brain obtains information about the body's core temperature and skin temperature.

....

....

....

(3 marks)

1 (c) Explain **two** ways in which the man's body may have helped prevent his core temperature from falling whilst he was in the sea.

....

....

....

....

....

(4 marks)

8

Leave blank

2 The diagram below shows an alveolus and a blood capillary.

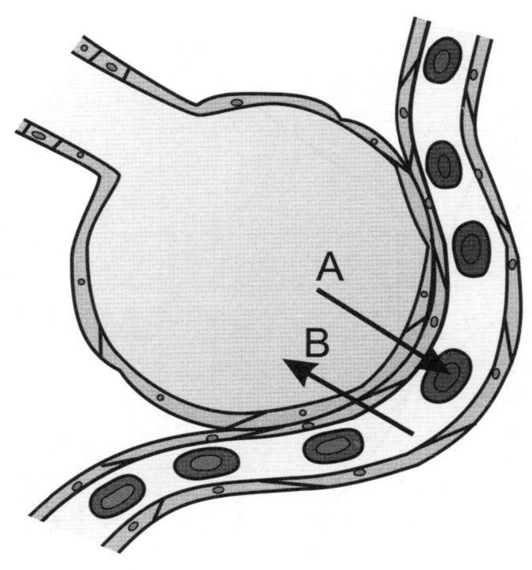

2 (a) The arrows on the diagram show the net movement of two gases, A and B.

Name gases **A** and **B**.

Gas A: ....

Gas B: ....

(1 mark)

2 (b) Describe how alveoli are adapted for gas exchange.

....

....

....

(3 marks)

4

Turn over for the next question

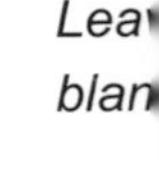

3 A scientist measured the rate of transpiration in two plants over 48 hours. The results are shown in the graph below.

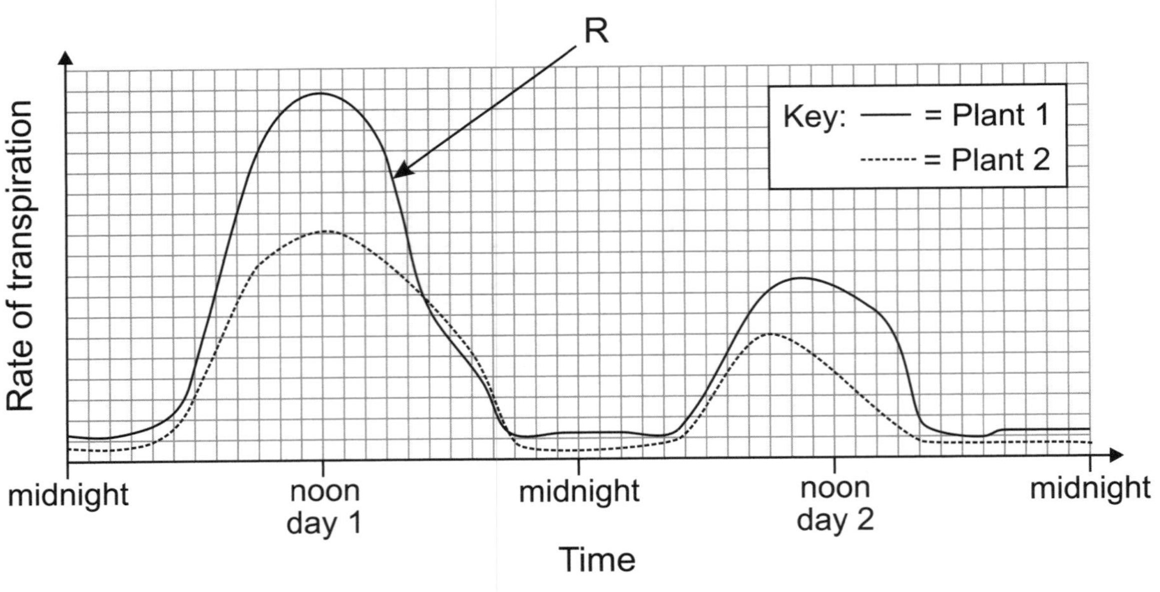

3 (a) At what time on **day 2** was the rate of transpiration highest for **plant 2**?

....

(1 mark)

3 (b) The rate of transpiration for both plants was slower on **day 2** than on **day 1**. Suggest **one** explanation for this.

....

....

....

(2 marks)

Leave blank

3 (c) At time **R** on the graph, plant 1 was wilting. Suggest **one** explanation for this.

....

....

(1 mark)

3 (d) Describe how a transpiration stream moves water through a plant.

....

....

....

....

....

....

(3 marks)

7

Turn over for the next question

4 Jenny is carrying out an experiment to investigate osmosis.

4 (a) What is osmosis?

....

....

(1 mark)

Jenny cut cylinders out of potatoes and has placed them into different concentrations of sugar solution, as shown in the diagram below.

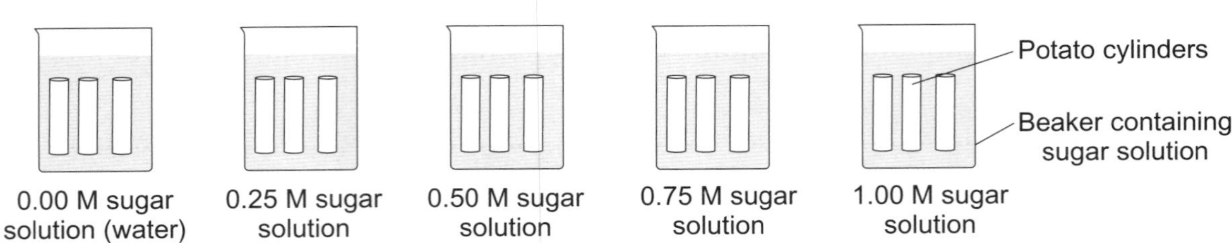

She measured the mass of the cylinders of potato before and after they had been placed in different concentrations of sugar solution for 20 minutes. Her results are shown below.

Concentration of sugar solution (molarity)	Experiment	Mass at start (g)	Mass at end (g)	Change in mass (g)	Mean change in mass (g)
0.00	1	1.9	2.57	+ 0.67	+ 0.67
	2	1.9	2.55	+ 0.65	
	3	1.9	2.59	+ 0.69	
0.25	1	1.9	2.15	+ 0.25	+ 0.23
	2	1.9	2.11	+ 0.21	
	3	1.9	2.12	+ 0.22	
0.50	1	1.9	1.72	– 0.18	– 0.16
	2	1.9	1.79	– 0.11	
	3	1.9	1.7	– 0.2	
0.75	1	1.9	1.51		
	2	1.9	1.45		
	3	1.9	1.49		
1.00	1	1.9	1.19	– 0.71	– 0.69
	2	1.9	1.25	– 0.65	
	3	1.9	1.18	– 0.72	

4 (b) Fill in the missing numbers in the results table above.

(2 marks)

Leave blank

4 (c) Draw a graph of the concentration of sugar solution against the average change in mass on the grid below.

Leave blank

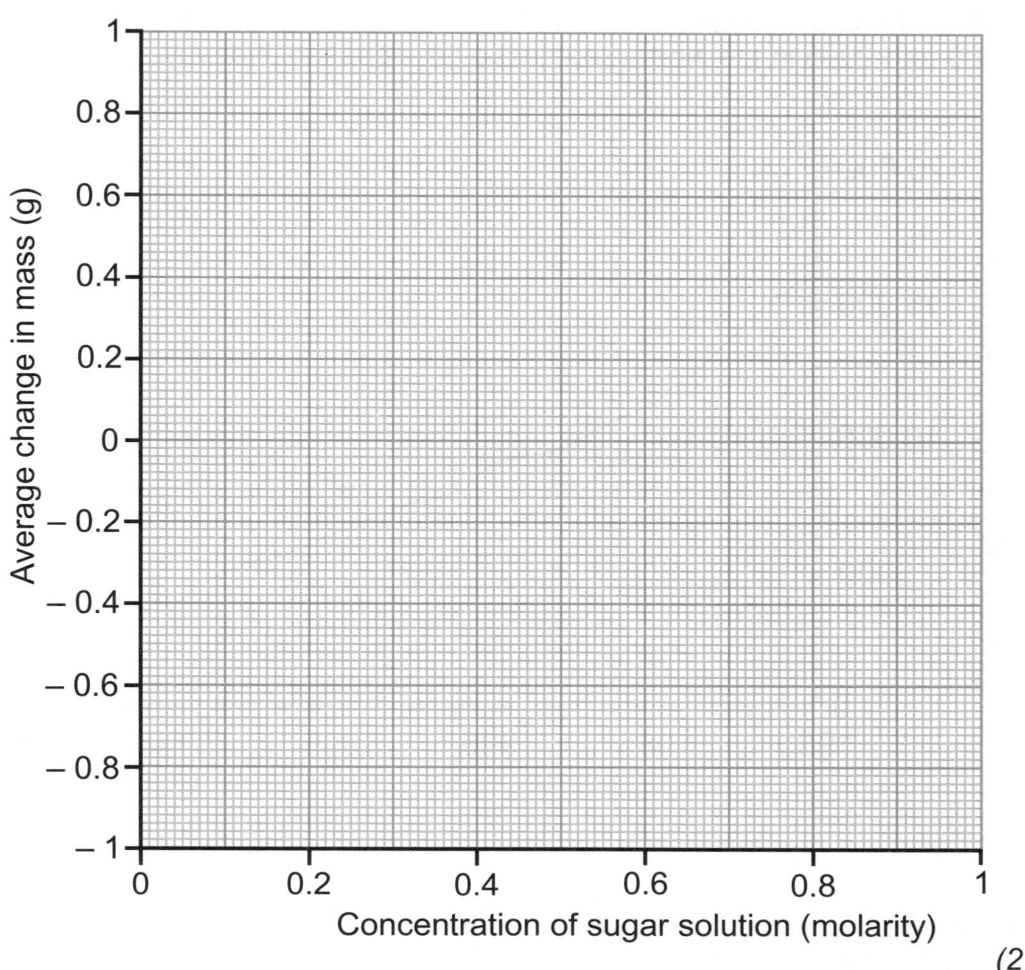

(2 marks)

4 (d) Use the graph to estimate the concentration of sugar inside the original potatoes. Explain your answer.

....

....

....

(2 marks)

4 (e) Suggest why Jenny repeated the experiment and took the mean of the results.

....

(1 mark)

8

Turn over for the next question

Leave blank

5 Many people fear that cod supplies from the North Sea may run out in the near future. To prevent this, cod stocks need to be fished sustainably.

The graph shows how the population of cod has changed between 1980 and 2005 in the North Sea, just off the coast of Norway.

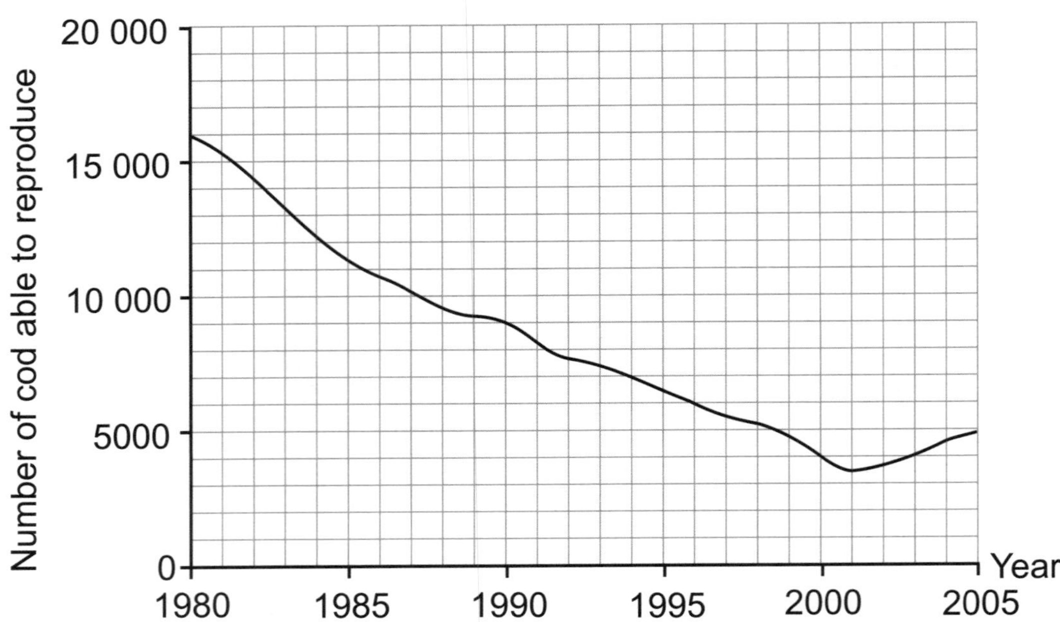

5 (a) Calculate the percentage reduction in North Sea cod numbers between 1980 and 2000.

....

....

....

(2 marks)

Leave blank

5 (b) Describe the trend shown by the graph and suggest reasons for the trend you have described.

....

....

....

....

....

....

....

(4 marks)

5 (c) Explain what is meant by producing food sustainably.

....

....

....

(1 mark)

7

Turn over for the next question

Leave blank

6 A biogas generator, like the one shown below, has been built near a town.

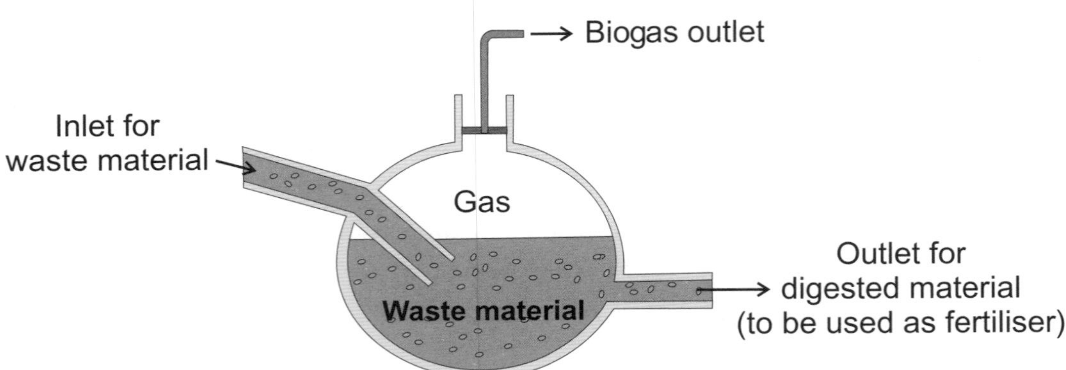

Animal and human waste together with agricultural waste are placed in the biogas generator. Biogas collects at the top of the generator and can be tapped off when needed.

6 (a) Describe how biogas is produced in the generator.

....

....
(1 mark)

6 (b) The biogas generator is constructed so that most of it is underground. This makes it easier to keep it at a constant temperature. Explain why biogas production is affected by temperature.

....

....
(1 mark)

6 (c) Before fitting the biogas generator, the town's inhabitants used coal as their main energy source.

Give **one** advantage of using biogas instead of coal.

....

....
(1 mark)

3

Leave blank

7 The diagram below shows a human heart.

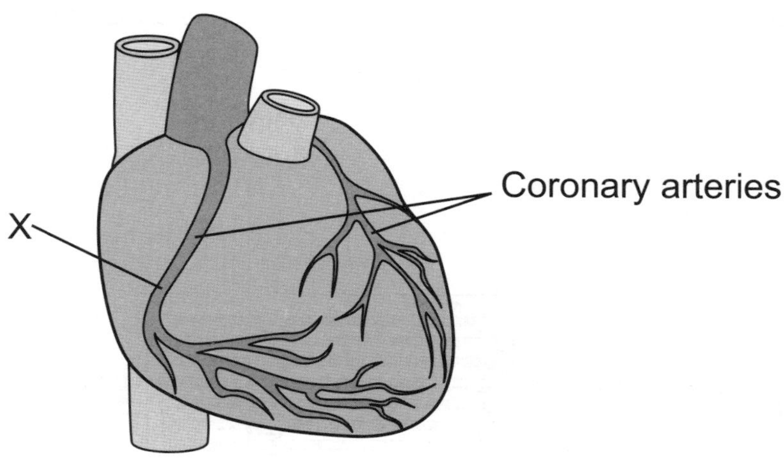

7 (a) Explain what would happen if the coronary artery was blocked at the point labelled **X**.

....

....

....

(2 marks)

7 (b) Malcolm has fatty deposits in the walls of one of his coronary arteries. They are beginning to block the blood supply to his heart muscle.

Malcolm's doctor recommends that he is treated using a stent.

7 (b) (i) Explain how having a stent fitted could help Malcolm's condition.

....

....

(1 mark)

7 (b) (ii) Suggest **one** potential disadvantage to Malcolm of having a stent fitted.

....

....

(1 mark)

4

Turn over for the next question

Leave blank

8 People suffering from kidney failure may be treated using a kidney dialysis machine.

The diagram below shows how one type of dialysis machine works.

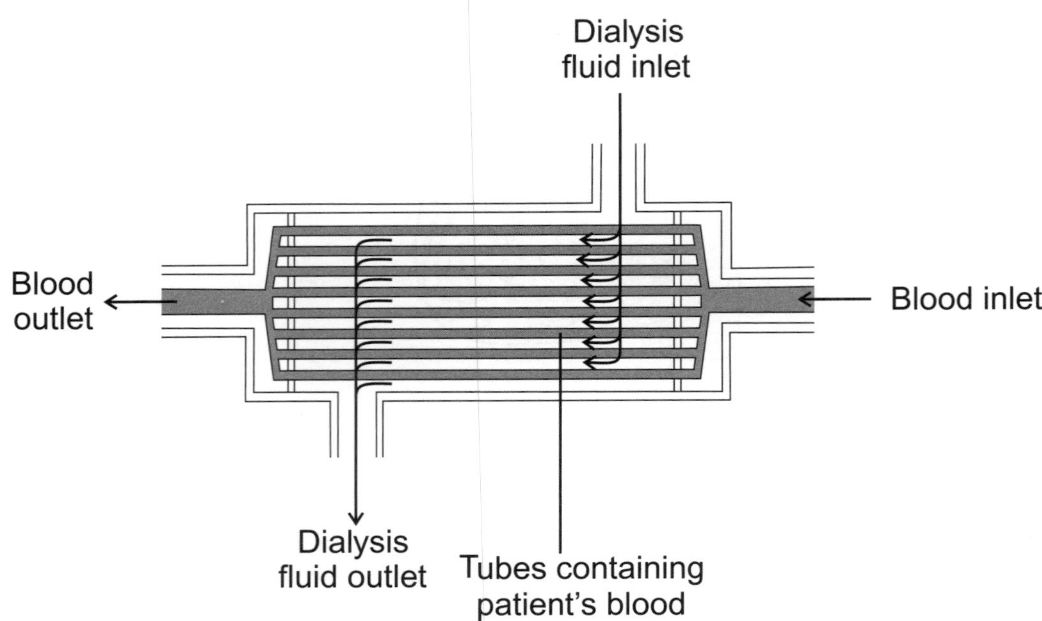

8 (a) Explain, as fully as you can, how a dialysis machine works.

....

....

....

....

....

....

(3 marks)

8 (b) People with kidney failure may also be treated by a kidney transplant.

Give **one** advantage and **one** disadvantage to the patient of having a kidney transplant rather than dialysis treatment.

Advantage:

....

....

Disadvantage:

....

....

(2 marks)

Leave blank

5

Turn over for the next question

Leave blank

9 Carbon dioxide can be sequestered in natural stores, like peat bogs.

9 (a) Explain how the destruction of peat bogs can affect global warming.

....

....

....

(2 marks)

9 (b) Name **two** other natural stores of carbon dioxide.

1. ....

2. ....

(2 marks)

4

Leave blank

10 A large proportion of pork produced in the UK comes from pigs that have been reared using intensive farming practices.

10(a) The diagram below shows how much of the energy supplied in pig food is transferred to pork meat.

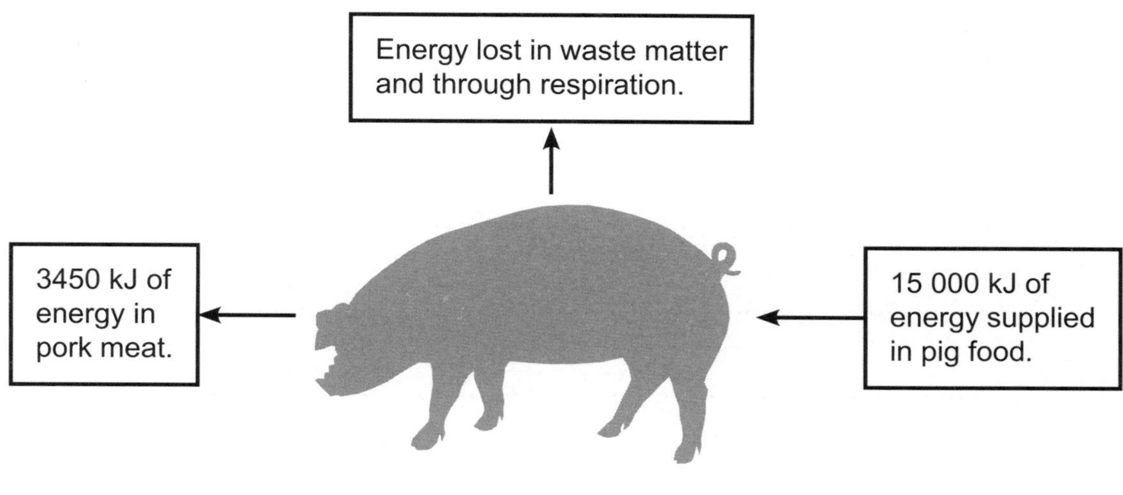

Calculate the percentage of energy in the pig's feed that is lost in waste matter and through respiration.

....

....

....

(2 marks)

10(b) Explain how intensive farming methods can reduce the energy lost from pigs in order to increase their growth.

....

....

....

(2 marks)

Question 10 continues on the next page

228

Leave blank

10(c) *In this question you will be assessed on the quality of your English, the organisation of your ideas and your use of appropriate specialist vocabulary.*

Evaluate the use of intensive farming practices to produce meat.

....

....

....

....

....

....

....

....

....

....

....

....

....

(6 marks)

10

END OF QUESTIONS

Page 23

Warm-Up Questions

1) E.g. because they are a good source of energy.
2) E.g. high blood pressure.
3) Any three of, e.g. slow growth in children / fatigue / poor resistance to infection / irregular periods in women.
4) increase
5) It increases your risk of heart disease.
6) E.g. is the report a scientific study, published in a reputable journal? / Was it written by a qualified person not connected with the people selling the product? / Was the sample of people asked/tested large enough to give reliable results? / Have there been other studies which found similar results?

Exam Questions

1 (a) Any one of, e.g. protein / fibre / minerals / fats ***(1 mark)***.
(b) Having a diet that is unbalanced/badly out of balance ***(1 mark)***.
(c) Any one of, e.g. arthritis / type 2 diabetes / high blood pressure / heart disease / some kinds of cancer ***(1 mark)***.

2 (a) $(40 \div 100) \times 512 = 204.8$ kcal OR $(512 \div 100) \times 40 = 204.8$ kcal
(2 marks for correct answer, otherwise 1 mark for correct working)
(b) Food B is healthier. It contains much less energy/carbohydrate/fat, so it is less likely to cause obesity ***(1 mark)***. It also contains more iron, which is an important mineral for health ***(1 mark)***. It contains more protein, which is important for growth and repair ***(1 mark)***.

3 (a) Dave ***(1 mark)***, energy ***(1 mark)***
(b) Exercise increases the amount of energy used by the body and decreases the amount stored as fat ***(1 mark)***. It also builds muscle so it helps to boost your metabolic rate ***(1 mark)***. The more energy you use (and the less fat you store), the less likely you are to become obese ***(1 mark)***.
(c) Any one of: e.g. his diet may be too high in carbohydrate/fat / he may have hormonal problems / he may have an underactive thyroid gland/ other inherited factor ***(1 mark)***.

Page 32

Warm-Up Questions

1) A microorganism that enters the body and causes disease.
2) Viruses replicate by invading your cells and using the cell machinery to produce many copies of themselves. Then they cause the cell to break open, releasing new viruses into your body.
3) Unique molecules on the surface of cells/pathogens/microorganisms.
4) To kill/harm pathogenic bacteria without killing your own body cells.
5) To prevent the growth of harmful pathogens.
6) A big outbreak of disease.
7) When a disease spreads all over the world.

Exam Questions

1 (a) Flu is caused by a virus ***(1 mark)*** and antibiotics are not effective against viruses ***(1 mark)***.
(b) Inappropriate use of antibiotics increases the chances of antibiotic-resistant strains of bacteria emerging ***(1 mark)***.

2 White blood cells ingest/engulf pathogens ***(1 mark)***, produce antibodies that kill pathogens ***(1 mark)*** and produce antitoxins that counteract the pathogenic toxins ***(1 mark)***.

3 When a person is vaccinated against typhoid, they are injected with dead/ inactive typhoid bacteria ***(1 mark)***. The dead/inactive bacteria carry antigens ***(1 mark)***, which cause the body to produce antibodies to attack them ***(1 mark)***. If live typhoid bacteria infect the body after this, white blood cells can rapidly mass produce antibodies to kill off the bacteria ***(1 mark)***.

Page 38

Warm-Up Questions

1) eyes, ears, nose, tongue, skin
2) as electrical impulses
3) muscles and glands
4) a synapse
5) glands
6) E.g. nerves carry messages faster than hormones. / Nerves act for a short time but hormones act for a long time.

Exam Questions

1 (a) A reflex/reflex action ***(1 mark)***
(b) (i) B ***(1 mark)***
(ii)D ***(1 mark)***
(c) When the electrical impulse reaches the end of the neurone, it stimulates the release of a chemical ***(1 mark)***. The chemical diffuses across the synapse to activate an electrical impulse in the next neurone ***(1 mark)***.
(d) Any one of, they minimise damage to the body (because they are so quick) / they help to prevent injury ***(1 mark)***.

2 FSH is produced by the pituitary gland ***(1 mark)***. It is carried in the blood plasma to other parts of the body ***(1 mark)***. It acts on target cells in the ovaries stimulating them to produce oestrogen ***(1 mark)***.

Page 46-47

Warm-Up Questions

1) Day 1 is when the bleeding starts.
2) The growth of a plant in response to light.
3) auxin
4) E.g. water / ions / temperature / blood sugar level.
5) This is the optimal temperature for most enzymes in the body.

Exam Questions

1 (a) It inhibits it ***(1 mark)***.
(b) FSH ***(1 mark)***
(c) day 14 ***(1 mark)***

2 (a) Keeping oestrogen levels permanently high inhibits production of FSH ***(1 mark)***, so no eggs mature / so egg development and production stop ***(1 mark)***.
(b) (i) E.g. low oestrogen pills have fewer side effects ***(1 mark)***.
(ii) progesterone ***(1 mark)***

3 (a) Katie. She will lose more water through her skin than Colin because she will be sweating more ***(1 mark)***.
(b) Katie. She will have more concentrated urine than Colin because she will be losing more water through sweating (and breathing) ***(1 mark)***.
(c) All the functions of your body which try to maintain a constant internal environment ***(1 mark)***.

4 (a) The right side ***(1 mark)***.
(b) Auxin is produced in the tip and moves backwards/down the stem ***(1 mark)***, so there is more auxin on the right side ***(1 mark)***. This makes the cells grow/elongate faster on the right side, so the stem grows to the left ***(1 mark)***.
(c) Because light would change the distribution of the auxin ***(1 mark)***.

5 (a) Selective weedkillers are made of plant hormones which only affect broad-leaved plants ***(1 mark)***. So they kill weeds, but not (cereal) crops ***(1 mark)***.
(b) E.g. rooting powder ***(1 mark)***

6 (a) kidney ***(1 mark)***
(b) brain ***(1 mark)***

7 How to grade your answer:

0 marks: No benefits or drawbacks of using the contraceptive pill or IVF are given.

1-2 marks: One or two benefits and drawbacks are suggested.

3-4 marks: Some benefits and drawbacks are given. The answer has a logical structure and spelling, grammar and punctuation are mostly correct.

5-6 marks: A number of benefits and drawbacks are given. The answer has a logical structure and uses correct spelling, grammar and punctuation.

Here are some points your answer may include:

The contraceptive pill:

The pill is over 99% effective at preventing pregnancy, although there is still a very slight chance of getting pregnant.

It can cause side-effects like headaches, nausea, irregular menstrual bleeding, and fluid retention.

It doesn't protect against sexually transmitted diseases.

IVF:

It can give an infertile couple a child.

Some women have a strong reaction to the hormones, e.g. abdominal pain, vomiting, dehydration.

Multiple births can happen if more than one embryo grows into a baby, which are risky for the mother and babies.

There are risks associated with most medical treatments, and IVF is no exception. People who decide to undergo IVF treatment should know and understand the risks, but if it's the only way they can have a child, then perhaps the benefits outweigh those risks.

Page 52

Warm-Up Questions

1) A substance that alters chemical reactions in the body.
2) To lower their risk of heart and circulatory disease.
3) A placebo is a substance that's like the real drug but doesn't do anything (e.g. a 'sugar pill' instead of a drug). Using a placebo allows the doctor to see the actual difference the drug makes.
4) Any two of, e.g. ecstasy, cannabis, heroin, cocaine.
5) Any one of, e.g. caffeine, alcohol, nicotine.

Exam Questions

1 (a) E.g. taking steroids increases muscle size ***(1 mark)*** so taking them can improve an athlete's performance ***(1 mark)***.

(b) E.g. taking steroids can have negative health effects. / The athlete may not want to gain an unfair advantage over other competitors. ***(1 mark)***

2 (a) Drinking alcohol slows reactions, so a driver might not react to a problem quickly enough to stop an accident happening ***(1 mark)***.

(b) If a person stops drinking alcohol they will suffer physical withdrawal symptoms ***(1 mark)***.

(c) Any two of, e.g. increased crime/violence / costs to the NHS / costs to economy through lost working days. ***(1 mark for each)***

3 (a) E.g. it stunted the growth of fetuses' arms and legs ***(1 mark)***.

(b) E.g. leprosy / some cancers ***(1 mark)***

4 (a) To make sure that it doesn't have any harmful side effects when the body is working normally ***(1 mark)***.

(b) A double-blind clinical trial means that neither the patient nor the doctor ***(1 mark)*** knows which patients have been given the drug and which the placebo until all the results have been gathered ***(1 mark)***. This is so the doctors monitoring the patients and analysing the results aren't subconsciously influenced by their knowledge ***(1 mark)***.

Revision Summary for Biology 1a (page 53)

2) Professional runner, mechanic, secretary

16)(a) Response A

(b) Response B

Page 58

Warm-Up Questions

1) Keeping the surface area to volume ratio to a minimum reduces heat loss.
2) E.g. bright warning colours to scare predators away.
3) E.g. lichens
4) The river is very polluted.
5) E.g. a rain gauge.

Exam Questions

1 (a) It camouflages them to make it easier for them to sneak up on prey/avoid predators ***(1 mark)***.

(b) Blubber provides insulation ***(1 mark)*** and acts as an energy store when food is scarce ***(1 mark)***.

(c) It makes it easier for them to shed water ***(1 mark)*** preventing cooling by evaporation ***(1 mark)***.

2 Any three of, e.g. has spines instead of leaves to reduce water loss / small surface area compared to volume reduces water loss from evaporation / storing water in its stem / extensive shallow root system to absorb water over a wide area / deep roots to access underground water ***(1 mark each)***.

3 (a) In a woodland area ***(1 mark)***.

(b) (i) competition ***(1 mark)***

(ii) The population of Species A is likely to decrease ***(1 mark)***, because the number of beetles available to eat will decrease ***(1 mark)*** as Species B will be feeding on them too ***(1 mark)***.

Page 63-64

Warm-Up Questions

1) A feeding level in a food chain or web.
2) Biomass is basically the mass of living material at a trophic level — how much it weighs.
3) So much energy is lost at each stage that there's not enough left to support more organisms after four or five stages.
4) A community where the materials taken out of the soil and used are balanced by those that are put back in.
5) Green plants and algae.
6) burning/combustion

Exam Questions

1 (a) 25 caterpillars $\times$ 2.5 g = 62.5 g ***(1 mark)***

(b) C. The mass of the organisms decreases at each trophic level as shown by this pyramid ***(1 mark)***.

(c) Their energy initially comes from the Sun ***(1 mark)***.

2 (a) Materials in living organisms are returned to the environment either in waste materials ***(1 mark)*** or when they die and decay ***(1 mark)***. Microorganisms break down the materials, returning them to the environment to be taken up again by organisms ***(1 mark)***.

(b) Any two of, e.g. warm / good oxygen supply / lots of decomposers ***(1 mark for each)***

3 Some of the energy taken in by the mice is lost to the surroundings as heat ***(1 mark)***. Some energy is lost in the waste material excreted by the mice ***(1 mark)***. Some of the material that makes up the mice is inedible, so energy from this material doesn't pass to the owl ***(1 mark)***.

4 (a) (i) A = decay / respiration *(1 mark)*.
(ii) B = eating / feeding *(1 mark)*.
(iii) C = respiration *(1 mark)*.
(b) There would be less photosynthesis and so more carbon dioxide in the atmosphere/less carbon dioxide removed from the atmosphere *(1 mark)*.
(c) photosynthesis *(1 mark)*

Page 69

Warm-Up Questions

1) a) eye colour
b) scar
c) weight
2) the nucleus
3) A short length of a chromosome that controls the development of different characteristics.
4) one parent

Exam Questions

1 (a) sperm and egg *(1 mark)*
(b) 23 *(1 mark)*
(c) 46 *(1 mark)*
(d) half *(1 mark)*
2 (a) Ruth and Mark have (inherited) different eye-colour genes *(1 mark)*.
(b) During sexual reproduction, an individual receives a mixture of genes/chromosomes from both parents *(1 mark)*. The combination that it receives determines what features it inherits *(1 mark)*.
3 (a) Yes *(1 mark)*. Flower colour is controlled by genes *(1 mark)* and the two plants have exactly the same genetic material *(1 mark)*.
(b) No *(1 mark)*. Environmental factors affect plant height as well as genes *(1 mark)*. Since the plants are in different environments, they will probably be different heights *(1 mark)*.

Page 74

Warm-Up Questions

1) A few plant cells are put in a growth medium with hormones, and they then grow into new plants that are clones of the parent plant.
2) By taking cuttings.
3) E.g. hundreds of "ideal" offspring can be produced each year.
4) A reduced gene pool is where there are fewer different alleles in a population.
5) E.g. insulin

Exam Questions

1 (a) E.g. to cut the gene out of the donor organism's DNA *(1 mark)*. To cut the DNA of the recipient organism *(1 mark)*.
(b) E.g. to give resistance to viruses/insects/herbicides *(1 mark)*.
(c) E.g. to produce milk containing substances (e.g. drugs) that can be used to treat human diseases. *(1 mark)*.
(d) Any two of, e.g. they could affect the numbers of other plants around the crop, reducing biodiversity / they could increase the risk of food allergies / they might not be safe / transplanted genes could transfer to other plants / super-weeds could develop. *(1 mark each)*

Make sure you can explain the pros and cons of genetic engineering because it's a really controversial issue — and it could easily come up in the exam.

2 (a) Remove the genetic material/nucleus from the unfertilised egg cell of a sheep *(1 mark)*. Insert a complete set of chromosomes from an adult sheep's body cell into the empty egg cell *(1 mark)*. Stimulate the egg cell with an electric shock to make it divide *(1 mark)*. When the embryo is a ball of cells, implant it into a female sheep/surrogate mother to develop *(1 mark)*.
(b) Female. Dolly is a clone, so she must have exactly the same genetic material as her parent *(1 mark)*.
(c) E.g. Cloning can lead to a "reduced gene pool". / It's possible that cloned animals might not be as healthy as normal ones. / Some people worry that it may lead to humans being cloned in the future. *(1 mark)*

Page 78

Warm-Up Questions

1) The idea that life on Earth began as simple organisms from which more complex organisms evolved.
2) Sexual reproduction and mutations.
3) Evolution is the gradual change/adaptation of a population of organisms over time. Natural selection is the process by which evolution occurs.
4) A change in an organism's DNA.
5) No — most mutations have no effect. Occasionally they can be beneficial. (Sometimes they can be harmful.)

Exam Questions

1 (a) Species C *(1 mark)*
(b) Yes, you would expect Species D to look similar to Species E because they share a recent common ancestor, so they are closely related/have similar genes *(1 mark)*.
2 (a) Individuals within a species show variation because of the differences in their genes *(1 mark)*. Some individuals are better adapted to their environment than others and these individuals will be more likely to survive and reproduce *(1 mark)*, passing on their characteristics to the next generation *(1 mark)*. Over generations, the useful characteristics (that lead to a better chance of survival) will become more common in the population *(1 mark)*.

Remember, individuals in a species are naturally selected for but individuals cannot evolve — only a species as a whole can evolve.

(b) E.g. his ideas went against common religious beliefs about how life on Earth developed. / He could not explain how new characteristics appeared or were inherited. / There wasn't enough evidence to convince many scientists because few other studies had been done. *(1 mark for each)*
(c) (i) He thought that if a characteristic was used a lot by an organism then it would become more developed during its lifetime *(1 mark)*. He believed that these acquired characteristics would then be passed on to the next generation *(1 mark)*.
(ii) Lamarck's hypothesis was rejected because experiments didn't support it *(1 mark)*. The discovery of genetics supported Darwin's idea because it provided an explanation of how organisms born with beneficial characteristics can pass them on *(1 mark)*.

Page 87

Warm-Up Questions

1) Plant cells have a rigid cell wall, they have a permanent vacuole and they contain chloroplasts.
2) Diffusion is the spreading out of particles from an area of high concentration to an area of low concentration.
3) (a) To carry oxygen.
(b) Any two of, e.g. concave shape gives the red blood cells a large surface area for absorbing oxygen / concave shape helps the red blood cells pass through capillaries to body cells / no nucleus maximises the space for haemoglobin.

4) differentiation
5) An organ system is a group of organs working together to perform a particular function.
6) Any five of, e.g. salivary glands / pancreas / liver / stomach / large intestine / small intestine.

Exam Questions

1 (a) C ***(1 mark)***
(b) Chlorophyll ***(1 mark)***
(c) E.g. it has a tall shape/a large surface area for absorbing carbon dioxide ***(1 mark)***.

2 (a) B — it has a higher concentration of glucose outside the cell than inside ***(1 mark)***, so glucose will diffuse into the cell ***(1 mark)***.
(b) E.g. oxygen ***(1 mark)***

Page 93-94

Warm-Up Questions

1) Carbon dioxide, water, (sun)light, chlorophyll.
2) A limiting factor is something that stops photosynthesis from happening any faster.
3)

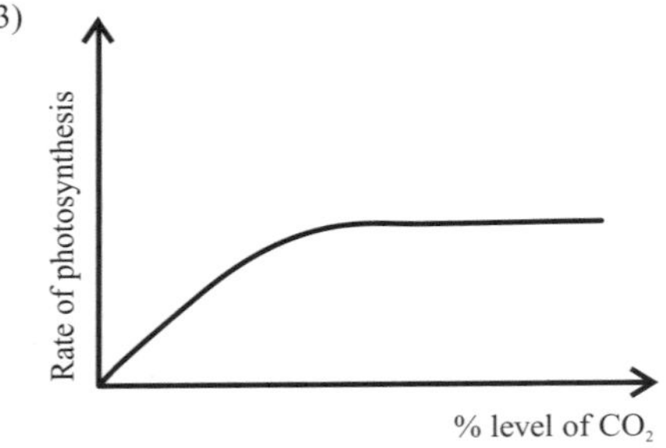

4) E.g. by using a paraffin heater.
5) respiration

Exam Questions

1 Making cell walls — cellulose ***(1 mark)***
Making proteins — amino acids ***(1 mark)***
Storing energy — starch ***(1 mark)***

2 (a) epidermis/epidermal tissue ***(1 mark)***
(b) Any two of, e.g. mesophyll tissue / xylem / phloem ***(1 mark each)***

3 (a) (i) At the higher temperature the molecules/enzymes work more rapidly / there are more collisions and more energetic collisions between reacting molecules, so the rate of photosynthesis is quicker. ***(1 mark)***
(ii) At 50 °C the enzymes are denatured/the plant dies. ***(1 mark)***
(b) In the experiment the rate was highest at this temperature ***(1 mark)***, but the optimum could actually be anywhere between 30 °C and 50 °C (where no measurements were made) ***(1 mark)***.

4 (a) By counting the number of bubbles produced/measuring the volume of gas produced, in a given time/at regular intervals ***(1 mark)***.
(b) (i) The rate of photosynthesis/number of bubbles/volume of gas ***(1 mark)***.
(ii) The light intensity ***(1 mark)***.
(c) E.g. carbon dioxide concentration in the water/temperature/the plant being used ***(1 mark)***.

5 (a) A label anywhere on the sloping part of the graph, before it levels off ***(1 mark)***.
(b) Carbon dioxide concentration / temperature / amount of chlorophyll / amount of water ***(1 mark)***.

6 (a) Chlorophyll ***(1 mark)***.
(b) (i)

(1 mark)

(ii) Plants need both chlorophyll and light to photosynthesise and produce starch — there is only chlorophyll in the green area of the plant ***(1 mark)***, and light can only reach parts of the leaf not covered by black paper ***(1 mark)***.

Page 98

Warm-Up Questions

1) Where an organism is found.
2) A quadrat is a square frame enclosing a known area.
3) The median is the middle value, in order of size, so it's 8.
4) transect

Exam Questions

1 (a) 21 ***(1 mark)***
(b) (i) 6 + 15 + 9 + 14 + 20 + 5 + 3 + 11 + 10 + 7 = 100 ***(1 mark)***
100/10 = 10 dandelions per m^2 ***(1 mark)***
(ii) 90 × 120 = 10 800 m^2 ***(1 mark)***
10 × 10 800 = 108 000 dandelions in field F ***(1 mark)***
(c) Anna's, because she used a larger sample size (20 quadrats per field, whereas Paul only used 10) ***(1 mark)***.

Page 104

Warm-Up Questions

1) A catalyst is a substance that increases the speed of a reaction, without being changed or used up in the reaction.
2) The optimum pH is the pH at which the enzyme works best.
3) They break down big molecules into smaller ones.
4) (a) amylase
(b) protease
(c) lipase
Proteases break down proteins, and lipases break down lipids (fats).
5) (a) sugars
(b) amino acids
(c) glycerol and fatty acids

Exam Questions

1 (a) The enzyme has a specific shape which will only fit with one type of substance ***(1 mark)***.
(b) In the wrong conditions (e.g. high temperatures), the bonds in the enzyme are broken/the enzyme changes shape, so the substance can no longer fit into it/the enzyme won't work anymore ***(1 mark)***.
If you heat a substance you supply it with energy and it moves about more. This helps things to react faster. But if you heat an enzyme too much, it jiggles about such a lot that it ends up breaking some of the bonds that hold it together and it loses its shape. A similar thing happens with pH — the wrong pH disrupts the bonds and the shape is changed.

2 (a)

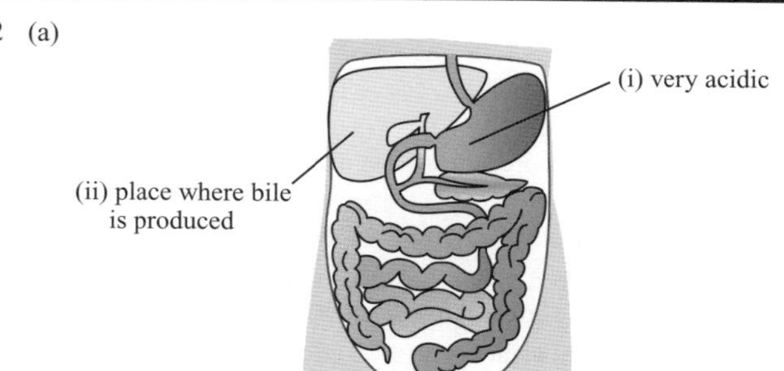

(1 mark for each)

The acidic part is the stomach.
The liver is where bile is produced.

(b) (i) It stores bile until it is ready to be released ***(1 mark)***.

(ii) It produces protease, amylase and lipase enzymes ***(1 mark)*** and releases them into the small intestine ***(1 mark)***.

3 (a) Accept answers between 38 °C and 40 °C ***(1 mark)***.

(b) Enzyme B, because it has an unusually high optimum temperature which it would need to work in the hot vent ***(1 mark)***.

Page 109

Warm-Up Questions

1) Respiration is the process of breaking down glucose to release energy, which happens in every cell.
2) Any three of, e.g. the heart rate increases / the breathing rate increases / respiration rate increases / more energy is released in the muscles / anaerobic respiration may begin.
3) glycogen
4) Proteases are used to pre-digest the protein in some baby foods so it's easier for a baby to digest.
5) carbohydrases

Exam Questions

1 (a) During vigorous exercise the body can't supply enough oxygen to the muscles ***(1 mark)***. It uses anaerobic respiration to provide energy without using oxygen, which keeps the muscles going for longer ***(1 mark)***.

(b) glucose → lactic acid + energy ***(1 mark)***.

(c) It causes a build up of lactic acid, which is painful ***(1 mark)*** and it doesn't release as much energy as aerobic respiration ***(1 mark)***.

2 (a) isomerase ***(1 mark)***

(b) Fructose is sweeter than glucose ***(1 mark)***. This means the food industry can use less of it in foods, which is good for making slimming foods ***(1 mark)***.

3 (a) Because during exercise the muscles need more energy from respiration, and this respiration requires oxygen ***(1 mark)***.

(b) Because there is an oxygen debt / oxygen is needed to break down the lactic acid that has built up ***(1 mark)***.

Page 114

Warm-Up Questions

1) deoxyribonucleic acid
2) mitosis
3) ovaries and testes / reproductive organs
4) 46
5) 23

Exam Questions

1 Before the cell starts to divide, the DNA is duplicated ***(1 mark)***. The cell then divides twice, during which the chromosomes line up in pairs and are pulled apart ***(1 mark)***. Four gametes are produced, each with a single set of chromosomes ***(1 mark)***.

2 (a) The results suggest that Mr X was at the crime scene, because his DNA profile has the same pattern as the DNA profile from the blood at the crime scene ***(1 mark)***.

(b) It is true that usually everyone's DNA is unique ***(1 mark)***, but identical twins have the same DNA and so would have identical genetic fingerprints ***(1 mark)***.

3 (a) (i) Each cell should contain only three chromatids ***(1 mark)***, and there should be one of each type ***(1 mark)*** as shown:

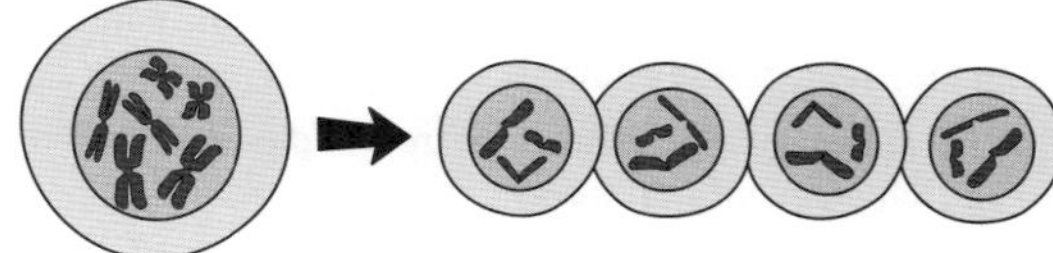

Remember that there are two divisions in meiosis. In the first division, one chromosome from each pair goes into each of two new cells. In the second division, both those cells divide again, with one half of each chromosome going into each of the new cells.

(ii) They contain half the genetic material that the original cell contained ***(1 mark)***.

(b) Any three of, e.g. it involves two divisions, instead of one / it halves the chromosome number, rather than keeping it constant / it produces genetically different cells, not genetically identical cells / it produces sex cells/gametes, not body cells ***(1 mark for each)***.

Page 119

Warm-Up Questions

1) It's the process by which a cell changes to become specialised for its job.
2) E.g. paralysis
3) a) XY
   b) XX

Exam Questions

1 (a) They are undifferentiated cells ***(1 mark)*** that can develop into different types of/specialised cells ***(1 mark)***.

(b) They could be grown into a particular type of cell, which can then be used to replace faulty cells ***(1 mark)***.

(c) Any one of: embryonic stem cells have the potential to develop into any kind of cell, whereas adult stem cells can only develop into certain types of cell / embryonic stem cells are more versatile than adult stem cells ***(1 mark)***.

(d) E.g. bone marrow ***(1 mark)***.

(e) How to grade your answer:

0 marks: No reasons for or against using embryos to create stem cells are given.

1-2 marks: There is a brief description of at least one reason for and one reason against using embryos to create stem cells for research.

3-4 marks: The answer gives at least two reasons for and two reasons against using embryos to create stem cells for research. The answer has a logical structure and spelling, grammar and punctuation are mostly correct.

5-6 marks: The answer gives at least three reasons for and three reasons against using embryos to create stem cells for research. The answer has a logical structure and uses correct spelling, grammar and punctuation.

Here are some points your answer may include:
Reasons for:

Some people believe that curing patients who already exist and are suffering is more important than the rights of embryos.

The embryos used in stem cell research are usually unwanted ones that would probably be destroyed if they weren't used for research.

Any research done on stem cells in the UK must follow strict guidelines.

Reasons against:

Some people feel that human embryos shouldn't be used for experiments
since each one is a potential human life.

Some people think scientists should concentrate on finding and developing other sources of stem cells, so people could be helped without having to use embryos.

2 50% or 1/2 ***(1 mark)***. The chances of the child being a boy are the same (50%) at each pregnancy ***(1 mark)***.

Page 126-127

Warm-Up Questions

1) They're different versions of the same gene.
2) The allele which causes cystic fibrosis is a recessive allele, so people can have one copy of the allele and not have the disorder/show any symptoms.
3) It's a genetic disorder where a baby is born with extra fingers or toes.
4) A cell is removed from the embryo and its genes are analysed so that genetic disorders can be detected.
5) 1:1

Exam Questions

1 (a) No, because polydactyly isn't a significant health issue / embryos are only screened for serious genetic disorders ***(1 mark)***.

(b) Certain types of gene increase the risk of cancer, but they aren't a definite indication that the person will develop cancer ***(1 mark)***. Also some types of cancer can be treated successfully ***(1 mark)***. It can be argued that it isn't right to destroy an embryo because it might develop a disease which could be treatable ***(1 mark)***.

(c) Any one of: e.g. it implies that people with genetic problems are undesirable. / The rejected embryos (which could have developed into humans) are destroyed. / They may be worried that it could lead to embryo screening being allowed for other traits. ***(1 mark)***

Extracts can be a bit scary — all that scientific information in a big wodge. Try reading the extract once, then reading the questions and then reading the extract again, underlining any useful bits. The extract's there to help you with the questions — so use it.

2 (a) White flowers ***(1 mark)***

(b) (i) FF ***(1 mark)***

(ii) ff ***(1 mark)***

(iii) Ff ***(1 mark)***

3 (a)

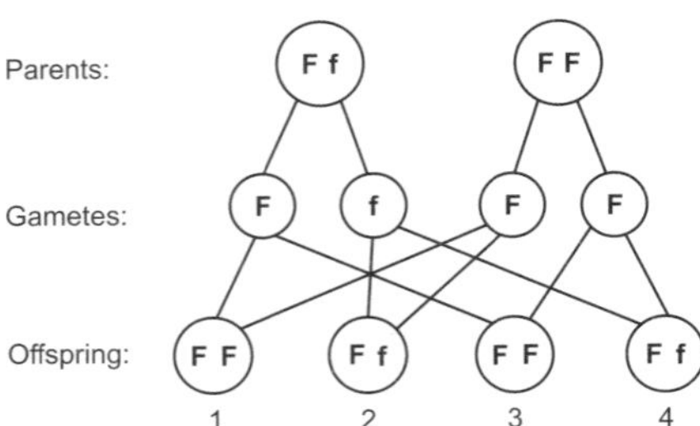

(1 mark for gametes correct, 1 mark for offspring correct)

(b) They will all be unaffected ***(1 mark)***.

(c) (i) 1 in 2 / 50% ***(1 mark)***

(ii) 2 and 4 ***(1 mark)***

Page 131

Warm-Up Questions

1) Fossils are the remains of organisms from many years ago, which are found in rocks.
2) E.g. an animal's burrow / a plant's roots / a footprint
3) Some fossils are destroyed by geological activity, e.g. the movement of tectonic plates may have crushed fossils already formed in the rocks.
4) A species that doesn't exist anymore.
5) Isolation is where populations of a species are separated.

Exam Questions

1 (a) Inside the amber there is no oxygen or moisture ***(1 mark)*** so the insect remains can't decay / so decay microbes can't survive ***(1 mark)***.

(b) E.g. a volcanic eruption / a collision with an asteroid ***(1 mark)***.

2 (a) Teeth don't decay easily so they can last a long time when buried ***(1 mark)***. They're eventually replaced by minerals as they decay (leaving a rock-like substance in the shape of the teeth) ***(1 mark)***.

(b) Parts of Stegosaurus that were made of soft tissue will have decayed away completely, without being fossilised ***(1 mark)***.

3 E.g. two populations of the original bird species became isolated/separated over the two islands due to a physical barrier (e.g. an earthquake) ***(1 mark)***. Conditions on the two islands were slightly different ***(1 mark)***. Each population showed genetic variation because they had a wide range of alleles ***(1 mark)***. Different characteristics became more common in each population due to natural selection ***(1 mark)***. Over time the two populations became so different that they couldn't interbreed any more ***(1 mark)***.

Revision Summary for Biology 2b (page 132)

24) BB and bb

Page 138

Warm-Up Questions

1) Water will move out of the animal cell by osmosis from an area of high water concentration to an area of low water concentration.
2) A partially permeable membrane only allows small molecules (e.g. water) to diffuse through it.
3) Diffusion and active transport.
4) They're thin, they have a large surface area, they have lots of blood vessels and they're often ventilated.
5) The intercostal muscles and diaphragm relax. The volume of the thorax decreases. This increases the pressure, so air is forced out.
6) alveoli

Exam Questions

1 (a) The diaphragm contracts ***(1 mark)***, and the intercostal muscles contract ***(1 mark)***. This increases the volume of the thorax ***(1 mark)***, and so decreases the pressure in the thorax, drawing air in ***(1 mark)***.

(b) They work by pumping air into the lungs, which expands the ribcage ***(1 mark)***. When they stop pumping, the ribcage relaxes and pushes air back out of the lungs ***(1 mark)***.

(c) E.g. they can cause damage to the lungs ***(1 mark)***.

2 (a) The potato cylinder in tube D, because this tube contains the most concentrated sugar solution so this cylinder will have lost the most water ***(1 mark)*** by osmosis ***(1 mark)***.

(b) Tube A contained distilled water, so some of the water moved by osmosis into the potato cylinder ***(1 mark)*** from an area of high water concentration to an area of low water concentration ***(1 mark)***.

Page 143

Warm-Up Questions

1) E.g. alveoli and villi.
2) Active transport.
3) (a) Xylem — transports water and minerals.
   Phloem — transports food substances/dissolved sugars.
   (b) Xylem — from the roots to the stem and leaves.
   Phloem — from the leaves to growing regions and storage organs.
4) Evaporation and diffusion.
5) (a) The roots.
   (b) The leaves.

Exam Questions

1 (a) The products of digestion move by diffusion down their concentration gradients into the blood ***(1 mark)***, and by active transport, against their concentration gradient ***(1 mark)***.
(b) E.g. they increase the surface area to maximise absorption ***(1 mark)***. They have a thin wall/a single layer of surface cells to reduce the distance across which diffusion occurs ***(1 mark)***. They have a good blood supply for the uptake of substances ***(1 mark)***.

2 (a) It has a hair-like shape that sticks out into the soil, creating a large surface area for diffusion/active transport ***(1 mark)***.
(b) The concentration of mineral ions is higher inside the root hair cell than in the soil around it ***(1 mark)***. So mineral ions are absorbed by active transport ***(1 mark)*** against a concentration gradient/using energy from respiration ***(1 mark)***.

Page 150

Warm-Up Questions

1) C pulmonary vein and vena cava, atria, ventricles, pulmonary artery and aorta
2) Carry blood to the heart.
3) Any four of, e.g. red blood cells / white blood cells / platelets / glucose / amino acids / carbon dioxide / hormones / urea / antibodies / antitoxins.
4) A mechanical device that is put into a person to pump blood if their own heart fails.
5) E.g. the artery can narrow again as stents can irritate the artery and make scar tissue grow.

Exam Questions

1 (a) E.g. they have a biconcave shape giving a large surface area for absorbing oxygen. / They have no nucleus, which gives more room to carry oxygen. / They contain haemoglobin which combines with oxygen to become oxyhaemoglobin ***(1 mark each)***.
(b) White blood cells ***(1 mark)***, which defend the body against disease ***(1 mark)***.

2 (a) (i) aorta, vena cava, pulmonary artery, pulmonary vein ***(1 mark each)***.
(ii) (right) atrium ***(1 mark)***
(b) (i) four ***(1 mark)***
(ii) valves ***(1 mark)***
(iii) Valves prevent the blood flowing backwards/in the wrong direction ***(1 mark)***.

Page 155

Warm-Up Questions

1) E.g. carbon dioxide and urea
2) thermoregulatory centre
3) It contains receptors that are sensitive to the temperature of the blood flowing through the brain. It also receives impulses from the skin, giving information about skin temperature.
4) E.g. hairs lie flat / sweat is produced by sweat glands and evaporates from the skin, which removes heat / the blood vessels supplying the skin dilate, so more blood flows close to the skin's surface, making it easier for heat to be lost to the environment.
5) They remove urea from the blood, adjust the blood's ion content and make sure blood contains the right amount of water.

Exam Questions

1 (a) X = kidney ***(1 mark)***
(b) To store urine ***(1 mark)***.

2 E.g. hairs stand on end, which traps a layer of warm air next to the skin / sweat production stops / blood vessels constrict to close off the skin's blood supply ***(1 mark for each)***.

3 (a) Urea, ions, and water ***(1 mark)***.
(b) Excess salt has to be removed from the body by the kidneys ***(1 mark)***. Reducing the amount of salt in the diet reduces the amount of work that the kidneys have to do / this reduces the chance of a dangerous build-up of salt between dialysis sessions ***(1 mark)***.

4 E.g. Ions ***(1 mark)*** replace those lost in sweat ***(1 mark)***. Sugar ***(1 mark)*** replaces the sugar that's used up by muscles during exercise ***(1 mark)***.

Page 159

Warm-Up Questions

1) Part of the kidney, where the blood is filtered and purified.
2) Waste substances build up in the blood and that person will lose their ability to control the levels of ions and water in their body. It could result in death.
3) About three times a week.
4) E.g. a donor with a tissue type that closely matches the patient is chosen. The patient is treated with drugs that suppress the immune system.

Exam Questions

1 The membranes between the blood and the capsule act like filters ***(1 mark)***, and protein molecules are too big to fit through ***(1 mark)***.

2 (a) (i) The urea diffuses out through the dialysis membrane ***(1 mark)***, because the concentration of urea in the blood is more than in the dialysis fluid/because the dialysis fluid contains no urea ***(1 mark)***.
(ii) The dialysis fluid contains the same concentration of glucose as healthy blood ***(1 mark)***, so there is no concentration gradient and no net movement of glucose ***(1 mark)***.
(b) (i) E.g. She will not have to have dialysis sessions three times every week for hours each time ***(1 mark)***.
(ii) Because the foreign antigens (on the donor kidney) can be attacked by the patient's antibodies ***(1 mark)***.

3 How to grade your answer:

0 marks: No clear description or explanation of the stages of urine production is given.

1-2 marks: There is some attempt to describe the stages of urine production but what happens at each stage is not explained.

3-4 marks: The stages of urine production are described and some explanation of what happens at each stage is given. The answer has a logical structure and spelling, grammar and punctuation are mostly correct.

5-6 marks: The stages of urine production are described and full explanations of what happens at each stage are given. The answer has a logical structure and uses correct spelling, grammar and punctuation.

Here are some points your answer may include:

The first stage is ultrafiltration, which happens in the Bowman's capsule.

A high pressure is built up in the blood, which squeezes water, urea, ions and sugar out of the blood and into the Bowman's capsule.

The second stage is reabsorption, which happens as the liquid flows along the nephron.

All the sugar is reabsorbed using active transport.

Sufficient ions are reabsorbed (excess ions are not) using active transport.

Sufficient water is reabsorbed.

The final stage is for any waste substances that are left to be released by the body. The remaining substances (including urea) travel out of the nephron, into the ureter and down to the bladder as urine.

Page 162

Warm-Up Questions

1) food / drink
2) the pancreas
3) It makes the liver remove glucose from the blood and turn it into glycogen.
4) (a) Insulin used to be extracted from the pancreases of pigs and cows.
   (b) E.g. it used to cause adverse reactions in some people.

Exam Questions

1 (a) (i) pancreas ***(1 mark)***
  (ii) liver ***(1 mark)***
  (b) (i) E.g. after eating a meal containing carbohydrate/sugar ***(1 mark)***.
  (ii) cellular metabolism / respiration ***(1 mark)***
  (iii) E.g. vigorous exercise ***(1 mark)***
  (iv) Glucagon makes the liver turn glycogen into glucose, which is released into the blood ***(1 mark)***.

2 (a) Type 1 diabetes is a condition where the pancreas produces little or no insulin ***(1 mark)***. The result is that a person's blood glucose can rise to a level that can kill them ***(1 mark)***.
  (b) Advantage — any one of, e.g. it's a permanent cure/there's no need for any more injections / the person can have a more normal diet / the person avoids all of the risks associated with diabetes that isn't properly controlled ***(1 mark)***.
  Disadvantage — any one of, e.g. there's a possibility of rejection / the person will need to take immunosuppressive drugs / it involves surgery, which always carries some risk ***(1 mark)***.

Page 172-173

Warm-Up Questions

1) E.g. Our increasing population means that we are producing more waste. / Many people are demanding a better standard of living and want luxuries to make life more comfortable, so waste is produced in making these products.
2) Any one of: e.g. household waste is buried in landfill sites / nuclear waste is buried underground / chemicals (e.g. herbicides and pesticides) are used on farmland.
3) It means CO_2 is locked up in natural stores.
4) The greenhouse effect is the process in which certain gases trap reflected heat and prevent it leaving the atmosphere.
5) Carbon dioxide and methane.
6) Peat bogs are drained to produce the peat that is used in compost. Draining peat bogs releases carbon dioxide, adding to the greenhouse effect. So using peat-free compost is better for the environment because it will reduce the demand for peat.

Exam Questions

1 (a) Between AD 1000 and AD 1800, the concentration stayed about the same (at about 280 ppm) ***(1 mark)***. Between AD 1800 and AD 2000 the concentration rose sharply, from about 280 ppm to about 330 ppm ***(1 mark)***.
  (b) Any two of: e.g. deforestation / destroying peat bogs / using cars/planes / burning fuel to heat our homes / industrial processes ***(1 mark each)***.

2 (a) Melting ice on land runs into the sea / the seawater becomes warmer and expands ***(1 mark)***.
  (b) Any two of, e.g. weather patterns may change in many parts of the world. / The distribution of many wild animal and plant species may change. / Biodiversity may be reduced. / There could be changes in migration patterns. ***(1 mark)***.

3 (a) E.g. sewage and toxic chemicals released from industry can pollute rivers. / Chemicals used on the land (e.g. fertilisers) can get washed into water. ***(1 mark)***.
  (b) Sulfur dioxide can cause acid rain ***(1 mark)***.
  (c) Any two from: e.g. building / farming / dumping waste / quarrying ***(1 mark for each)***

4 (a) The two sets of data show the same pattern/increase at the same time ***(1 mark)***.
  (b) Any one of: e.g. a relationship between two things doesn't necessarily prove that one causes another / it could be a coincidence / some other factor may have caused both increases ***(1 mark)***.

5 (a) E.g. there would be fewer trees to carry out photosynthesis ***(1 mark)***, which absorbs/removes the greenhouse gas carbon dioxide from the air ***(1 mark)***.
  (b) Using the trees as fuel would contribute more to global warming because combustion releases the carbon in the wood as carbon dioxide ***(1 mark)***.

Page 177

Warm-Up Questions

1) Fermentation is when bacteria or yeast break sugars down by anaerobic respiration.
2) E.g. gasohol, ethanol.
3) E.g. cost, convenience, efficiency and position.
4) An inlet for waste material, an outlet for the digested material and an outlet for the biogas.
5) It will slow down.

Exam Questions

1 (a) methane ***(1 mark)***
  (b) Advantage — any one of, e.g. they are mechanically loaded and emptied, this has to be done manually in batch generators / they don't have to be continuously cleaned / they produce biogas all the time ***(1 mark)***.
  Disadvantage — e.g. they are more expensive to set up than batch generators ***(1 mark)***.
  (c) The rate of biogas production is faster at higher temperatures. Nigeria and Brazil have higher average temperatures than England and Denmark ***(1 mark)***.

2 (a) Biological waste (e.g. sewage / food scraps / animal dung / remains of plants) ***(1 mark)***.
  (b) (i) Because of the unpleasant smell / possibility of harmful bacteria in the waste ***(1 mark)***.
  It's really just common sense that something which is busy fermenting poo and rubbish will smell. Don't be afraid to give common sense answers — examiners like to see that you can relate science to real life.
  (ii) So it is convenient for adding animal/plant waste ***(1 mark)***.

(c) Any two of, e.g. it is carbon neutral / it produces less sulfur/nitrogen oxides/acid rain / harmful methane is burned away / it is cheap/ readily available / the digested material can be used as a fertiliser / (potentially harmful) waste is disposed of / it saves the damaging effects of mining the coal ***(1 mark for each)***.

Page 182

Warm-Up Questions

1) A fermenter is a big container full of liquid culture medium, which microorganisms can grow and reproduce in.
2) Any three of, e.g. it's an efficient way of producing protein to feed people. / The microorganisms grow very quickly. / The microorganisms don't need much space. / The microorganisms can feed on waste material that would be no good for feeding animals.
3) Any three of, e.g. the crowded conditions on factory farms can aid the spread of disease / intensively farmed animals are given antibiotics so, as a result of eating their meat, antibiotics may be less effective in humans / keeping intensively farmed animals warm uses extra fossil fuels / intensively farmed animals may be forced to eat sources of food they wouldn't naturally eat.
4) They are declining.

Exam Questions

1 (a) It's used to make meat substitutes for vegetarian meals ***(1 mark)***.

(b) *Fusarium* ***(1 mark)***.

(c) (i) glucose syrup ***(1 mark)***

(ii) aerobic conditions ***(1 mark)***

(iii) purification ***(1 mark)***

2 C is the most efficient because there are fewer steps in this food chain ***(1 mark)*** so less energy is lost ***(1 mark)***.

3 (a) To prevent disease (which may be more likely in the warm, crowded conditions) ***(1 mark)***.

(b) The disease organisms may develop resistance to the antibiotics, which makes the disease harder to treat ***(1 mark)***.

(c) This reduces the energy the cattle lose as heat ***(1 mark)***. Keeping them inside means they use less energy because they move less, and using less energy means they'll need less food and so cost less money ***(1 mark)***.

Revision Summary for Biology 3b (page 183)

10) The fact that one glacier is melting doesn't mean that all glaciers are melting. One glacier melting doesn't mean that the average global temperature is rising. You'd need to collect a lot more data from around the whole world over a long period of time.

14) (a) Biogas is suitable because waste from the goats and cows can be used in the biogas generator.
Advantages: villagers won't have to spend time collecting wood, digested material could be used to fertilise soil, and waste would be disposed of, reducing disease.
Disadvantages: biogas production slows down in cold conditions, so they might need an alternative fuel source in winter.

(b) Their conclusion isn't valid. Possible reasons: the amounts spread on the ground might have been different, the weather in the two places might have been different, the species of crop might have been different, etc.

Exam Paper — Unit Biology 1

1 (a) E.g. type 2 diabetes / high blood pressure / heart disease / arthritis / some cancers ***(1 mark)***.

(b) E.g. no, because more people on the study diet took regular exercise during the study than people on the normal diet ***(1 mark)***. This could have caused their weight loss rather than the diet ***(1 mark)***.

2 (a) X. It's the one that causes the biggest clear patch around the disc (where the antibiotic has killed the bacteria) ***(1 mark)***.

(b) The diameter of the clear zone around the antibiotic ***(1 mark)***.

The dependent variable is the thing that you measure.

(c) The bacteria could have developed resistance to the antibiotic ***(1 mark)***. Bacteria can mutate ***(1 mark)***. Sometimes the mutations cause them to become resistant to an antibiotic ***(1 mark)***. The individual resistant bacteria will survive and reproduce, so the population of the resistant strain would have increased ***(1 mark)***.

3 (a) The rate at which all the chemical reactions in the body take place ***(1 mark)***.

(b) $(7 \times 30) + (14 \times 10) = 350$ kJ
(2 marks for correct answer, otherwise 1 mark for correct working)

It's always a good idea to show your working — if you don't get the right answer you could still pick up some marks if you were on the right tracks.

(c) $760 \div 40 = 19$ minutes
(2 marks for correct answer, otherwise 1 mark for correct working)

4 (a) Measles, mumps and rubella ***(1 mark for all 3 answers correct)***.

(b) How to grade your answer:

0 marks: No relevant information is given.

1-2 marks: There is a brief description of how a vaccine works. The answer mentions use of dead or inactive microorganisms.

3-4 marks: There is some description of how a vaccine works. The answer mentions use of dead or inactive microorganisms and antibodies. The answer has a logical structure and spelling, grammar and punctuation are mostly correct.

5-6 marks: There is a detailed description of how a vaccine works. The answer mentions use of dead or inactive microorganisms, antigens, antibodies and white blood cells. The answer has a logical structure and uses correct spelling, grammar and punctuation.

Here are some points your answer may include:

The body is injected with dead or inactive microorganisms.

These microorganisms are harmless but carry antigens.

The antigens cause your white blood cells to produce antibodies.

Antibodies attack/kill the microorganisms.

If live microorganisms of the same type appear again the white blood cells rapidly mass-produce antibodies.

These kill the microorganisms before an illness can develop.

5 (a) Their reaction time was very fast ***(1 mark)***. Their response was involuntary/automatic ***(1 mark)***.

If you have to think about what response to give then it's not a reflex action.

(b) (i) relay neurone ***(1 mark)***

(ii) The pain stimulus is detected by receptors in the skin ***(1 mark)***. The impulse travels along a sensory neurone to the central nervous system/spinal cord ***(1 mark)***. When the impulse reaches a synapse between the sensory neurone and a relay neurone, it triggers chemicals to be released ***(1 mark)***. These chemicals cause impulses to be sent along the relay neurone ***(1 mark)***. When the impulse reaches a synapse between the relay neurone and a motor neurone, chemicals are released again which cause impulses to be sent along the motor neurone ***(1 mark)***. The impulse then reaches the muscle, which contracts to move your hand away from the source of pain ***(1 mark)***.

6 (a) An individual that is genetically identical to its parent ***(1 mark)***.

(b) B, because the genes in the new cell come from the body cell ***(1 mark)***.

(c) Remove the nucleus from an unfertilised egg cell/cell A ***(1 mark)***. Insert a complete set of chromosomes from an adult body cell/ cell B into the empty egg cell ***(1 mark)***. Stimulate the egg cell with an electric shock to make it divide ***(1 mark)***. When the embryo is a ball of cells, implant it into a surrogate mother/an adult female to develop ***(1 mark)***.

(d) How to grade your answer:

0 marks: No reasons for or against animal cloning are given.

1-2 marks: There is a brief description of one reason for and one reason against animal cloning.

3-4 marks: At least two reasons for and two reasons against animal cloning are given. The answer has a logical structure and spelling, grammar and punctuation are mostly correct.

5-6 marks: The answer gives at least three reasons for and three reasons against animal cloning. The answer has a logical structure and uses correct spelling, grammar and punctuation.

Here are some points your answer may include:

For:

Cloning animals allows farmers to produce lots of ideal offspring quickly.

Studying animal clones could lead to greater understanding of the development of the embryo.

Studying animal clones could lead to greater understanding of ageing and age-related disorders.

Cloning could be used to help to preserve endangered species.

Against:

Cloning leads to a reduced gene pool.

If a population are all closely related and a new disease appears, they could all be wiped out.

Cloned animals may not be as healthy as normal ones.

Animal cloning could lead to attempts at human cloning in the future.

7 (a) D, because the biomass of the organisms decreases at each trophic level ***(1 mark)***.

(b) (130 ÷ 1100) × 100% = 11.8%
(2 marks for correct answer, otherwise 1 mark for correct working)

(c) Any two of, e.g. energy is used for respiration/movement/growth / energy is lost in waste materials / energy is lost as heat
(1 mark for each correct answer).

(d) Energy is lost at each level of a food chain ***(1 mark)***. After about five levels the amount of energy being passed on is not sufficient to support another level of organisms ***(1 mark)***.

8 (a) (i) the dark variety ***(1 mark)***

(ii) The dark variety is better camouflaged so less likely to be eaten by predators ***(1 mark)*** so more survive to breed and pass this characteristic on to the next generation ***(1 mark)***.
It makes sense that if an organism blends in with its background it'll be harder for predators to spot it.

(b) (i) Town B — it contains a higher proportion of dark moths ***(1 mark)***.

(ii) 77% – 25% = 52% ***(2 marks for correct answer, otherwise 1 mark for correctly reading both values off the graph)***

9 (a) At point X, CO_2 is being removed from the atmosphere by photosynthesis ***(1 mark)***. At point Y, CO_2 is being released into the atmosphere by plants and animals respiring ***(1 mark)***. At point Z, carbon compounds in the plants are being transferred to animals as they eat the plants ***(1 mark)***.

(b) Microorganisms break down waste products and dead organisms ***(1 mark)*** and release carbon dioxide into the atmosphere as they respire/cause decay ***(1 mark)***.

Exam Paper — Unit Biology 2

1 (a) (i) Number of clover Jeremy counted per m^2 = (89 × 2) – 96 = 82 ***(1 mark)***.
Mean number of buttercups per m^2 = (57 + 63) ÷ 2 = 60 ***(1 mark)***.

(ii) 50 × 70 = 3500 m^2
6 × 3500 = 21 000 dandelions
(2 marks for correct answer, otherwise 1 mark for correct working)
All you have to do is multiply the number of dandelions found in 1 m^2 by the total area of the field.

(b) E.g. they could take a larger sample size by using more quadrats / sampling more areas ***(1 mark)***. They could choose the areas of the field to sample at random ***(1 mark)***.

2 (a) oxygen ***(1 mark)***
Remember, plants give off oxygen when they photosynthesise.

(b) The volume of gas collected would decrease because when the lamp is turned off the light intensity will decrease ***(1 mark)***, so the rate of photosynthesis will decrease too ***(1 mark)***.

(c) Carbon dioxide is needed for photosynthesis ***(1 mark)***, so adding it to the water ensures that the rate of photosynthesis is not limited by a lack of carbon dioxide ***(1 mark)***.

(d) The enzymes needed for photosynthesis work more slowly at low temperatures, so the rate of photosynthesis will be slower at low temperatures ***(1 mark)***. But if the temperature is too hot, the enzymes are denatured so photosynthesis won't happen ***(1 mark)***. The temperature could be controlled, for example by putting the beaker into a warm water bath to keep the temperature constant ***(1 mark)***.

(e) Any three of, e.g. for respiration / for making cellulose for cell walls / for making amino acids/proteins / to store as starch / to convert into fats and oils for storage in seeds ***(1 mark for each correct use)***.

3 (a) An organ is a group of tissues that work together to perform a certain function ***(1 mark)***.

(b) E.g. muscular tissue ***(1 mark)*** — contracts to move the stomach wall and churn up food ***(1 mark)***. Glandular tissue ***(1 mark)*** — makes/secretes digestive juices to digest food ***(1 mark)***.

4 (a) Cell membrane ***(1 mark)***. It controls what enters and leaves the cell ***(1 mark)***.

(b) How to grade your answer:

0 marks: No relevant information is given.

1-2 marks: There is a brief description of one similarity and one difference between plant and animal cells.

3-4 marks: There is a description of two similarities and two differences between plant and animal cells. The answer has a logical structure and spelling, grammar and punctuation are mostly correct.

5-6 marks: A detailed description of three similarities and three differences between plant and animal cells is given. The answer has a logical structure and uses correct spelling, grammar and punctuation.

Here are some points your answer may include:

Similarities:

Both plant and animal cells have a nucleus, which controls the cell's activities.

Both plant and animal cells contain cytoplasm, which is where most of the cell's chemical reactions take place.

Plant cells and animal cells both have a cell membrane.

Mitochondria are found in both plant cells and animal cells.

Ribosomes are found in both plant cells and animal cells.

Differences:

Chloroplasts are present in plant cells, but not in animal cells.

Plant cells have a cell wall, but animal cells do not.

Plant cells contain a permanent vacuole, but animal cells do not.

5 (a) Each new plant would have inherited one allele for round seed coats and one allele for wrinkled seed coats ***(1 mark)***. Since all the offspring had round seed coats, this allele must be dominant ***(1 mark)***.

(b) (i) E.g.

Parents' genotype: Rr Rr

Gametes' genotype: R r R r

Offspring's genotype: RR Rr Rr rr

(1 mark for each correct level)

(ii) 5474 ÷ 1850 = 2.96 (to 2 d.p.), so the ratio is 2.96:1
(2 marks for correct answer rounded to two decimal places, otherwise 1 mark for correct working)

(iii) Because fertilisation is a random process / the genetic diagram only shows the probability ***(1 mark)***.

(c) E.g. because scientists in Mendel's time had no knowledge of genes or DNA, so they did not understand the significance of his work ***(1 mark)***.

6 (a) (i) As the rate of work increases Nancy's blood lactic acid concentration also increases ***(1 mark)***. At higher rates of work Nancy's blood lactic acid concentration increases more quickly ***(1 mark)***.

(ii) During vigorous exercise the body can't supply enough oxygen to the muscles so they start to respire anaerobically as well as aerobically ***(1 mark)***. Anaerobic respiration produces lactic acid ***(1 mark)***. The harder the muscles work, the more they'll resort to anaerobic respiration and the more lactic acid they'll produce ***(1 mark)***.

(b) Nancy's pulse rate and breathing rate will remain high after her race ***(1 mark)***. This is because after vigorous exercise the body has an oxygen debt ***(1 mark)***. Her pulse rate and breathing rate remain high to help oxidise the lactic acid that has built up ***(1 mark)***.

7 (a) (i) Approximately 37 °C (accept values between 35 °C and 40 °C) ***(1 mark)***.

(ii) The increasing temperature causes the enzyme to change shape/ denature ***(1 mark)***. This means that it no longer matches the shape of the starch, so cannot catalyse its breakdown, so the time taken for the reaction to be complete increases ***(1 mark)***.

(iii) E.g. proteases ***(1 mark)***, lipases ***(1 mark)***.

(b) Any two of: e.g. proteases are used to pre-digest proteins in some baby foods. / Carbohydrases are used to turn starch syrup into sugar syrup. / Isomerases are used to turn glucose syrup into fructose syrup. ***(1 mark for each valid answer)***

(c) How to grade your answer:

0 marks: No advantages or disadvantages of using enzymes in industry are given.

1-2 marks: There is a brief description of one advantage and one disadvantage of using enzymes in industry.

3-4 marks: At least two advantages and two disadvantages of using enzymes in industry are given. The answer has a logical structure and spelling, grammar and punctuation are mostly correct.

5-6 marks: The answer gives at least three advantages and three disadvantages of using enzymes in industry. The answer has a logical structure and uses correct spelling, grammar and punctuation.

Here are some points your answer may include:

Advantages:

Enzymes speed up reactions without the need for high temperatures and pressures.

This means energy is saved, so costs are lower.

Enzymes are specific, so they only catalyse the reaction you want them to.

Enzymes work for a long time, so after the initial cost of buying, they can be continually used.

Disadvantages:

Enzymes can be expensive to produce.

Enzymes can be denatured at high temperatures.

Enzymes can be denatured by changes in pH.

Contamination of the enzyme with other substances can affect the reaction.

Exam Paper — Unit Biology 3

1 (a) 37 °C ***(1 mark)***

(b) The thermoregulatory centre of the brain ***(1 mark)*** contains receptors that monitor the temperature of blood flowing past them ***(1 mark)*** and receive information from temperature receptors in the skin ***(1 mark)***.

(c) Blood vessels close to the surface of the skin would have constricted ***(1 mark)*** to reduce the amount of heat lost from the skin ***(1 mark)***. His muscles would also have contracted causing shivering ***(1 mark)***, which generates heat ***(1 mark)***.

2 (a) Gas A = oxygen Gas B = carbon dioxide
(1 mark for both answers correct)

A fairly easy one to get you started. The job of the lungs is to transfer oxygen to the blood and remove waste carbon dioxide from it.

(b) They provide a large surface area for diffusion to occur across ***(1 mark)***. They have thin walls, which decreases the distance for diffusion to occur across ***(1 mark)***. They have a good blood supply to assist quick absorption ***(1 mark)***.

3 (a) 9 a.m. ***(1 mark)***

(b) Any one of, e.g. day 2 was colder, so the water evaporated/diffused slower. / Day 2 was less windy, so the water vapour was carried away slower. / Day 2 was wetter/more humid, so there was a smaller diffusion gradient ***(1 mark for reason, 1 mark for explanation)***.

(c) The plant has lost too much water/has lost water faster than it could be replaced through the roots ***(1 mark)***.

(d) Transpiration creates a slight shortage of water in the leaf ***(1 mark)***. More water is drawn up from the rest of the plant through the xylem vessels to replace it ***(1 mark)***. This in turn means that more water is drawn up from the roots, and so there's a constant transpiration stream of water through the plant ***(1 mark)***.

4 (a) Osmosis is the movement of water molecules across a partially permeable membrane from a region of high water concentration to a region of low water concentration ***(1 mark)***.

(b) Experiment 1: change in mass = 1.51 – 1.9 = –0.39 g
Experiment 2: change in mass = 1.45 – 1.9 = –0.45 g
Experiment 3: change in mass = 1.49 – 1.9 = –0.41 g
(1 mark for calculating all three of these values correctly)
Mean change in mass = (–0.39 + –0.45 + –0.41) ÷ 3 = –0.42 g
(1 mark for correctly calculating the mean)

(c)

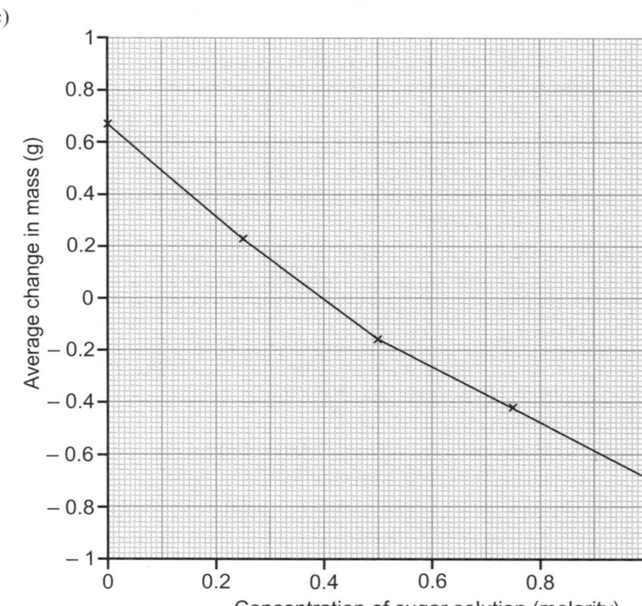

(1 mark for points plotted correctly, 1 mark for line. If answer to part (b) was incorrect, allow one incorrect value plotted at 0.75 M)

(d) The concentration of sugar inside the original potatoes was approximately 0.4 M ***(1 mark)***. This is the point where there was no change in weight of the potato cylinders, therefore no net movement of water, because the concentrations on both sides of the (partially permeable) membrane are the same ***(1 mark)***.

(e) To give more reliable results *(1 mark)*.

Repeating an experiment also means that you should be able to spot any glaring errors — like reading the balance wrongly in the experiment above.

5 (a) 16 000 – 4000 = 12 000
% reduction = (12 000 ÷ 16 000) × 100 = 75%
(2 marks for correct answer, otherwise 1 mark for correct working)

(b) E.g. the number of cod able to reproduce declined from 16 000 to about 3500 between 1980 and 2001 *(1 mark)*. The number then rose to about 5000 by 2005 *(1 mark)*. Cod numbers may have declined because levels of fishing increased / larger/better fishing nets were used so more cod were caught *(1 mark)*. They may have risen because of the introduction of fishing quotas / restrictions on the type/size of nets that could be used *(1 mark)*.

(c) Producing enough food without using resources faster than they renew *(1 mark)*.

6 (a) Biogas is produced by anaerobic fermentation of waste material by several different types of bacteria *(1 mark)*.

(b) Temperature affects the rate of bacterial respiration. If the temperature is not kept at the optimum for bacterial respiration the rate of biogas production will decrease. *(1 mark)*.

If it is too cold the bacteria will respire slowly and produce biogas too slowly. If it is too hot the bacteria will die.

(c) Any one of, e.g. it's a sustainable fuel / the raw materials are cheap / the raw materials are readily available / it doesn't produce particulates (produces less pollution) / it conserves finite resources / it acts as a waste removal system *(1 mark)*.

7 (a) The blood supply to the area below the blockage would be cut off/ reduced *(1 mark)*. Not enough oxygen and glucose would reach this part of the heart muscle, resulting in damage/death of the muscle tissue/a heart attack *(1 mark)*.

(b) (i) A stent will keep Malcolm's coronary artery open, making sure that enough blood can reach his heart muscle *(1 mark)*.

(ii) Any one of, e.g. he would have to undergo surgery to have the stent fitted / he would have to take drugs to stop blood clotting on the stent / his artery could narrow again over time *(1 mark)*.

8 (a) The person's blood flows between partially permeable membranes *(1 mark)*. The dialysis fluid contains the same concentration of glucose and mineral ions as the blood, which ensures that glucose and other useful mineral ions are not lost *(1 mark)*. Urea diffuses out of the blood into the dialysis fluid *(1 mark)*.

(b) Advantage: any one of, e.g. the transplant provides a permanent cure / the patient does not need to undergo dialysis two or three times every week / the patient can eat a more normal diet *(1 mark)*.

Disadvantage: any one of, e.g. the patient's immune system might reject the transplanted kidney / patients have to take immunosuppressive drugs, which makes them susceptible to infections *(1 mark)*.

9 (a) When a peat bog is drained, the peat starts to decompose and release carbon dioxide *(1 mark)*. Destroying peat bogs adds more carbon dioxide to the atmosphere, which can add to global warming *(1 mark)*.

(b) Any two from: e.g. oceans / lakes / ponds / green plants
(1 mark for each correct answer).

10 (a) 15 000 – 3450 = 11 550
% energy lost = (11 550 ÷ 15 000) × 100 = 77%
(2 marks for correct answer, otherwise 1 mark for correct working)

(b) The pigs are kept close together in small pens, so they're warm and can't move about *(1 mark)*. This saves them wasting energy on movement, and stops them giving out so much energy as heat *(1 mark)*.

(c) How to grade your answer:

0 marks: No discussion of the advantages or disadvantages of using intensive farming practices to produce meat.

1-2 marks: There is a brief description of one advantage and one disadvantage of using intensive farming practices to produce meat.

3-4 marks: There is a discussion of the use of intensive farming practices to produce meat. The answer contains at least one advantage and one disadvantage, and covers at least four points in total. The answer has a logical structure and spelling, grammar and punctuation are mostly correct.

5-6 marks: A detailed discussion of the use of intensive farming practices to produce meat is given. The answer contains at least two advantages and two disadvantages, and covers at least six points in total. The answer has a logical structure and uses correct spelling, grammar and punctuation.

Here are some points your answer may include:

Advantages:

The transfer of energy from the animal feed to the animal is more efficient / less energy is wasted.

The animals will grow faster on less food.

This makes the meat cheaper for the farmer to produce, and cheaper for us to buy.

We can produce more food more quickly to feed a growing world population.

Disadvantages:

Some people think that forcing animals to live in unnatural and uncomfortable conditions is cruel.

The crowded conditions on factory farms create a favourable environment for the spread of diseases.

Antibiotics that are given to the animals to prevent disease can become less effective as human medicines.

Fossil fuels are often burned to keep the animals warm, so more fuel is used than if they were in their natural environment.

A lot of fish is used as food for intensively farmed animals, which harms fish stocks.

Index

Index

Index

Make sure you're not missing out on another superb CGP revision book that might just save your life...

...order your **free** catalogue today.

CGP customer service is second to none

We work very hard to despatch all orders the **same day** we receive them, and our success rate is currently 99.9%. We send all orders by **overnight courier** or **First Class** post.
If you ring us today you should get your catalogue or book tomorrow. Irresistible, surely?

- Phone: 0870 750 1252 (Mon-Fri, 8.30am to 5.30pm)
- Fax: 0870 750 1292
- e-mail: orders@cgpbooks.co.uk
- Post: CGP, Kirkby-in-Furness, Cumbria, LA17 7WZ
- Website: www.cgpbooks.co.uk

...or you can ask at any good bookshop.

BAS44